REDEMPTION SONGS

A CHOICE COLLECTION OF

ONE THOUSAND HYMNS
AND CHORUSES

FOR EVANGELISTIC MEETINGS
SOLOISTS, CHOIRS, THE HOME

LONDON
PICKERING & INGLIS LTD.

PICKERING & INGLIS LTD

29 Ludgate Hill, London EC4M 7BP
26 Bothwell Street, Glasgow G2 6PA

INDEX TO SUBJECTS

"Printed in Spain

4791

REDEMPTION SONGS

PRAISE AND OPENING

1 ALL hail the power of Jesu's name!
Let angels prostrate fall ;
Bring forth the royal diadem,
And crown Him Lord of all.

2 Crown Him, ye martyrs of your God,
Who from His altar call ;
Extol the stem of Jesse's rod,
And crown Him Lord of all.

3 Ye chosen seed of Israel's race,
A remnant weak and small,
Hail Him who saves you by His grace,
And crown Him Lord of all.

4 Ye Gentile sinners, ne'er forget
The wormwood and the gall ;
Go, spread your trophies at His feet,
And crown Him Lord of all.

5 Let every kindred, every tribe,
On this terrestrial ball,
To Him all majesty ascribe,
And crown Him Lord of all.

6 O that with yonder sacred throng
We at His feet may fall,
Join in the everlasting song,
And crown Him Lord of all !

2 BREAK Thou the bread of life,
Dear Lord, to me,
As Thou didst break the loaves
Beside the sea.
Beyond the sacred page
I seek Thee, Lord ;
My spirit pants for Thee,
O Living Word !

2 Break Thou the bread of life,
O Lord, to me,
That hid within my heart
Thy Word may be :
Mould Thou each inward thought,
From self set free,
And let my steps be all
Controlled by Thee.

3 Open Thy Word of Truth,
That I may see
Thy message written clear
And plain for me ;

Then in sweet fellowship
Walking with Thee,
Thine image on my life
Engraved will be.

4 Bless Thou the truth, dear Lord,
To me, to me,
As Thou didst bless the bread
By Galilee :
Then shall all bondage cease,
All fetters fall ;
And I shall find my peace,
My All in All !

3 WE come before Thy throne to-day,
Thy promised presence claim ;
O come and enter now our hearts,
And set our souls aflame.

Lord, send Thy blessing, Lord, send Thy
blessing,
Lord, send Thy blessing on our waiting souls.

2 We know that Thou art present here,
Thy grace to us reveal ;
We fain would know Thy blessed will,
Thy holy presence feel.

3 O send to us Thy quickening power,
All guilt and dross remove ;
O let our waiting hearts be filled,
Dear Saviour, with Thy love.

4 Accept the homage that we bring,
O Lord, we humbly pray ;
Bestow Thy richest blessings now,
And meet with us to-day.

4 THE name of Jesus is so sweet,
I love its music to repeat ;
It makes my joys full and complete,
The precious name of Jesus.

" Jesus," oh, how sweet the name !
" Jesus," every day the same ;
" Jesus," let all saints proclaim
Its worthy praise for ever.

2 I love the name of Him Whose heart
Knows all my griefs and bears a part;
Who bids all anxious fears depart—
I love the name of Jesus.

3 That name I fondly love to hear,
It never fails my heart to cheer,
Its music dries the falling tear ;
    Exalt the name of Jesus !

4 No word of man can ever tell
How sweet the name I love so well ;
Oh, let its praises ever swell !
    Oh, praise the name of Jesus !

5 WHEN upon life's billows you are
        tempest tossed,
When you are discouraged, thinking
    all is lost,
Count your many blessings, name
    them one by one,
And it will surprise you what the
    Lord hath done.

Count your blessings, name them one by one,
Count your blessings, see what God hath done ;
Count your blessings, name them one by one,
And it will surprise you what the Lord hath
    done.

2 Are you ever burdened with a load
    of care ?
Does the cross seem heavy you are
    called to bear ?
Count your many blessings, every
    doubt will fly,
And you will be singing as the days
    go by.

3 When you look at others with their
    lands and gold,
Think that Christ has promised you
    His wealth untold,
Count your many blessings, money
    cannot buy
Your reward in heaven, nor your
    home on high.

4 So amid the conflict, whether great
    or small,
Do not be discouraged, God is over
    all,
Count your many blessings, angels
    will attend,
Help and comfort give you to your
    journey's end.

6 GOD is here, and that to bless us
        With the Spirit's quickening
        power :
See, the cloud already bending,
Waits to drop the grateful shower.

Let it come, O Lord, we pray Thee,
    Let the shower of blessing fall ;
We are waiting, we are waiting,
    Oh, revive the hearts of all.

2 God is here ! we feel His presence
    In this consecrated place ;
But we need the soul refreshing
    Of His free, unbounded grace.

3 God is here ! oh, then, believing,
    Bring to Him our one desire,
That His love may now be kindled,
    Till its flame each heart inspire.

4 Saviour, grant the prayer we offer,
    While in simple faith we bow,
From the windows of Thy mercy
    Pour us out a blessing now.

7 TO God be the glory, great things
        He hath done,
So loved He the world that He gave
    us His Son,
Who yielded His life an atonement
    for sin,
And opened the Life Gate that all
    may go in.

Praise the Lord, praise the Lord,
    Let the earth hear His voice !
Praise the Lord, praise the Lord,
    Let the people rejoice !
O come to the Father, through Jesus the Son,
And give Him the glory, great things He hath
    done.

2 O perfect redemption, the purchase
    of blood,
To every believer the promise of God ;
The vilest offender who truly believes,
That moment from Jesus a pardon
    receives.

3 Great things He hath taught us,
    great things He hath done,
And great our rejoicing through
    Jesus the Son ;
But purer, and higher, and greater
    will be
Our wonder, our transport when
    Jesus we see.

8 WHO is on the Lord's side ?
        Who will serve the King ?
Who will be His helpers,
    Other lives to bring ?
Who will leave the world's side ?
    Who will face the foe ?
Who is on the Lord's side ?
    Who for Him will go ?
By Thy call of mercy,
    By Thy grace divine,
We are on the Lord's side,
    Saviour, we are Thine !

2 Not for weight of glory,
Nor for crown and palm,
Enter we the army,
  Raise the warrior psalm ;
But for love that claimeth
  Lives for whom He died :
He whom Jesus nameth
  Must be on His side !
By Thy love constraining,
  By Thy grace divine,
We are on the Lord's side,
  Saviour, we are Thine !

3 Jesus, Thou hast bought us.
  Not with gold or gem,
But with Thine own life-blood
  For Thy diadem ;
With Thy blessing filling
  All who come to Thee,
Thou hast made us willing,
  Thou hast made us free.
By Thy grand redemption,
  By Thy grace divine,
We are on the Lord's side,
  Saviour, we are Thine !

4 Fierce may be the conflict,
  Strong may be the foe ;
But the King's own army
  None can overthrow :
Round His standard ranging,
  Victory is secure,
For His truth unchanging
  Makes the triumph sure.
Joyfully enlisting,
  By Thy grace divine,
We are on the Lord's side,
  Saviour, we are Thine !

9 I MUST have the Saviour with me,
  For I dare not walk alone,
I must feel His presence near me,
  And His arm around me thrown.

Then my soul....shall fear no ill,....
Let Him lead....me where He will,....
I will go without a murmur,
  And His footsteps follow still.

2 I must have the Saviour with me,
  For my faith, at best, is weak ;
He can whisper words of comfort,
  That no other voice can speak.

3 I must have the Saviour with me,
  In the onward march of life,
Through the tempest and the sun-
    shine,
  Through the battle and the strife.

4 I must have the Saviour with me,
  And His eye the way must guide,
Till I reach the vale of Jordan,
  Till I cross the rolling tide.

10 HERE in Thy name we are
    gathered,
  Come and revive us, O Lord ;
" There shall be showers of blessing,"
  Thou hast declared in Thy Word.

Oh, graciously hear us,
  Graciously hear us, we pray :
Pour from Thy windows upon us
  Showers of blessing to-day.

2 Oh ! that the showers of blessing
  Now on our souls may descend,
While at the footstool of mercy
  Pleading Thy promise we bend !

3 " There shall be showers of blessing,"
  Promise that never can fail ;
Thou wilt regard our petition ;
  Surely our faith will prevail.

4 Showers of blessing, we need them,
  Showers of blessing from Thee ;
Showers of blessing, oh, grant them !
  Thine all the glory shall be.

11 MY song shall be of Jesus,
  His mercy crowns my days,
He fills my cup with blessings,
  And tunes my heart to praise ;
My song shall be of Jesus,
  The precious Lamb of God,
Who gave Himself my ransom,
  And bought me with His blood.

2 My song shall be of Jesus,
  When sitting at His feet,
I call to mind His goodness,
  In meditation sweet :
My song shall be of Jesus,
  Whatever ill betide ;
I'll sing the grace that saves me,
  And keeps me at His side.

3 My song shall be of Jesus,
  While pressing on my way,
To reach the blissful region
  Of pure and perfect day ;
And when my soul shall enter
  The gate of Eden fair,
A song of praise to Jesus
  I'll sing for ever there.

12 PRAISE Him! praise Him! Jesus
    our blessed Redeemer,
    Sing, O earth, His wonderful love
      proclaim.
Hail Him! hail Him! highest
    archangels in glory,
    Strength and honour give to His
      holy name.
Like a shepherd Jesus will guard
    His children,   [day long.
    In His arms He carries them all
O ye saints that dwell on the moun-
    tain of Zion,
    Praise Him! praise Him! ever
      in joyful song.

2 Praise Him! praise Him! Jesus, our
    blessed Redeemer,
    For our sins He suffered and bled
      and died ;
He, our rock, our hope of eternal
    salvation.
    Hail Him! hail Him! Jesus the
      crucified.   [sorrow,
Loving Saviour, meekly enduring
    Crowned with thorns that cruelly
      pierced His brow ;
Once for us rejected, despised, and
    forsaken,   [now.
    Prince of Glory, ever triumphant

3 Praise Him! praise Him! Jesus our
    blessed Redeemer,
    Heavenly portals, loud with
      hosannahs ring.   [ever,
Jesus, Saviour, reigneth for ever and
    Crown Him, crown Him, Prophet
      and Priest and King !
Death is vanquished! tell it with
    joy ye faithful,   [grave ?
    Where is now thy victory, boasting
Jesus lives! no longer thy portals
    are cheerless,
    Jesus lives, the mighty and strong
    to save.

13 STANDING on the promises of
    Christ our King,   [ring :
    Through eternal ages let His praises
Glory in the highest, I will shout
    and sing,
    Standing on the promises of God.

Stand...ing, stand...ing,
Standing on the promises of God my Saviour,
    Stand...ing, stand...ing,
I'm standing on the promises of God.

2 Standing on the promises that
    cannot fail,
When the howling storms of doubt
    and fear assail,   [prevail,
By the living Word of God I shall
    Standing on the promises of God.

3 Standing on the promises I now can
    see   [blood for me ;
Perfect, present cleansing in the
Standing in the liberty where Christ
    makes free,
    Standing on the promises of God.

4 Standing on the promises of Christ
    the Lord,
Bound to Him eternally by love's
    strong cord,   [sword,
Overcoming daily with the Spirit's
    Standing on the promises of God.

14 THE wondrous work the Lord has
    done
Let every voice proclaim !
And for the work of grace begun,
The wondrous battle fought and won,
Give glory to His name !

We pleaded for the Spirit,
    He came in mighty power !
We pleaded for the droppings,
    And, lo, He sent the shower !

2 Unto the Lord doth praise belong,
    O tell it everywhere !
Let every ransomed soul prolong
The loud hosannah of the song—
    The Lord doth answer prayer !

3 We'll sing the power of Jesus' name,
    And His atoning blood ;
To-day and evermore the same,
The vilest sinner to reclaim,
    And bring him back to God.

4 Let every heart and every tongue
    As one united host   [done—
Praise God for what His arm hath
Praise God the Father, God the Son,
    And God the Holy Ghost !

15 COME, O my soul, my every power
    awaking,
    Look unto Him whose goodness
      crowns thy days ;
While into song angelic choirs are
    breaking,
    O let thy voice in thankful tribute
      raise !

Tell how alone the path of death He trod ;
Tell how He lives, thine Advocate with God ;
Lift up thy voice, while heaven's triumphant
throng
Swell at His feet the everlasting song.

2 Think, O my soul, how patiently He
    sought thee,   [steep,
    Far, far away upon the mountain
    Then in His arms how tenderly He
    brought thee,   [ing sheep.
    Home to His fold a weary, wander-

3 Sing, O my soul, and let thy pure
    devotion
    Rise to His throne, thy Saviour,
    Friend, and Guide ;
    Sing of His love, that, like a mighty
    ocean   [beside.
    Flows unto thee, and all the world

4 Soon, O my soul, thine earthly house
    forsaking,
    Soon shalt thou rise the better
    land to see ;   [awaking,
    Then will thy harp, a nobler strain
    Praise Him who died to purchase
    life for thee.

16 O LOVE, that wilt not let me go,
    I rest my weary soul in Thee ;
    I give Thee back the life I owe,
    That in Thine ocean depths, its flow
    May richer, fuller be.

2 O Light, that followest all my way,
    I yield my flickering torch to Thee ;
    My heart restores its borrowed ray,
    That in Thy sunshine's blaze, its day
    May brighter, fairer be.

3 O Joy, that seekest me through pain,
    I cannot close my heart to Thee ;
    I trace the rainbow through the rain,
    And feel the promise is not vain,
    That morn shall tearless be.

4 O Cross, that liftest up my head,
    I dare not ask to fly from Thee ;
    I lay in dust life's glory dead,   [red,
    And from the ground, there blossoms
    Life that shall endless be.

17 I WILL sing of my Redeemer,
    And His wondrous love to me ;
    On the cruel Cross He suffered,
    From the curse to set me free.

    Sing, oh sing...of my Redeemer,...
      With His blood...He purchased me,...
    On the Cross...He sealed my pardon,...
      Paid the debt...and made me free....

2 I will tell the wondrous story,
    How my lost estate to save,
    In His boundless love and mercy,
    He the ransom freely gave.

3 I will praise my dear Redeemer,
    His triumphant power I'll tell,
    How the victory He giveth,
    Over sin, and death, and hell.

4 I will sing of my Redeemer,
    And His heavenly love to me ;
    He from death to life hath brought me,
    Son of God, with Him to be.

18 THE God of Abraham praise
    Who reigns enthroned above,
    Ancient of everlasting days,
    And God of love !
    Jehovah ! great I AM !
    By earth and heaven confest.
    I bow, and bless the sacred Name,
    For ever blest.

2 The God of Abraham praise,
    At whose supreme command
    From earth I rise, and seek the joys
    At His right hand.
    I all on earth forsake,
    Its wisdom, fame, and power ;
    And Him my only portion make,
    My shield and tower.

3 He by Himself hath sworn ;
    I on His oath depend ;
    I shall, on eagles' wings upborne,
    To heaven ascend.
    I shall behold His face,
    I shall His power adore,
    And sing the wonders of His grace
    For evermore.

4 There dwells the Lord our King,
    The Lord our righteousness,
    Triumphant o'er the world and sin :
    The Prince of Peace.
    On Zion's sacred height
    His kingdom still maintains,
    And glorious with His saints in light,
    For ever reigns.

5 The whole triumphant host
    Give thanks to God on high ;
    " Hail, Father, Son, and Holy Ghost ! "
    They ever cry.
    Hail, Abraham's God and mine !
    I join the heavenly lays ;
    All might and majesty are Thine,
    And endless praise.

19 MY Shepherd is the Lamb,
The living Lord, who died ;
With all things good I ever am
By Him supplied.
He richly feeds my soul
With blessings from above,
And leads me where the rivers roll
Of endless love.

2 My soul He doth restore
Whene'er I go astray ;
He makes my cup of joy run o'er
From day to day.
His love, so full, so free,
Anoints my head with oil ;
Mercy and goodness follow me,
Fruit of His toil.

3 When faith and hope shall cease,
And love abides alone,
Then shall I see Him face to face,
And know as known.
Still shall I lift my voice,
His praise my song shall be ;
And I will in His love rejoice
Who died for me.

20 WITH harps and with vials there
stand a great throng
In the presence of Jesus and sing
this new song.

Unto Him who hath loved us and washed us
from sin,
Unto Him be the glory for ever ! Amen !

2 All these once were sinners, defiled
in His sight,
Now arrayed in pure garments in
praise they unite.

3 He maketh the rebel a priest and
a king,
He hath bought us and taught us
this new song to sing.

4 How helpless and hopeless we
sinners had been,
If He never had loved us till cleansed
from our sin ?

5 Aloud in His praises our voices
shall ring,
So that others, believing, this new
song shall sing.

21 HARK, hark, my soul ! angelic
songs are swelling
O'er earth's green fields and
ocean's wave-beat shore ;

How sweet the truth those blessed
strains are telling
Of that new life when sin shall
be no more !

Angels of Jesus, angels of light,
Singing to welcome the pilgrims of the night !

2 Onward we go, for still we hear them
singing, [bids you come : "
" Come, weary souls, for Jesus
And through the dark, its echoes
sweetly ringing, [home.
The music of the gospel leads us

3 Far, far away, like bells at evening
pealing,
The voice of Jesus sounds o'er
land and sea,
And laden souls, by thousands
meekly stealing,
Kind Shepherd, turn their weary
steps to Thee.

4 Angels, sing on, your faithful watches
keeping ;
Sing us sweet fragments of the
songs above,
Till morning's joy shall end the
night of weeping,
And life's long shadows break in
cloudless love.

22 FOR all the Lord has done for me,
I never will cease to praise Him ;
And for His grace so rich and free,
I never will cease to praise Him.

I never will cease to praise Him,
My Saviour ! My Saviour !
I never will cease to praise Him,
He's done so much for me.

2 He gives me strength for every day,
I never will cease to praise Him ;
He leads and guides me all the way,
I never will cease to praise Him.

3 Although the world His love neglect,
I never will cease to praise Him ;
I could not such a friend reject,
I never will cease to praise Him.

4 He saves me every day and hour,
I never will cease to praise Him ;
Just now I feel His cleansing power,
I never will cease to praise Him.

5 While on my journey here below,
I never will cease to praise Him ;
And when to that bright world I go,
I never will cease to praise Him.

23 O GOD of Bethel, by whose hand
    Thy people still are fed,
Who through this weary pilgrimage
    Hast all our fathers led ;

2 Our vows, our prayers we now present
    Before Thy throne of grace :
God of our fathers, be the God
    Of their succeeding race.

3 Through each perplexing path of life
    Our wandering footsteps guide ;
Give us each day our daily bread,
    And raiment fit provide.

4 O spread Thy covering wings around,
    Till all our wanderings cease,
And at our Father's loved abode,
    Our souls arrive in peace.

5 Such blessings from Thy gracious
    hand
    Our humble prayers implore ;
And Thou shalt be our chosen God,
    And portion evermore.

24 AWAKE, my soul, and with the
    sun
Thy daily stage of duty run ;
Shake off dull sloth, and joyful rise,
To pay the morning sacrifice.

2 Wake, and lift up thyself, my heart,
And with the angels bear thy part,
Who all night long unwearied sing
High praise to the eternal King.

3 Lord, I my vows to Thee renew ;
Disperse my sins as morning dew ;
Guard my first springs of thought
    and will,
And with Thyself my spirit fill.

4 Direct, control, suggest, this day,
All I design, or do, or say,   [might,
That all my powers, with all their
In Thy sole glory may unite.

25 HOLY, holy, holy, Lord God
    Almighty !
    Early in the morning our song
      shall rise to Thee ;
Holy, holy, holy, merciful and
    mighty,   [Trinity !
    God in Three Persons, blessed

2 Holy, holy, holy ! all the saints
    adore Thee,
    Casting down their golden crowns
      around the glassy sea ;

Cherubim and seraphim falling down
    before Thee,
    Which wert, and art, and evermore
      shalt be.

3 Holy, holy, holy ! though the dark-
    ness hide Thee,
    Though the eye of sinful man Thy
      glory may not see ;
Only Thou art holy ! there is none
    beside Thee.
    Perfect in power, in love, and
      purity.

4 Holy, holy, holy, Lord God Almighty !
    All Thy works shall praise Thy
      name, in earth, and sky, and sea ;
Holy, holy, holy, merciful and
    mighty,
    God in Three Persons, blessed
      Trinity !

26 ALL people that on earth do
    dwell,   [voice ;
    Sing to the Lord with cheerful
Him serve with mirth, His praise
    forth tell !
    Come ye before Him and rejoice.

2 Know that the Lord is God indeed ;
    Without our aid He did us make :
We are His flock, He doth us feed,
    And for His sheep, He doth
      us take.

3 Oh, enter then His gates with praise,
    Approach with joy His courts
      unto ;
Praise, laud, and bless His Name
    always,
    For it is seemly so to do.

4 For why ? the Lord our God is good,
    His mercy is for ever sure ;
His truth at all times firmly stood,
    And shall from age to age endure.

27 JESUS has loved me—wonderful
    Saviour !
    Jesus has loved me, I cannot tell
      why ;   [less,
Came He to rescue sinners all worth-
    My heart He conquered, for Him
    I would die.

    Glory to Jesus—wonderful Saviour !
    Glory to Jesus, the One I adore ;
    Glory to Jesus—wonderful Saviour !
    Glory to Jesus, and praise evermore.

2 Jesus has saved me—wonderful
 Saviour! [how;
 Jesus has saved me, I cannot tell
All that I know is He was my ransom,
 Dying on Calvary with thorns
 on His brow.

3 Jesus will lead me—wonderful
 Saviour!
 Jesus will lead me, I cannot tell
 where; [sorrow,
But I will follow through joy or
 Sunshine or tempest, sweet peace
 or despair.

4 Jesus will crown me—wonderful
 Saviour! [when;
 Jesus will crown me, I cannot tell
White throne of splendour hail I
 with gladness,
 Crowned with the plaudits of
 angels and men.

28 CLEANSED in our Saviour's
 precious blood,
Filled with the fulness of our God,
Walking by faith the path He trod,
 Hallelujah! hallelujah!

2 Leaning our heads on Jesus' breast,
Knowing the joy of that sweet rest,
Finding in Him, the chief, the best,
 Hallelujah! hallelujah!

3 Kept by His power from day to day,
Held by His hand, we cannot stray,
Glory to glory all the way,
 Hallelujah! hallelujah!

4 Living in us His own pure life,
Giving us rest from inward strife,
From strength to strength, from
 death to life,
 Hallelujah! hallelujah!

5 Oh, what a Saviour we have found,
Well may we make the world resound,
With one continual, joyous sound,
 Hallelujah! hallelujah!

29 NOW in a song of grateful praise,
 To Thee, O Lord, my voice I'll
 raise;
With all Thy saints I'll join to tell,
My Jesus has done all things well.

And above the rest this note shall swell,
This note shall swell, this note shall swell,
And above the rest this note shall swell,
My Jesus has done all things well.

2 How sov'reign, wonderful and free,
Has been Thy love to sinful me!
Thou sav'dst me from the jaws of
 hell;
My Jesus has done all things well.

3 Since e'er my soul has known His
 love,
What mercies He has made me
 prove!
Mercies which do all praise excel!
My Jesus has done all things well.

4 And when to that bright world I rise,
And join the anthems of the skies,
Above the rest this note shall swell,
My Jesus has done all things well.

30 COME, sing, my soul, and praise
 the Lord,
Who hath redeemed thee by His
 blood;
Delivered thee from chains that
 bound,
And brought thee to redemption
 ground.

Redemption ground, the ground of peace!
Redemption ground, O wondrous grace!
Here let our praise to God abound,
Who saves us on redemption ground!

2 Once from my God I wandered far,
And with His holy will made war:
But now my songs to God abound;
I'm standing on redemption ground.

3 Oh, joyous hour when God to me
A vision gave of Calvary:
My bonds were loosed, my soul
 unbound;
I sang upon redemption ground.

4 No works of merit now I plead,
But Jesus take for all my need;
No righteousness in me is found,
Except upon redemption ground.

5 Come, weary soul, and here find rest;
Accept redemption, and be blest:
The Christ who died by God is
 crowned
To pardon on redemption ground.

31 WORTHY, worthy, is the Lamb,
 Worthy, worthy, is the Lamb,
 Worthy, worthy, is the Lamb,
 That was slain.

Praise Him, hallelujah! Praise Him, hallelujah!
Praise Him, hallelujah! Praise the Lamb!

2 We the crown of life shall wear,
 We the palm of victory bear,
 All our Father's blessings share,
  In the Lamb.

3 And when landed safe above,
 In the kingdom of His love,
 We shall all the fulness prove
  Of the Lamb.

4 Now revive Thy work, O Lord,
 By Thy Spirit and Thy Word ;
 Now revive Thy work, O Lord,
  Through the Lamb.

5 Strike the stoutest sinner through,
 Start the cry, " What must I do ? "
 Make him weep till born anew,
  Through the Lamb.

32 PRAISE, my soul, the King of
    heaven ;
 To His feet thy tribute bring ;
Ransomed, healed, restored, forgiven,
 Who like thee His praise shall sing ?
  Praise Him ! praise Him !
  Praise the everlasting King !

2 Praise Him for His grace and favour
 To our fathers in distress ;
Praise Him, still the same as ever,
 Slow to chide, and swift to bless :
  Praise Him ! praise Him !
  Glorious in His faithfulness !

3 Father-like He tends and spares us ;
 Well our feeble frame He knows ;
In His hands He gently bears us,
 Rescues us from all our foes :
  Praise Him ! praise Him !
  Widely as His mercy flows.

4 Angels, help us to adore Him,
 Ye behold Him face to face !
Sun and moon, bow down before Him,
 Dwellers all in time and space.
  Praise Him ! praise Him !
  Praise with us the God of grace !

33 LOOK, ye saints, the sight is
    glorious ;
 See the " Man of Sorrows " now
From the fight return victorious :
 Every knee to Him shall bow !
  Crown Him ! crown Him !
  Crowns become the Victor's brow.

2 Crown the Saviour ! Angels, crown
  Him !
 Rich the trophies Jesus brings :

In the seat of power enthrone Him,
 While the vault of Heaven rings !
  Crown Him ! crown Him !
  Crown the Saviour King of kings !

3 Sinners in derision crowned Him,
 Mocking thus the Saviour's claim :
Saints and angels crowd around Him,
 Own His title, praise His name.
  Crown Him ! crown Him !
  Spread abroad the Victor's fame.

4 Hark ! those bursts of acclamation !
 Hark ! those loud triumphant
  chords !
Jesus takes the highest station,
 Oh, what joy the sight affords !
  Crown Him ! crown Him !
  King of kings and Lord of lords !

34 WHO is He in yonder stall,
 At whose feet the shepherds fall ?
 'Tis the Lord, O wondrous story,
 'Tis the Lord, the King of Glory !
 At His feet we humbly fall—
 Crown Him, crown Him Lord of all !

2 Who is He in deep distress,
 Fasting in the wilderness ?

3 Who is He the people bless
 For His word of gentleness ?

4 Who is He to Whom they bring
 All the sick and sorrowing ?

5 Who is He Who stands and weeps
 At the grave where Lazarus sleeps ?

6 Who is He the gathering throng
 Greet with loud triumphant song ?

7 Lo, at midnight, who is He
 Prays in dark Gethsemane ?

8 Who is He on yonder tree
 Dies in grief and agony ?

9 Who is He Who from the grave
 Comes to succour, help, and save ?

10 Who is He Who from His throne
 Rules through all the world alone ?

35 WE are never, never weary of the
    grand old song ;
 Glory to God, hallelujah !
We can sing it loud as ever with our
  faith more strong :
 Glory to God, hallelujah !

O, the children of the Lord have a right to
 shout and sing,
For the way is growing bright, and our souls
 are on the wing,   [King !
We are going by-and-bye to the palace of a
 Glory to God, hallelujah !

2 We are lost amid the rapture of
   redeeming love ;
Glory to God, hallelujah !
We are rising on its pinions to the
   hills above ;
Glory to God, hallelujah !

3 We are going to a palace that is built
   of gold ;
Glory to God, hallelujah !
Where the King in all His splendour
   we shall soon behold ;
Glory to God, hallelujah !

4 There we'll shout redeeming mercy
   in a glad new song ;
Glory to God, hallelujah !
There we'll sing the praise of Jesus
   with the blood-washed throng ;
Glory to God, hallelujah !

36 WE praise Thee, O God, for the
   Son of Thy love,
For Jesus, who died and is now gone
   above.

> Hallelujah ! Thine the glory !
> Hallelujah ! Amen !
> Hallelujah ! Thine the glory !
> Revive us again.

2 We praise Thee, O God, for Thy
   Spirit of light,
Who has shown us our Saviour, and
   scattered our night.

3 All glory and praise to the Lamb that
   was slain,
Who has borne all our sins, and has
   cleansed every stain.

4 All glory and praise to the God of all
   grace,
Who has bought us, and sought us,
   and guided our way.

5 Revive us again ; fill each heart with
   Thy love ;
May each soul be rekindled with fire
   from above.

37 MY God, I have found
   The thrice blessed ground,
Where life and where joy and true
   comfort abound.

> Hallelujah ! Thine the glory !
> Hallelujah ! Amen !
> Hallelujah ! Thine the glory !
> Revive us again.

2 'Tis found in the blood
  Of Him who once stood
My refuge and safe y, my surety
  with God.

3 He bore on the tree
  The sentence for me,·
And now both the Surety and sinner
  are free.

4 And though here below
  'Mid sorrow and woe,
My place is in heaven with Jesus,
  I know.

5 And this I shall find,
  For such is His mind,
He'll not be in glory and leave me
  behind.

38 REJOICE and be glad ! the
   Redeemer has come !
Go look on His cradle, His Cross,
   and His tomb.

Sound His praises, tell the story of Him who
   was slain !
Sound His praises, tell with gladness, He liveth
   again !

2 Rejoice and be glad ! it is sunshine
   at last !
The clouds have departed, the
   shadows are past.

3 Rejoice and be glad ! for the blood
   hath been shed ;
Redemption is finished, the price
   hath been paid.

4 Rejoice and be glad ! now the pardon
   is free !
The Just for the unjust had died on
   the tree.

5 Rejoice and be glad ! for the Lamb
   that was slain
O'er death is triumphant, and liveth
   again.

6 Rejoice and be glad ! for our King
   is on high ;
He pleadeth for us on His throne
   in the sky.

7 Rejoice and be glad for He cometh
   again ;
He cometh in glory, the Lamb that
   was slain.

Sound His praises, tell the story of Him who
   was slain !
Sound His praises, tell with gladness, He cometh
   again !

39 WE plough the fields and scatter
   The good seed o'er the land,
But it is fed and watered
   By God's Almighty Hand ;
He sends the snow in winter,
   The warmth to swell the grain,
The breezes and the sunshine,
   And soft refreshing rain.

   All good gifts around us
      Are sent from Heaven above,
   Then thank the Lord, O thank the Lord,
      For all His love.

2 He only is the Maker
   Of all things near and far ;
He paints the wayside flower,
   He lights the evening star ;
The winds and waves obey Him,
   By Him the birds are fed ;
Much more to us His children
   He gives our daily bread.

3 We thank Thee, then, O Father,
   For all things bright and good,
The seed-time and the harvest,
   Our life, our health, our food.
Accept the gifts we offer
   For all Thy love imparts,
And, what Thou most desirest,
   Our humble, thankful hearts.

40 O COME all ye faithful,
   Joyfully triumphant,
To Bethlehem hasten now with glad
   accord ;
      Lo ! in a manger
      Lies the King of Angels !

      O come, let us adore Him,
      O come, let us adore Him,
      O come, let us adore Him,
         Christ the Lord !

2 Raise, raise, choirs of angels,
   Songs of loudest triumph ;
Through heaven's high arches be
   your praises poured :
      Now to our God be
      Glory in the highest !

3 Amen ! Lord, we bless Thee,
   Born for our salvation,
O Jesus ! for ever be Thy name adored;
      Word of the Father,
      Now in flesh appearing.

41 HOW firm a foundation, ye saints
      of the Lord,
   Is laid for your faith in His excellent
      Word !

What more can He say than to you
      He hath said,
You who unto Jesus for refuge have
      fled.

2 Fear not, I am with thee, O be not
      dismayed !
I, I am thy God, and will still give
      thee aid ;
I'll strengthen thee, help thee, and
      cause thee to stand,
Upheld by My righteous, omnipotent
      hand.

3 When through the deep waters I call
      thee to go,
The rivers of grief shall not thee
      overflow ;
For I will be with thee in trouble to
      bless,   [distress.
And sanctify to thee thy deepest

4 The soul that on Jesus hath leaned
      for repose,
I will not, I will not desert to its foes;
That soul, though all hell should
      endeavour to shake,
I'll never, no never, no never forsake!

42 HARK ! the herald angels sing,
   " Glory to the new-born King,
Peace on earth and mercy mild,
God and sinners reconciled."
Joyful, all ye nations rise,
Join the triumph of the skies ;
With the angelic host proclaim,
" Christ is born in Bethlehem."

      Hark ! the herald angels sing,
      " Glory to the new-born King."

2 Christ, by highest heaven adored,
Christ, the everlasting Lord,
Late in time behold Him come,
Offspring of a Virgin's womb.
Veiled in flesh the God-head see !
Hail, the Incarnate Deity !
Pleased as Man with man to dwell,
Jesus our Emmanuel.

3 Hail, the heaven-born Prince of
      Peace !
Hail, the Sun of righteousness !
Light and life to all He brings,
Risen with healing in His wings.
Mild He lays His glory by,
Born that man no more may die,
Born to raise the sons of earth,
Born to give them second birth.

43 TEN thousand times ten thousand,
In sparkling raiment bright,
The armies of the ransomed saints
Throng up the steeps of light.
'Tis finished, all is finished,
Their fight with death and sin ;
Fling open wide the golden gates,
And let the victors in.

2 What rush of Alleluias
Fill all the earth and sky !
What ringing of a thousand harps
Bespeak the triumph nigh !
O day, for which creation
And all its tribes were made !
O joy, for all its former woes
A thousandfold repaid !

3 Oh, then what raptured greetings
On Canaan's happy shore,
What knitting severed friendships up,
Where partings are no more !
Then eyes with joy shall sparkle
That brimmed with tears of late ;
Orphans no longer fatherless,
Nor widows desolate.

44 HE hath spoken, " Be still," the
Rebuker of seas :
The command was for me, and my
heart is at ease ;
He hath hushed into silence the
waves and the winds,
By applying His blood, and removing
my sins.

He's the Prince of peacemakers, all glory to God,
To redeem me, and cleanse me, He shed His
own blood ;
My adoption is sealed, I'm a child of the King,
And for ever and ever of Jesus I'll sing.

2 He hath quickened my soul by a
life from above,
It was done by the Spirit, its essence
is love ;
He hath pardoned and washed me
as white as the snow,
And my heart with His love does
this moment o'erflow.

3 He's a wonderful Jesus, this Saviour
of mine,
He's the great Son of God, a Redeemer Divine ;
He's my Strength, and my Wisdom,
my Life and my Lord,
And enthroned in my heart to be
loved and adored.

4 I will love Him, and serve Him from
now till I die,
For His love fills my heart, and His
beauty my eye ;
He's the fairest and dearest of all
to my soul,
And our lives shall be one, while
eternities roll.

45 REST of the weary, Joy of the sad ;
Hope of the dreary, Light of the
glad ;
Home of the stranger, Strength to
the end ;
Refuge from danger, Saviour and
Friend.

2 Pillow where, lying, love rests its
head ;
Peace of the dying, Life of the dead ;
Path of the lowly, Prize at the end ;
Breath of the holy, Saviour and
Friend.

3 When my feet stumble, I to Thee cry,
Crown of the humble, Cross of the high;
When my steps wander, over me bend,
Truer and fonder, Saviour and
Friend.

4 Ever confessing Thee, I will raise
Unto Thee blessing, glory and praise:
All my endeavour, world without
end,
Thine to be ever, Saviour and Friend.

46 SING on, ye joyful pilgrims,
Nor think the moments long ;
My faith is heavenward rising
With every tuneful song ;
Lo ! on the mount of blessing,
The glorious mount, I stand,
And, looking over Jordan,
I see the promised land.

Sing on ; oh ! blissful music !
With every note you raise
My heart is filled with rapture,
My soul is lost in praise.

2 Sing on, ye joyful pilgrims,
While here on earth we stay,
Let songs of home and Jesus
Beguile each fleeting day ;
Sing on the grand old story
Of His redeeming love,
The everlasting chorus
That fills the realms above.

3 Sing on, ye joyful pilgrims,
    The time will not be long
Till in our Father's kingdom
    We swell a nobler song,
Where those we love are waiting
    To greet us on the shore,
We'll meet beyond the river,
    Where surges roll no more.

47 O GOD, our help in ages past,
    Our hope for years to come,
Our shelter from the stormy blast,
    And our eternal home !

2 Under the shadow of Thy throne
    Thy saints have dwelt secure ;
Sufficient is Thine arm alone,
    And our defence is sure.

3 Before the hills in order stood,
    Or earth received her frame,
From everlasting Thou art God,
    To endless years the same.

4 A thousand ages in Thy sight
    Are like an evening gone, [night
Short as the watch that ends the
    Before the rising sun.

5 Time, like an ever rolling stream,
    Bears all its sons away ;
They fly forgotten, as a dream
    Dies at the opening day.

6 O God, our help in ages past,
    Our hope for years to come,
Be Thou our guard while troubles last,
    And our eternal home.

48 ETERNAL Father, strong to save,
    Whose arm hath bound the rest-
    less wave,
Who bidd'st the mighty ocean deep
    Its own appointed limits keep ;
O hear us when we cry to Thee
For those in peril on the sea.

2 O Christ, whose voice the waters
    heard,   [word,
And hushed their raging at Thy
Who walkedst on the foaming deep,
And calm amid the storm didst sleep ;
O hear us when we cry to Thee
For those in peril on the sea.

3 O Holy Spirit, Who did'st brood
Upon the waters dark and rude,
And bid their angry tumult cease,
And give, for wild confusion, peace ;
O hear us when we cry to Thee
For those in peril on the sea.

4 O Trinity of love and power,
Our brethren shield in danger's hour ;
From rock and tempest, fire and foe,
Protect them, wheresoe'er they go ;
Thus evermore shall rise to Thee
Glad hymns of praise from land and
    sea.

49 O LORD of heaven and earth and
    sea,
    To Thee all praise and glory be ;
How shall we show our love to Thee,
    Who givest all ?

2 Thou didst not spare Thine only Son,
But gav'st Him for a world undone ;
And freely with the Blessed One
    Thou givest all.

3 We lose what on ourselves we spend,
We have as treasure without end
Whatever Lord, to Thee, we lend,
    Who givest all.

4 To Thee, from whom we all derive
Our life, our gifts, our power to give !
O may we ever with Thee live,
    Who givest all !

50 THE Church's one foundation
    Is Jesus Christ her Lord ;
She is His new creation
    By water and the word.
From heav'n He came and sought her
    To be His holy bride ;
With His own blood He bought her
    And for her life He died.

2 Elect from every nation,
    Yet one o'er all the earth,
Her charter of salvation
    One Lord, one faith, one birth.
One holy name she blesses,
    Partakes one holy food,
And to one hope she presses,
    With every grace endued.

3 Though with a scornful wonder
    Men see her sore oppressed,
By schisms rent asunder,
    By heresies distressed,
Yet saints their watch are keeping,
    Their cry goes up, " How long ? "
And soon the night of weeping
    Shall be the morn of song.

4 'Mid toil and tribulation,
    And tumult of her war,
She waits the consummation
    Of peace for evermore ;

Till with the vision glorious
  Her longing eyes are blest,
And the great Church victorious
  Shall be the Church at rest.

5 Yet she on earth hath union
  With God the Three in One,
And mystic sweet communion
  With those whose rest is won.
O happy ones and holy !
  Lord, give us grace that we
Like them, the meek and lowly,
  On high may dwell with Thee.

51 O JESUS, I have promised
    To serve Thee to the end ;
Be Thou for ever near me,
  My Master and my Friend !
I shall not fear the battle
  If Thou art by my side,
Nor wander from the pathway
  If Thou wilt be my Guide.

2 O let me feel Thee near me ;
  The world is ever near,
I see the sights that dazzle,
  The tempting sounds I hear ;
My foes are ever near me,
  Around me and within ;
But, Jesus, draw Thou nearer,
  And shield my soul from sin.

3 O let me hear Thee speaking
  In accents clear and still,
Above the storms of passion,
  The murmurs of self-will.
O speak to reassure me,
  To hasten or control ;
O speak, and make me listen,
  Thou Guardian of my soul !

4 O Jesus, Thou hast promised
  To all who follow Thee,
That where Thou art in glory
  There shall Thy servant be ;
And, Jesus, I have promised,
  To serve Thee to the end :
O give me grace to follow,
  My Master and my Friend !

52 STAND up, stand up for Jesus !
  Ye soldiers of the cross ;
Lift high His royal banner,
  It must not suffer loss.
From vict'ry unto vict'ry
  His army shall He lead,
Till every foe is vanquished,
  And Christ is Lord indeed.

Stand up, stand up for Jesus !
  Ye soldiers of the cross ;
Lift high His royal banner,
  It must not suffer loss.

2 Stand up ! stand up for Jesus !
  The trumpet call obey ;
Forth to the mighty conflict,
  In this His glorious day !
" Ye that are men, now serve Him,"
  Against unnumbered foes ;
Let courage rise with danger,
  And strength to strength oppose.

3 Stand up ! stand up for Jesus !
  Stand in His strength alone ;
The arm of flesh will fail you—
  Ye dare not trust your own ;
Put on the gospel armour,
  And, watching unto prayer,
Where duty calls, or danger,
  Be never wanting there.

4 Stand up ! stand up for Jesus !
  The strife will not be long ;
This day, the noise of battle,
  The next the victor's song.
To him that overcometh,
  A crown of life shall be ;
He with the King of glory
  Shall reign eternally.

53 THINE arm, O Lord, in days of
    old,
  Was strong to heal and save ;
It triumphed o'er disease and death,
  O'er darkness and the grave.
To Thee they went, the blind, the
    dumb,
  The palsied and the lame,
The leper with his tainted life,
  The sick with fevered frame.

2 And lo ! Thy touch brought life and
    health,   [sight :
  Gave speech, and strength, and
And youth renewed and frenzy
    calmed
Owned Thee the Lord of light ;
And now, O Lord, be near to bless,
  Almighty as of yore,
In crowded street, by restless couch,
  As by Gennesareth's shore.

3 Be Thou our great Deliverer still,
  Thou Lord of life and death ;
Restore and quicken, soothe and
    bless,
  With Thine Almighty breath.

To hands that work, and eyes that
    see,
  Give wisdom's heavenly lore,
That whole and sick and weak and
    strong
  May praise Thee evermore.

54 ROLLING downward through the
    midnight,   [song ;
  Comes a glorious burst of heavenly
'Tis a chorus full of sweetness—
  And the singers are an angel throng.

" Glory ! glory in the highest !
  On the earth good-will and peace to men ! "
Down the ages send the echo ;
  Let the glad earth shout again !

2 Wond'ring shepherds see the glory,
  Hear the word the shining ones
    declare ;
At the manger fall in worship,
  While the music fills the quiv'ring
    air.

3 Christ the Saviour, God's Anointed,
  Comes to earth our fearful debt
    to pay ;
Man of sorrows, and rejected,
  Lamb of God, that takes our sin
    away.

55 OH, bliss of the purified ! bliss of
    the free !
I plunge in the crimson tide opened
    for me ;   [I stand,
O'er sin and uncleanness exulting
And point to the print of the nails
    in His hand.

  Oh, sing of His mighty love !
  Sing of His mighty love !
  Sing of His mighty love,
    Mighty to save !

2 Oh, bliss of the purified ! Jesus is
    mine !   [I pine ;
No longer in dread condemnation
In conscious salvation I'll sing of
    His grace,   [face.
Who lifted upon me the light of His

3 Oh, bliss of the purified ! bliss of the
    pure !
No wound hath the soul that His
    blood cannot cure ;
No sorrow bowed head but may
    sweetly find rest ;
No tears—but may dry them on
  Jesus's 'breast.

4 Oh, Jesus the crucified ! Thee will
    I sing.!
My blessed Redeemer, my God, and
    my King !
My soul, filled with rapture, shall
    shout o'er the grave,
And triumph in death in the
    " Mighty to save."

56 SING, O sing, the dear old story
    Of our Saviour's matchless love;
Sing of Jesus and His glory
    With the ransomed host above.

  Sing, O sing the love of Jesus—
    Sound His praises far and near ;
  Sing the wondrous story over,
    Till the whole wide world shall hear.

2 Sing of love to you so precious,
  Tell, in song, how Jesus died ;
Let sweet music draw the millions
  To the dear Redeemer's side.

3 Ye redeemed ones, sing the story !
  Sing it o'er and o'er again,
Until every tribe and nation
  Join to sing the glad refrain.

57 O FOR a thousand tongues to sing
    My great Redeemer's praise,
The glories of my God and King,
    The triumphs of His grace !

2 My gracious Master and my God,
    Assist me to proclaim,
And spread through all the earth
    abroad
    The honour of Thy name.

3 Jesus ! the name that charms our
    fears,
    That bids our sorrows cease ;
'Tis music in the sinner's ears,
    'Tis life and health and peace.

4 He breaks the power of cancelled sin,
    He sets the prisoner free ;
His blood can make the foulest clean,
    His blood avails for me.

58 O FOR a faith that will not shrink
    Though pressed by many a foe,
That will not tremble on the brink
    Of poverty or woe ;

2 That will not murmur nor complain
    Beneath the chastening rod,
But, in the hour of grief or pain,
    Can lean upon its God.

3 A faith that shines more bright and
    clear
  When tempests rage without,
That when in danger knows no fear,
  In darkness feels no doubt.

4 A faith that keeps the narrow way
  Till life's last spark is fled,
And with a pure and heavenly ray
  Lights up a dying bed.

5 Lord, give me such a faith as this,
  And then, whate'er may come,
I taste even now the hallowed bliss
  Of an eternal home.

59 COME let us to the Lord our God
  With contrite hearts return :
Our God is gracious, nor will leave
  The desolate to mourn.

2 His voice commands the tempest
    forth,
  And stills the stormy wave ;
And though His arm be strong to
    smite,
  'Tis also strong to save.

3 Long hath the night of sorrow
    reigned,
  The dawn shall bring us light ;
God shall appear, and we shall rise
  With gladness in His sight.

4 Our hearts, if God we seek to know,
  Shall know Him and rejoice ;
His coming like the morn shall be,
  Like morning songs His voice.

5 As dew upon the tender herb,
  Diffusing fragrance round ;
As showers that usher in the spring,
  And cheer the thirsty ground,

6 So shall His presence bless our souls
  And shed a joyful light ;
That hallowed morn shall chase away
  The sorrows of the night.

60 HARK, the glad sound, the
    Saviour comes,
  The Saviour promised long :
Let every heart prepare a throne,
  And every voice a song.

2 He comes, the prisoners to release,
  In Satan's bondage held :
The gates of brass before Him burst,
  The iron fetters yield.

3 He comes from thickest films of vice
  To clear the mental ray,
And on the eyeballs of the blind,
  To pour celestial day.

4 He comes, the broken heart to bind,
  The bleeding soul to cure,
And with the treasures of His grace
  To enrich the humble poor.

5 Our glad hosannas, Prince of Peace,
  Thy welcome shall proclaim ;
And heaven's eternal arches ring
  With Thy beloved name.

61 O THOU, my soul, bless God the
    Lord,
  And all that in me is
Be stirred up, His holy name
  To magnify and bless.

2 Bless, O my soul, the Lord thy God,
  And not forgetful be
Of all His gracious benefits
  He hath bestowed on thee.

3 All thine iniquities who doth
  Most graciously forgive ;
Who thy diseases all and pains
  Doth heal, and thee relieve.

4 Who doth redeem thy life, that thou
  To death may'st not go down :
Who thee with loving kindness doth
  And tender mercies crown.

62 I TO the hills will lift mine eyes,
    From whence doth come mine
    aid ;
My safety cometh from thee Lord,
  Who heaven and earth hath made.

2 Thy foot He'll not let slide, nor will
  He slumber that thee keeps :
Behold, He that keeps Israel,
  He slumbers not, nor sleeps.

3 The Lord thee keeps, the Lord thy
    shade
  On thy right hand doth stay :
The moon by night thee shall not
    smite,
  Nor yet the sun by day.

4 The Lord shall keep thy soul : He
    shall
  Preserve thee from all ill ;
Henceforth thy going out and in
  God keep for ever will.

63 TO Him that loved the souls of
men,
And washed us in His blood,
To royal honours raised our head,
And made us priests to God ;

2 To Him let every tongue be praise,
And every heart be love !
All grateful honours paid on earth,
And nobler songs above !

3 Behold, on flying clouds He comes !
His saints shall bless the day ;
While they that pierced Him sadly
mourn
In anguish and dismay.

4 I am the First, and I the Last,
Time centres all in Me ;
Th' Almighty God, who was, and is,
And evermore shall be.

64 WHAT though no flow'rs the fig-
tree clothe,
Though vines their fruit deny,
The labour of the olive fail,
And fields no meat supply ?

2 Though from the fold, with sad sur-
My flock cut off I see ;   [prise,
Though famine pine in empty stalls,
Where herds were wont to be ;

3 Yet in the Lord will I be glad,
And glory in His love ;
In Him I'll joy, who will the God
Of my salvation prove.

4 He to my tardy feet shall lend
The swiftness of the roe ;
Till, rais'd on high, I safely dwell
Beyond the reach of woe.

5 God is the treasure of my soul,
The source of lasting joy ;
A joy which want shall not impair,
Nor death itself destroy.

65 REVIVE Thy work, O Lord !
Thy mighty arm make bare ;
Speak with the voice that wakes
the dead,
And make Thy people hear !
Revive Thy work, O Lord,
While here to Thee we bow ;
Descend, O gracious Lord, descend
Oh, come and bless us now !

2 Revive Thy work, O Lord !
Disturb this sleep of death ;
Quicken the smould'ring embers now
By Thine Almighty breath.

3 Revive Thy work, O Lord !
Create soul-thirst for Thee ;
And hung'ring for the Bread of life,
Oh, may our spirits be !

4 Revive Thy work, O Lord !
Exalt Thy precious name :
And by the Holy Ghost, our love
For Thee and Thine inflame.

66 I WILL sing the wondrous story
Of the Christ who died for me ;
How He left His home in glory,
For the Cross on Calvary.
Yes, I'll sing the wondrous story
Of the Christ who died for me ;
Sing it with the saints in glory,
Gathered by the crystal sea.

2 I was lost ; but Jesus found me—
Found the sheep that went astray ;
Threw His loving arms around me,
Drew me back into His way.

3 I was bruised ; but Jesus healed me—
Faint was I from many a fall ;
Sight was gone and fears possessed
me ;
But He freed me from them all.

4 Days of darkness still come o'er me ;
Sorrow's paths I often tread ;
But the Saviour still is with me,
By His hand I'm safely led.

5 He will keep me till the river
Rolls its waters at my feet ;
Then He'll bear me safely over,
Where the loved ones I shall meet.

67 LOVE divine, all love excelling,
Joy of heaven, to earth come
down !
Fix in us Thy humble dwelling,
All Thy faithful mercies crown.
Jesus, Thou art all compassion,
Pure, unbounded love Thou art ;
Visit us with Thy salvation,
Enter every trembling heart.

2 Breathe, oh, breathe Thy loving
Spirit
Into every troubled breast !
Let us all in Thee inherit,
Let us find the promised rest ;
Take away the love of sinning,
Alpha and Omega be ;
End of faith, as its beginning,
Set our hearts at liberty.

3 Come, almighty to deliver,
  Let us all Thy grace receive !
Suddenly return, and never,
  Never more Thy temples leave,
Thee we would be always blessing,
  Serve Thee as Thy hosts above,
Pray, and praise Thee without ceas-
  Glory in Thy perfect love.   [ing,

4 Finish then Thy new creation,
  Pure and spotless may we be ;
Let us see our whole salvation
  Perfectly secured by Thee !
Changed from glory into glory,
  Till in Heaven we take our place ;
Till we cast our crowns before Thee,
  Lost in wonder, love, and praise.

68 THE Head that once was crowned
    with thorns
  Is crowned with glory now :
A royal diadem adorns
  The mighty Victor's brow.

2 The highest place that heaven affords
  Is His by sovereign right :
The King of kings and Lord of lords,
  He reigns in perfect light.

3 The joy of all who dwell above,
  The joy of all below
To whom He manifests His love,
  And grants His name to know.

4 To them the Cross, with all its shame,
  With all its grace, is given :
Their name, an everlasting name,
  Their joy, the joy of heaven.

69 ARISE, my soul, arise,
    Shake off thy guilty fears !
The bleeding sacrifice
  In my behalf appears ;
Before the throne my Surety stands,
His name is written on His hands.

2 He ever lives above
  For me to intercede ;
His all-redeeming love,
  His precious blood will plead ;
His blood atoned for all our race,
And sprinkles now the throne of
  grace.

3 Five bleeding wounds He bears,
  Received on Calvary ;
They pour effectual prayers,
  They strongly plead for me ;
" Forgive him, oh, forgive," they cry,
" Nor let that ransomed sinner die."

4 My God is reconciled,
  His pard'ning voice I hear ;
He owns me for His child,
  I can no longer fear ;
With confidence I now draw nigh,
And " Father, Abba Father ! " cry.

70 THERE is no name so sweet on
    earth,
  No name so sweet in heaven,
The name, before His wondrous
    birth,
  To Christ the Saviour given.
    We love to sing of Christ our King,
    And hail Him blessed Jesus !
    For there's no word ear ever heard
    So dear, so sweet as " Jesus."

2 And when He hung upon the tree
  They wrote this name above Him,
That all might see the reason we
  For evermore must love Him.

3 So now, upon His Father's throne—
  Almighty to release us
From sin and pain—He ever reigns
  The Prince and Saviour, Jesus.

4 O Jesus ! by that matchless Name
  Thy grace shall fail us never ;
To-day as yesterday the same,
  Thou art the same for ever !

71 IN the field with their flocks
    abiding,
  They lay on the dewy ground ;
And glimmering under the starlight
  The sheep lay white around,
When the light of the Lord spread
    o'er them,
  And lo ! from the heaven above,
An angel leaned from the glory
  And sang his song of love—
    He sang, that first sweet Christmas,
    The song that shall never cease,
    " Glory to God in the highest,
    On earth good-will and peace."

2 " To you in the City of David,
  A Saviour is born to-day ! "
And suddenly a host of the heavenly
    ones
  Flashed forth to join the lay.
O never hath sweeter message
  Thrilled home to the souls of men,
And the heavens themselves have
    never heard
  A gladder choir, till then.

For they sang that Christmas carol,
    That never on earth shall cease,
" Glory to God in the highest,
    On earth good-will and peace."

3 And the shepherds came to the
    manger,
  And gazed on the Holy Child ;
And calmly o'er that rude cradle
    The Virgin Mother smiled ;
And the sky, in the starlight silence,
    Seem'd full of the angel lay ;
" To you in the City of David
    A Saviour is born.to-day ; "

O they sang—and I ween that never
    The carol on earth shall cease,
" Glory to God in the highest,
    On earth good-will and peace."

72 WE sing the praise of Him who
    died,
Of Him who died upon the Cross,
The sinner's hope—though men
    deride,
  For Him we count the world but
    loss.

2 Inscribed upon the Cross we see,
  In shining letters, " God is Love!"
The Lamb who died upon the tree
  Has brought us mercy from above.

3 The Cross, it takes our guilt away,
  It holds the fainting spirit up ;
It cheers with hope the gloomy day,
  And sweetens every bitter cup.

4 It makes the coward spirit brave,
  And nerves the feeble arm for
    fight ;
It takes its terror from the grave,
  And gilds the bed of death with
    light.

73 O WORSHIP the King all glorious
    above,
  O gratefully sing His power and His
    love,
Our Shield and Defender, the
    Ancient of Days,
Pavilioned in splendour, and girded
    with praise.

2 O tell of His might, O sing of His
    grace,
  Whose robe is the light, whose
    canopy space.

His chariots of wrath deep thunder-
    clouds form,
And dark is His path on the wings
    of the storm.

3 This earth with its store of wonders
    untold,
Almighty, Thy power hath founded
    of old,
Hath 'stablished it fast by a change-
    less decree,
And round it hath cast, like a mantle,
    the sea.

4 Thy bountiful care what tongue can
    recite ?
It breathes in the air ; it shines in
    the light ;
It streams from the hills ; it descends
    to the plain,
And sweetly distils in the dew and
    the rain.

74 YE servants of God,
    Your Master proclaim,
  And publish abroad
    His Wonderful Name ;
The Name all victorious
    Of Jesus extol ;
His kingdom is glorious,
    And rules over all.

2 God ruleth on high,
    Almighty to save ;
And still He is nigh,
    His presence we have !
The great congregation
    His triumph shall sing,
Ascribing salvation
    To Jesus our King.

3 " Salvation to God
    Who sits on the throne "
Let all cry aloud,
    And honour the Son.
The praises of Jesus
    All angels proclaim,
Fall down on their faces,
    And worship the Lamb.

4 Then let us adore
    And give Him His right,
All glory and power,
    All wisdom and might ;
All honour and blessing,
    With angels above ;
And thanks never-ceasing,
    And infinite love.

THE GOSPEL

75 I AM a stranger here within a
  foreign land,
My home is far away upon a golden
  strand ;
Ambassador to be of realms beyond
  the sea,
I'm here on business for my King.

> This is the message that I bring,
> A message angels fain would sing :
> " Oh, be ye reconciled,"
> Thus saith my Lord and King,
> " Oh, be ye reconciled to God ! "

2 This is the King's command, that
  all men everywhere
Repent and turn away from sin's
  seductive snare ;
That all who will obey, with Him
  shall reign for aye,
And that's my business for my King.

3 My home is brighter far than
  Sharon's rosy plain,
Eternal life and joy throughout its
  vast domain ;
My Sovereign bids me tell how
  mortals there may dwell,
And that's my business for my King.

76 THAT grand word, " Whosoever,"
  is ringing through my soul,
Whosoever will may come ;
In rivers of salvation the living
  waters roll,
Whosoever will may come.

> Oh, that " Who...soev...er ! "
> Whosoever will may come ;
> The Saviour's invitation is freely sounding
> Whosoever will may come. [still,

2 Whenever this sweet message in
  God's own Word I see,
Whosoever will may come ;
I know 'tis meant for sinners, I
  know 'tis meant for me,
Whosoever will may come.

3 I heard the loving message, and now
  to others say,
Whosoever will may come ;
Seek now the precious Saviour, and
  He'll be yours to-day,
Whosoever will may come.

4 To God be all the glory ! His only
  Son He gave,
Whosoever will may come ;

And those who come believing, He'll
  to the utmost save,
Whosoever will may come.

77 UNDER the burden of guilt and
  care,
Many a spirit is grieving,
Who in the joy of the Lord might
  share,
Life everlasting receiving.

> Life ! life ! eternal life !
> Jesus alone is the Giver !
> Life ! life ! abundant life !
> Glory to Jesus for ever !

2 Burdened one, why will you longer
  bear
Sorrows from which He releases ?
Open your heart and rejoicing share
Life " more abundant " in Jesus.

3 Leaving the mountain, the streamlet
  grows,
Flooding the vale with a river ;
So, from the hill of the Cross there
  flows
Life " more abundant " for ever.

4 Oh for the floods on the thirsty land !
Oh for a mighty revival !
Oh for a sanctified, fearless band,
Ready to hail its arrival.

78 WOULD you be free from your
  burden of sin ?
There's power in the blood, power
  in the blood.
Would you o'er evil a victory win ?
There's wonderful power in the
  blood.

> There is power,..power,..wonder-working
>   power,
> In the blood..of the Lamb,..
> There is power,..power,..wonder-working
>   power.
> In the precious blood of the Lamb.

2 Would you be free from your passion
  and pride ?
There's power in the blood, power
  in the blood.
Come for a cleansing to Calvary's
  tide,
There's wonderful power in the
  blood.

3 Would you be whiter, much whiter
      than snow ?
   There's power in the blood, power
      in the blood.   [flow,
   Sin stains are lost in its life-giving
   There's wonderful power in the
      blood.

4 Would you do service for Jesus your
      King ?
   There's power in the blood, power
      in the blood.
   Would you live daily His praises to
      sing ?
   There's wonderful power in the
      blood.

79 YOU may have the joy-bells
         ringing in your heart,
   And a peace that from you never
      will depart ;
         Walk the straight and narrow
            way,
         Live for Jesus every day,
   He will keep the joy-bells ringing
      in your heart.

      Joy..bells....ringing in your heart,
      Joy..bells....ringing in your heart ;
      Take the Saviour here below,
      With you everywhere you go ;
      He will keep the joy-bells
      Ringing in your heart.

2 Love of Jesus in its fulness you may
      know,
   And this love to those around you
      sweetly show;
         Words of kindness always say,
         Deeds of mercy do each day,
   Then He'll keep the joy-bells ringing
      in your heart.

3 You will meet with trials as you
      journey home,
   Grace sufficient He will give to over-
      come ;
         Though unseen by mortal eye,
         He is with you, ever nigh,
   And He'll keep the joy-bells ringing
      in your heart.

4 Let your life speak well of Jesus
      every day,
   Own His right to every service you
      can pay ;
         Sinners you can help to win,
         If your life is pure and clean,
   And you keep the joy-bells ringing in
      your heart.

80   THEY tell me the story of Jesus
            is old,
         And they ask that we preach
            something new;
      They say that the Babe and the Man
         of the cross   [do.
      For the wise of this world will not

   It can never grow old, it can never grow old,
   Though a million times over the story is told;
   While sin lives unvanquished, and death rules
      the world,
   The story of Jesus can never grow old.

2 Yet the story is old, as the sunlight
      is old,
      Though it's new every morn all
         the same;
   As it floods all the world with its
      gladness and light,
      Kindling far away stars by its
         flame.

3 For what can we tell to the weary of
      heart,   [sin?
      If we preach not salvation from
   And how can we comfort the souls
      that depart,
      If we tell not how Christ rose again?

4 So, with sorrow we turn from the
      wise of this world
      To the wanderers far from the fold;
   With hearts for the message they'll
      join in our song,
      That the story can never grow old.

81   WAS it for me, for me alone,
            The Saviour left His glorious
               throne,
      The dazzling splendours of the sky ?
      Was it for me He came to die ?

      It was for me,....yes, all for me,....
      O love of God,.....so great, so free,....
      O wondrous love,....I'll shout and sing,....
      He died for me,.....my Lord and King !

2 Was it for me sweet angel strains
   Came floating o'er Judea's plains,
   That starlight night so long ago ?
   Was it for me God planned it so ?

3 Was it for me the Saviour said,
   " Pillow thy weary, aching head,
   Trustingly on thy Saviour's breast?"
   Was it for me ? Can I thus rest ?

4 Was it for me He wept and prayed,
   My load of sin before Him laid,
   That night within Gethsemane ?
   Was it for me, that agony ?

5 Was it for me He bowed His head
  Upon the Cross, and freely shed
  His precious blood—that crimson
    tide ?
  Was it for me the Saviour died ?

82 THERE'S a hill lone and grey, in
    a land far away,
  In a country beyond the blue sea,
  Where beneath that fair sky went a
    Man forth to die   [me.
  For the world and for you and for
    Oh, it bows down the heart,
    And the tear-drops will start
      When in memory that grey hill I see,
    For 'twas there on its side
    Jesus suffered and died,
      To redeem a poor sinner like me.

2 Behold ! faint on the road, 'neath a
    world's heavy load,
  Comes a thorn-crowned Man on
    the way,
  With a cross He is bowed, but still on
    through the crowd   [grey.
  He's ascending that hill lone and

3 Hark ! I hear the dull blow of the
    hammer swung low ;
  They are nailing my Lord to the
    tree,
  And the cross they upraise while the
    multitude gaze
  On the blest Lamb of dark
    Calvary.

4 How they mock Him in death, to
    His last labouring breath,
  While His friends sadly weep o'er
    the way !
  But though lonely and faint, still no
    word of complaint
  Fell from Him on the hill lone and
    grey.

5 Then the darkness came down and
    the rocks rent around,   [air ;
  And a cry pierced the grief-laden
  'Twas the voice of our King who
    received death's dark sting,
  All to save us from endless despair.

6 Let the sun hide its face, let the earth
    reel apace,
  Over men who their Saviour have
    slain ;
  But behold from the sod, comes the
    blest Lamb of God,
  Who was slain and is risen again.

83 COME, sinner, behold what Jesus
      hath done,
  Behold how He suffered for thee !
  They crucified Him, God's innocent
    Son,
  Forsaken, He died on the tree !
    They crucified Him, they crucified Him,
    They nailed Him to the tree ;
    And so there He died, a King crucified
    To save a poor sinner like me.

2 From heaven He came, He loved
    you—He died ;
  Such love as His never was known;
  Behold, on the Cross your King
    crucified,   [throne !
  To make you an heir to His

3 No pitying eye, a saving arm, none,
  He saw us and pitied us then ;
  Alone, in the fight, the victory He
    won ;
  O praise Him, ye children of men !

4 They crucified Him, and yet He
    forgave,   [cried ;
  " My Father, forgive them," He
  What must He have borne, the
    sinner to save,
  When under the burden He died !

5 So what will you do with Jesus your
    King ?   [last ?
  Say, how will you meet Him at
  What plea in the day of wrath will
    you bring,
  When offers of mercy are past ?

84 THE atoning blood is flowing—
      Let all the tidings hear ;
  The gospel word is showing
    How sinners may draw near.
  The atoning blood's relieving
    The prisoners from their chains,
  And sinners in believing
    Lose all their guilty stains.
    It is the blood,....the precious blood,....
    It is the blood,....the precious blood,....
  It is the blood that maketh an atonement for
    the soul.

2 The atoning blood is saving
    Sinners of deepest dye,
  And multitudes are having
    Free titles to the sky.
  The atoning blood is healing
    The souls that sin had slain ;
  Rejoicing saints are feeling
    The promised " latter rain."

3 The atoning blood is bringing
  Poor lost ones to the fold,
And heavenly hosts are singing
  O'er multitudes untold.
The atoning blood is speaking
  To every precious soul
Who is salvation seeking,
  " Believe, and be made whole."

4 The atoning blood is staying
  The great avenging rod,
While men are still delaying
  To yield themselves to God.
The atoning blood is sealing
  The world's eternal doom ;
But, to thy soul appealing,
  Says, " Lost one, to Me come."

85 THERE is no love like the love
    of Jesus—
    Never to fade or fall,
Till into the fold of the peace of God
  He has gathered us all.
Jesus' love, precious love,
  Boundless and pure and free ;
Oh, turn to that love weary wandering soul,
  Jesus pleadeth with thee !

2 There is no eye like the eye of Jesus,
  Piercing so far away ;   [light
Ne'er out of the sight of its tender
  Can the wanderer stray.

3 There is no voice like the voice of
    Jesus—
  Tender and sweet its chime,
Like musical ring of a flowing spring
  In the bright summer time.

4 There is no heart like the heart of
    Jesus,
    Filled with a tender love ;
No throb nor throe that our hearts
    can know,
  But He feels it above.

86 A HAND all bruised and bleeding
    is knocking at the door,
    Is knocking at the door of your
      heart ;
It is the hand of Jesus, who long has
    knocked before,   [depart.
    Though oft you have told Him to
Oh, don't you hear Him knocking, knocking
    at the door ?
He's knocking at the door to come in ;
He wants an invitation to cross your threshold
    o'er,
Then Jesus will save you from all sin.

2 How often when in sickness, your
    body racked with pain,
  This knocking resounded in your
      ears !
How often in the night-time the
    knock would come again,
  So loud it would fill your soul with
      fears !

3 While standing by the casket of
    some departed friend,
  With sorrow your heart was sick
      and sore ;
What caused that train of thinking
    of how your life would end ?
  That hand was then knocking at
      the door.

4 Why will you keep Him knocking ?
    why don't you let Him in ?
  He'll fill your pathway with
      delight ;
That hand so torn and bleeding will
    wash away your sin,
  Oh, welcome the Saviour in
      to-night.

87 COME away to Jesus ; He is
    willing to forgive,
  His love will shine around you every
    moment that you live ;
  You'll find Him good and true, the
    pilgrim journey through,
  He'll do better for you than this
    world can do.
He'll do better for you than this world can do,
He's a mighty Saviour, He is good and true ;
He'll save you by His grace, until you see His
    face,
He'll do better for you than this world can do.

2 Come away to Jesus ; let illusive
    trifles go,
  For everlasting blessing He is able to
    bestow ;
  He'll answer when you pray, He'll
    take your sins away,
  Lead you up and onward to His
    perfect day.

3 Come away to Jesus ; from your
    earthly idols part,
  And take His great salvation, for it
    satisfies the heart ;
  He'll open to your view His treasures
    ever new,
  He'll do better for you than this
    world can do.

88 OH, the best friend to have is
Jesus,
When the cares of life upon you roll ;
He will heal the wounded heart,
He will strength and grace impart;
Oh, the best friend to have is Jesus.

The best friend to have is Je..sus,
The best friend to have is Je..sus.
He will help you when you fall,
He will hear you when you call ;
Oh, the best friend you have is Jesus.

2 What a friend I have found in Jesus !
Peace and comfort to my soul He
brings ;
Leaning on His mighty arm,
I will fear no ill or harm ;
Oh, the best friend to have is Jesus.

3 Though I pass through the night of
sorrow,
And the chilly waves of Jordan roll,
Never need I shrink or fear,
For my Saviour is so near ;
Oh, the best friend to have is Jesus.

4 When at last to our home we gather
With the loved ones who have gone
before,
We will sing upon the shore,
Praising Him for evermore ;
Oh, the best friend to have is Jesus.

89 " MAN of Sorrows," what a name
For the Son of God who came
Ruined sinners to reclaim !
Hallelujah ! what a Saviour !

2 Bearing shame and scoffing rude,
In my place condemned He stood ;
Sealed my pardon with His blood :
Hallelujah ! what a Saviour !

3 Guilty, vile, and helpless we,
Spotless Lamb of God was He,
" Full atonement," can it be ?
Hallelujah ! what a Saviour !

4 Lifted up was He to die,
" It is finished," was His cry,
Now in heaven exalted high ;
Hallelujah ! what a Saviour !

5 When He comes, our glorious King,
All His ransomed home to bring,
Then anew this song we'll sing :
Hallelujah ! what a Saviour !

90 WHEN I think of Him who hath
loved me so, [woe,
Who left His home for this vale of
Was cradled in a manger low—
Oh, it's a precious old story !

Oh, the dear old story, the precious story,
That fills my heart with grace and glory,
The sweetest song in heaven I'll sing,
'Twill be...the old, old story !

2 How He healed the sick and restored
the blind, [pined,
And cheered the heart that in sorrow
The tender Saviour, loving, kind,
Oh, it's a precious old story !

3 As wearied He sat at Samaria's well,
The story of love did sweetly tell,
His gracious words of mercy fell,
Oh, it's a precious old story !

4 My griefs He carried, my sorrows
bore, [He wore,
His brow was scarred by the thorns
But now He reigns for evermore,
Oh, it's a precious old story !

91 IS there any one can help us, one
who understands our hearts,
When the thorns of life have
pierced them till they bleed ;
One who sympathises with us, who
in wondrous love imparts
Just the very, very blessing that
we need ?

Yes, there's One,...only One,...
The blessed, blessed Jesus, He's the One !
When afflictions press the soul,
When waves of trouble roll,
And you need a friend to help you,
He's the One.

2 Is there anyone can help us, who can
give a sinner peace,
When his heart is burdened down
with pain and woe ;
Who can speak the word of pardon
that affords a sweet release,
And whose blood can wash and
make us white as snow ?

3 Is there anyone can help us, when
the end is drawing near,
Who will go through death's dark
waters by our side ;
Who will light the way before us, and
dispel all doubts and fear,
And will bear our spirits safely o'er
the tide ?

92 BY Samaria's wayside well,
Once a blessed message fell
On a woman's thirsty soul,
Long ago ;
And to eyes that long were sealed
Was the glorious light revealed,
Through a fountain that was opened
Long ago.

There's a fountain that was opened
Long ago, long ago,
For the healing of the nation is its flow ;
Along the line of ages the prophets and the sages
Caught the singing of its waters,
Long ago....

2 And a little captive maid
By a leper undismayed,
Told to him a simple story
Long ago ;
That the stream where he might lave
Had alone the power to save,
Through his trust in that old fountain,
Long ago.

3 And a woman in a crowd,
Without word or cry aloud,
Just stooped down and touched His
garment
Long ago ;
As her urgent need appealed,
So her sinful soul was healed
In that fountain that was opened
Long ago.

4 As the eunuch tried to read
Philip taught him of his need,
And baptized him in the stream
Long ago ;
As the outward seal and sign
Of an inward work divine,
That was wrought through that old
fountain
Long ago.

93 " WHOSOEVER heareth ! "
shout, shout the sound !
Send the blessed tidings all the world
around :   [man is found :
Spread the joyful news wherever
" Whosoever will may come."

" Whosoever will ! " " whosoever will ! "
Send the proclamation over vale and hill ;
'Tis the loving Father calls the wanderer home ;
" Whosoever will may come."

2 Whosoever cometh need not delay ;
Now the door is open, enter while
you may ;   [Way ;
Jesus is the true and only Living
" Whosoever will may come."

3 " Whosoever will ! " the promise is
secure ;
" Whosoever will," for ever shall
endure ;   [more ;
" Whosoever will "—'tis life for ever-
" Whosoever will may come."

94 " THOUGH your sins be as
scarlet,
They shall be as white as snow ;
Though they be red....like crimson,
They shall be as wool ;
Though your sins be as scarlet,
They shall be as white as snow."

2 Hear the voice that entreats you,
Oh, return ye unto God !
Hs is of great....compassion,
And of wondrous love ;
Hear the voice that entreats you,
Oh, return ye unto God !

3 He'll forgive your transgressions,
And remember them no more ;
" Look unto Me,....ye people,"
Saith the Lord your God ;
He'll forgive your transgressions,
And remember them no more.

95 SOFTLY and tenderly Jesus is
calling—
Calling for you and for me.
See on the portals He's waiting and
watching—
Watching for you and for me.

Come home,...come home,...
Ye who are weary, come home,...
Earnestly, tenderly Jesus is calling—
Calling, " O sinner, come home ! "

2 Why should we tarry when Jesus is
pleading,—
Pleading for you and for me ?
Why should we linger and heed not
His mercies,—
Mercies for you and for me ?

3 Time is now fleeting, the moments
are passing,—
Passing from you and from me.
Shadows are gathering, death-beds
are coming,—
Coming for you and for me.

4 Oh, for the wonderful love He has
promised,—
Promised for you and for me.
Though we have sinned He has
mercy and pardon,—
Pardon for you and for me.

96 COME, sinners, to the Living One,
He's just the same Jesus
As when He raised the widow's son,
The very same Jesus.

> The very same Jesus,
> The wonder-working Jesus ;
> Oh ! praise His name, He's just the same,
> The very same Jesus.

2 Come, feast upon the Living Bread,
He's just the same Jesus
As when the multitudes He fed,
The very same Jesus.

3 Come, tell Him all your griefs and
fears,
He's just the same Jesus
As when He shed those loving tears,
The very same Jesus.

4 Still follow Him for clearer light,
He's just the same Jesus [sight,
As when He gave the blind their
The very same Jesus.

5 Then calm 'midst waves of trouble
He's just the same Jesus [be,
As when He hushed the raging sea,
The very same Jesus.

6 Some day our raptured eyes shall see
He's just the same Jesus,
Oh, blessed day for you and me !
The very same Jesus.

97 WONDROUS love of Jesus !
spread the news around—
Pardon freely offered, what a joyful
sound ! [free ;
Jesus, loving Saviour, died to set me
Oh ! that blessed " Whosoever,"
that means me.

> Pardon freely offered all who will believe ;
> Whosoever cometh Jesus will receive ;
> Jesus, loving Saviour, died to set us free :
> Hallelujah ! " Whosoever," that means me.

2 " Whosoever " means me better
than my name, [same ?
Any one, every one, is not that the
Believing is salvation, present, full,
and free ; [means me.
" Whosoever " is the message, that

3 Whosoever cometh may the promise
claim, [every stain.
Precious blood of Jesus cleanseth
The Son of God has loved me,
wonder, can it be ?
" Whosoever," saith the Saviour,
that means me.

4 Do not trust your feelings, trust His
Word alone,
Prayer can never save you, tears
cannot atone.
Finished ! cried the Saviour ; noth-
ing now to do,
Come, believe this " Whosoever," that
means you.

98 I'VE a message from the Lord,
hallelujah !
The message unto you I'll give,
'Tis recorded in His Word, halle-
lujah ! [live."
It is only that you " look and

> " Look and live,"...my brother, live,...
> Look to Jesus now and live ;
> 'Tis recorded in His Word, Hallelujah !
> It is only that you " look and live."

2 I've a message full of love, hallelujah!
A message, O my friend, for you ;
'Tis a message from above, halle-
lujah !
Jesus said it, and I know 'tis true.

3 Life is offered unto you, hallelujah !
Eternal life your soul shall have,
If you'll only look to Him, halle-
lujah !
Look to Jesus, who alone can save.

99 WHAT can wash away my stain ?
Nothing but the blood of Jesus ;
What can make me whole again ?
Nothing but the blood of Jesus.

> Oh, precious is the flow
> That makes me white as snow ;
> No other fount I know,
> Nothing but the blood of Jesus.

2 For my cleansing this I see—
Nothing but the blood of Jesus ;
For my pardon this my plea,—
Nothing but the blood of Jesus.

3 Nothing can for sin atone,
Nothing but the blood of Jesus ;
Nought of good that I have done,
Nothing but the blood of Jesus.

4 This is all my hope and peace—
Nothing but the blood of Jesus ;
He is all my righteousness—
Nothing but the blood of Jesus.

5 Now by this I overcome ;
Nothing but the blood of Jesus !
Now by this I'll reach my home :
Nothing but the blood of Jesus.

00 OUT in the desert, seeking,
         seeking,
  Sinner, 'tis Jesus seeking for thee ;
Tenderly calling, calling, calling,
  " Hither, thou lost one, oh, come
    unto Me."

Jesus is seeking, Jesus is calling,
  Why dost thou linger, why tarry away ?
Run to Him quickly, say to Him gladly,
  Lord, I am coming, coming to-day.

2 Still He is waiting, waiting, waiting,
  Oh, what compassion beams in
    His eye,
Hear Him repeating, gently, gently,
  " Come to the Saviour, oh, why
    wilt thou die ? "

3 Lovingly pleading, pleading, plead-
    ing,
  Mercy, though slighted, bears with
    thee yet ;
Thou canst be happy, happy, happy,
Come, ere thy life star for ever
    shall set.

4 Spirits in glory, watching, watching,
  Long to behold thee safe in the
    fold ;
Angels are waiting, waiting, waiting,
  When shall thy story with rapture
    be told ?

101 WE'RE bound for the land of
    the pure and the holy,
  The home of the happy, the
    kingdom of love ;
Ye wanderers from God in the broad
  road of folly,   [above ?
Oh ! say, will you go to the Eden
Will you go?
Oh ! say, will you go to the Eden above?

2 In that blessed land neither sighing
    nor anguish
  Can breathe in the fields where the
    glorified rove ;
Ye heart-burdened ones, who in
  misery languish,   [above ?
Oh ! say, will you go to the Eden

3 March on, happy pilgrims, the land
    is before you,
  And soon its ten thousand delights
    we shall prove ;
Yes, soon we shall march o'er the
    hills of bright glory,
  And drink the pure joys of the
    Eden above ?

102 THERE'S a stranger at the door,
    Let....Him in....
He has been there oft before,
    Let....Him in....
Let Him in, ere He is gone,
Let Him in, the Holy One,
Jesus Christ, the Father's Son,
    Let....Him in....

2 Open now to Him your heart,
    Let....Him in ;....
If you wait He will depart,
    Let....Him in ;....
Let Him in, He is your Friend,
He your soul will sure defend,
He will keep you to the end,
    Let....Him in....

3 Hear you now His loving voice ?
    Let....Him in ;....
Now, oh now, make Him your choice,
    Let....Him in ;....
He is standing at the door,
Joy to you He will restore,
And His name you will adore,
    Let....Him in....

4 Now admit the heavenly Guest,
    Let....Him in ;....
He will make for you a feast,
    Let....Him in ;....
He will speak your sins forgiven,
And when earth ties all are riven,
He will take you home to heaven,
    Let....Him in.....

103 CHRIST has for sin atonement
    made,
  What a wonderful Saviour !
We are redeemed ! the price is paid :
  What a wonderful Saviour !

What a wonderful Saviour is Jesus, my Jesus!
What a wonderful Saviour is Jesus, my Lord !

2 I praise Him for the cleansing blood,
  What a wonderful Saviour !
That reconciled my soul to God,
  What a wonderful Saviour !

3 He dwells within me day by day,
  What a wonderful Saviour !
And keeps me faithful all the way,
  What a wonderful Saviour !

4 He gives me overcoming power,
  What a wonderful Saviour !
And triumph in each conflict hour,
  What a wonderful Saviour !

5 To Him I've given all my heart,
    What a wonderful Saviour !
The world shall never share a part,
    What a wonderful Saviour !

104 BLESSED be the fountain of
        blood,
    To a world of sinners revealed ;
Blessed be the dear Son of God ;
    Only by His stripes are we healed.
Though I've wandered far from His
        fold,   [woe,
    Bringing to my heart pain and
Wash me in the blood of the Lamb,
    And I shall be whiter than snow.

Whit - - er than the snow....
Whit - - er than the snow,....
Wash me in the blood of the Lamb,....
And I shall be whiter than snow.....

2 Thorny was the crown that He wore,
    And the cross His body o'ercame ;
Grievous were the sorrows He bore,
    But He suffered thus not in vain.
May I to that Fountain be led,
    Made to cleanse my sins here
        below ;
Wash me in the blood that He shed,
    And I shall be whiter than snow.

3 Father, I have wandered from Thee,
    Often has my heart gone astray ;
Crimson do my sins seem to me :
    Water cannot wash them away.
Jesus, to that Fountain of Thine,
    Leaning on Thy promise I go,
Cleanse me by Thy washing divine,
    And I shall be whiter than snow.

105 COME to Jesus, come to Jesus,
    Come to Jesus just now ;
    Just now come to Jesus,
    Come to Jesus just now.

    2 He will save you.
    3 He is able.
    4 Only trust Him.
    5 Call upon Him.
    6 He will hear you.
    7 Look to Jesus.
    8 He'll forgive you.
    9 Don't reject Him.
    10 Hallelujah. Amen.

106 BEHOLD Me standing at the
        door,
And hear Me pleading evermore,

With gentle voice, oh, heart of sin,
May I come in ? may I come in ?

Behold Me standing at the door,
And hear Me pleading evermore ;
Say, weary heart, opprest with sin,
May I come in? may I come in?

2 I bore the cruel thorns for thee,
    I waited long and patiently,
Say, weary heart, opprest with sin
May I come in ? may I come in ?

3 I would not plead with thee in vain
    Remember all My grief and pain !
I died to ransom thee from sin,
May I come in ? may I come in ?

4 I bring thee joy from heaven above
    I bring thee pardon, peace, and love
Say, weary heart, opprest with sin,
May I come in ? may I come in ?

107 THERE is a story sweet to hear
        I love to tell it too ;
It fills my heart with hope and cheer.
    'Tis old, yet ever new.

    'Tis old,....yet ever new,
    'Tis old,....yet ever new,
    I know,....I feel 'tis true,
    'Tis old, yet ever new.

2 It tells me God the Son came down
    From glory's throne to die,
That I might live and wear a crown,
    And reign with Him on high.

3 It says He bore the Cross for me,
    And suffered in my place,
That I from sin might ransomed be,
    And praise Him for His grace.

4 Oh wondrous love, so great, so vast,
    So boundless and so free !
Lord, at Thy feet myself I cast :
    My all I give to Thee !

108 ONE there is above all others,
        Oh, how He loves !
His is love beyond a brother's,
        Oh, how He loves !
Earthly friends may fail or leave us,
One day soothe, the next day grieve
    us,
But this Friend will ne'er deceive us,
    Oh, how He loves !

2 'Tis eternal life to know Him,
        Oh, how He loves !   [Him,
Think, oh think, how much we owe
    Oh, how He loves !

With His precious blood He bought
  us,
In the wilderness He sought us,
To His fold He safely brought us,
  Oh, how He loves !

We have found a Friend in Jesus,
  Oh, how He loves !
'Tis His great delight to bless us,
  Oh, how He loves !
How our hearts delight to hear Him,
Bid us dwell in safety near Him !
Why should we distrust or fear Him ?
  Oh, how He loves !

Through His name we are forgiven,
  Oh, how He loves !
Backward shall our foes be driven,
  Oh, how He loves !
Best of blessings He'll provide us,
Nought but good shall e'er betide us,
Safe to glory He will guide us,
  Oh, how He loves !

109   HARK ! 'tis the Shepherd's
               voice I hear,
Out in the desert dark and drear,
Calling the lambs who've gone astray,
Far from the Shepherd's fold away.

> Bring them in, bring them in,
> Bring them in from the fields of sin ;
> Bring them in bring them in,
> Bring the wandering ones to Jesus.

2 Who'll go and help this Shepherd
     kind,
  Help Him the wandering lambs to
     find ?
  Who'll bring the lost ones to the fold,
  Where they'll be sheltered from the
     cold ?

3 Out in the desert hear their cry ;
  Out on the mountain wild and high ;
  Hark ! 'tis the Master speaks to
     thee,   [be."
  " Go, find My lambs, where'er they

110   THERE'S not a Friend like the
               lowly Jesus,
  No, not one ! no, not one !
None else can heal all our soul's
  diseases,
  No, not one ! no, not one !

Jesus knows all about our struggles,
He will guide till the day is done.
There's not a friend like the lowly Jesus,
No, not one ! no, not one !

2 No friend like Him is so high and
     holy,
     No, not one ! no, not one !
  And yet no friend is so meek and
     lowly,
     No, not one ! no, not one !

3 There's not an hour that He is not
     near us,
     No, not one ! no, not one !
  No night so dark but His love can
     cheer us,
     No, not one ! no, not one !

4 Did ever saint find this Friend for-
     sake him ?
     No, not one ! no, not one !
  Or sinner find that He would not
     take him ?
     No, not one ! no, not one !

5 Was e'er a gift like the Saviour given?
     No, not one ! no, not one !
  Will He refuse us a home in heaven ?
     No, not one ! no, not one !

111   WHENE'ER we meet you
               always say,
     What's the news ?
  Pray what's the order of the day ?
     What's the news ?
  Oh ! I have got good news to tell,
  My Saviour hath done all things well,
  And triumphed over death and hell,
     That's the news.

2 The Lamb was slain on Calvary,
     That's the news,
  To set a world of sinners free,
     That's the news.
  For us He bowed His sacred head,
  For us His precious blood was shed :
  And now He's risen from the dead,
     That's the news.

3 The Lord has pardoned all my sin,
     That's the news.
  I feel the witness now within,
     That's the news.
  And since He took my guilt away,
  And taught me how to watch and
     pray,
  I'm happy now, from day to day,
     That's the news.

4 And Jesus Christ can save you too,
     That's the news.
  Your sinful heart He can renew,
     That's the news.

This moment, if for sin you grieve,
This moment, if you do believe,
A ready pardon you'll receive,
    That's the news.

5 And then if anyone should say,
    What's the news ?
Oh, tell them you've begun to pray,
    That's the news.
That you have joined the conquering
    band,   [mand
And now with joy at God's com-
You're marching to the better land,
    That's the news.

112 WE'RE marching on to heaven
    above,
    Will you go ?
To sing the Saviour's dying love—
    Will you go ?   [shore,
Millions have reached that blissful
Their trials and their labours o'er,
And yet there's room for millions
    more—
    Will you go ?

2 The way to heaven is strait, but plain,
    Will you come ?
Repent, believe, be born again,
    Will you come ?
Christ offers pardon free to all,
Who will accept His loving call,
And at His feet repentant fall—
    Will you come ?

3 How blessed 'tis to serve Him here !
    Praise the Lord !
Redeemed from every doubt and fear
    Praise the Lord !
Though tribulation cross our way,
Affliction or adversity,
Yet Jesus saves us every day,
    Praise the Lord !

4 And when our day of fighting's o'er,
    Home at last !
We'll praise Him on the other shore,
    Home at last !
We'll join again in songs of praise
With those who see the Master's face,
And ever sing redeeming grace—
    Home at last !

113 COME, for the feast is spread ;
    Hark to the call !
Come to the Living Bread,
    Broken for all ;

Come to His " house of wine,"
Low on His breast recline,
All that He hath make thine ;
    Come, sinner, come.

2 Come, where the fountain flows—
    River of life—
Healing for all thy woes,
    Doubting and strife :
Millions have been supplied,
No one was e'er denied ;
Come to the crimson tide,
    Come, sinner, come.

3 Come to the Throne of Grace,
    Boldly draw near ;
He who would win the race
    Must tarry here ;
Whate'er thy want may be,
Here is the grace for thee,
Jesus thy only plea ;
    Come, Christian, come.

4 Jesus, we come to Thee,
    Oh, take us in !
Set Thou our spirits free ;
    Cleanse us from sin ;
Then, in yon land of light,
All clothed in robes of white,
Resting not day nor night,
    Thee will we sing.

114 GOD loved the world of sinners
    lost
    And ruined by the fall,
Salvation full at highest cost,
    He offers free to all.

> Oh, 'twas love, 'twas wondrous love,
>   The love of God to me ;
> It brought my Saviour from above,
>   To die on Calvary.

2 Eternal praises, Lord, to Thee,
    Thou blessed Son of God ;
For Thy deep love in cleansing me,
    In Thy most precious blood !

3 Even now by faith, I know I'm
    Thine,
    'Tis in Thy faithful Word ;
Oh, height, oh, depth of love divine,
    In Thee, the risen Lord !

4 Oh, help me, Lord, to spread Thy
    fame,
    And tell of all Thy grace,
To all the world Thy love proclaim,
    Until I see Thy face.

115 JESUS, my Saviour, to Bethlehem came,
Born in a manger to sorrow and
shame ;
Oh, it was wonderful—blest be His
name !
Seeking for me, for me !

Seeking for me ! for me !..
Seeking for me ! for me !..
Oh, it was wonderful—blest be His Name !
Seeking for me, for me !

2 Jesus, my Saviour, on Calvary's tree,
Paid the great debt, and my soul He
set free ;   [be ?
Oh, it was wonderful—how could it
Dying for me, for me !

Dying for me ! for me !..
Dying for me ! for me !..
Oh, it was wonderful—how could it be?
Dying for me, for me !

3 Jesus, my Saviour, the same as of
old,   [fold,
When I was wand'ring afar from the
Gently and long He did plead with
my soul,
Calling for me, for me !

Calling for me ! for me !..
Calling for me ! for me !..
Gently and long did He plead with my soul,
Calling for me, for me !

4 Jesus, my Saviour, shall come from
on high—
Sweet is the promise as weary years
fly ;   [sky,
Oh, I shall see Him descending the
Coming for me, for me !

Coming for me ! for me !
Coming for me ! for me !..
Oh, I shall see Him descending the sky,
Coming for me, for me !

116 OH, sing of Jesus, "Lamb of
God,"
Who died on Calvary !
And for a ransom shed His blood
For you, and even me !

I'm redeem'd,...I'm redeem'd,..
Through the blood of the Lamb that
was slain,..
I'm redeem'd,..I'm redeem'd,..
Hallelujah to God and the Lamb !

2 Oh, wondrous power of love divine !
So rich, so full, so free !
It reaches out to all mankind,
Embraces even me !
B

3 All glory now to Christ the Lord,
And evermore shall be !
He hath redeemed a world of sin,
And ransomed even me !

117 ONE there is who loves thee,
Waiting still for thee ;
Canst thou yet reject Him ?
None so kind as He !
Do not grieve Him longer,
Come, and trust Him now !
He has waited all thy days ;
Why waitest thou ?

One there is who loves thee,
Oh, receive Him now !
He has waited all the day ;
Why waitest thou ?

2 Graciously He woos thee,
Do not slight His call ;
Though thy sins are many,
He'll forgive them all.
Turn to Him, repenting,
He will cleanse thee now ;
He is waiting at thy heart :
Why waitest thou ?

3 Jesus still is waiting ;
Sinner, why delay ?
To His arms of mercy
Rise and haste away !
Only come believing,
He will save thee now ;
He is waiting at the door,
Why waitest thou ?

118 A RULER once came to Jesus
by night,   [light ;
To ask Him the way of salvation and
The Master made answer in words
true and plain,
" Ye must be born again."...

" Ye must be born again !
" Ye must be born again !
" I verily, verily say unto you—
" Ye must be born again ! "

2 Ye children of men, attend to the
word   [Lord,
So solemnly uttered by Jesus, the
And let not this message to you be
in vain,
" Ye must be born again."...

3 O ye who would enter the glorious rest,
And sing with the ransomed the song
of the blest ;   [obtain,
The life everlasting if ye would
" Ye must be born again."...

4 A dear one in heaven thy heart
    yearns to see,
  At the beautiful gates may be
    watching for thee ;
  Then list to the note of this solemn
    refrain,
  " Ye must be born again.".....

119 WILL you come, will you come,
    with your poor broken heart,
    Burdened and sin oppressed ?
  Lay it down at the feet of the
    Saviour and Lord,
  Jesus will give you rest.

    O happy rest, sweet happy rest,
    Jesus will give you rest...   [faith ?
  Oh ! why won't you come in simple trusting
    Jesus will give you rest.

2 Will you come, will you come ? there
    is mercy for you,
  Balm for your aching breast :
  Only come as you are and believe
    on His name,
  Jesus will give you rest.

3 Will you come, will you come ? you
    have nothing to pay ;
  Jesus who loves you best,
  By His death on the cross purchased
    life for your soul ;
  Jesus will give you rest.

4 Will you come, will you come ? how
    He pleads with you now !
  Fly to His loving breast ;
  And whatever your sin or your
    sorrow may be,
  Jesus will give you rest.

120 'TIS the grandest theme
    through the ages rung ;
  'Tis the grandest theme for a mortal
    tongue ;
  'Tis the grandest theme that the
    world e'er sung :
  " Our God is able to deliver thee."

    He is a..ble to deliver thee,
    He is a..ble to deliver thee ;
  Tho' by sin opprest, go to Him for rest ;
    Our God is able to deliver thee.

2 'Tis the grandest theme in the earth
    or main ;   [strain ;
  'Tis the grandest theme for a mortal
  'Tis the grandest theme, tell the
    world again :
  " Our God is able to deliver thee."

3 'Tis the grandest theme, let the
    tidings roll   [soul :
  To the guilty heart, to the sinful
  Look to God in faith, He will make
    thee whole :
  " Our God is able to deliver thee."

121 THERE is a green hill far away,
    Without a city wall,
  Where the dear Lord was crucified,
  Who died to save us all.

    Oh, dearly, dearly has he loved !
    And we must love Him too ;
    And trust in His redeeming love,
    And try His works to do.

2 We may not know, we cannot tell
    What pains He had to bear ;
  But we believe it was for us
  He hung and suffered there.

3 He died that we might be forgiven,
    He died to do us good,
  That we might go at last to heaven,
  Saved by His precious blood.

4 There was no other good enough
    To pay the price of sin ;
  He only could unlock the gate
  Of heaven, and let us in.

122 HAVE you any room for Jesus,
    He who bore your load of sin ?
  As He knocks and asks admission,
  Sinner, will you let Him in ?

    Room for Jesus, King of glory,
    Hasten now, His word obey !
    Swing the heart's door widely open,
    Bid Him enter while you may.

2 Room for pleasure, room for business
    But for Christ the crucified,
  Not a place that He can enter,
    In your heart for which He died ?

3 Have you any time for Jesus,
    As in grace He calls again ?
  Oh, to-day is time accepted,
    To-morrow you may call in vain !

4 Room and time now give to Jesus,
    Soon will pass God's day of grace ;
  Soon thy heart left cold and silent,
    And thy Saviour's pleading cease.

123 COME to the Saviour, make no
    delay ;
  Here in His Word He has shown us
    the way ;

Here in our midst He's standing
  to-day,
    Tenderly saying, " Come ! "
Joyful, joyful will the meeting be,
When from sin our hearts are pure and free,
And we shall gather, Saviour, with Thee,
  In our eternal home.

2 " Suffer the children ! " oh, hear His
    voice !   [rejoice ;
  Let every heart leap forth and
  And let us freely make Him our
    choice,
    Do not delay, but come.

3 Think once again, He's with us
    to-day ;   [obey ;
  Heed now His blest command, and
  Hear now His accents tenderly say,
  " Will you, My children, come ? "

124 SINNER, how thy heart is
          troubled !
    God is coming very near ;
  Do not hide thy deep emotion,
    Do not check that falling tear.
      Oh, be saved, His grace is free !
      Oh, be saved, He died for thee !

2 Jesus now is bending o'er thee,
    Jesus lowly, meek, and mild ;
  To the Friend who died to save thee,
    Wilt thou not be reconciled ?

3 Art thou waiting till the morrow ?
    Thou may'st never see its light !
  Come at once ! accept His mercy :
    He is waiting—come to-night !

4 With a lowly contrite spirit,
    Kneeling at the Saviour's feet,
  Thou canst feel, this very moment,
    Pardon—precious, pure and sweet.

5 Let the angels bear the tidings
    Upward to the courts of heaven !
  Let them sing, with holy rapture,
    O'er another soul forgiven !

125 GOD is calling the prodigal,
          come without delay,
  Hear, oh, hear Him calling, calling
    now for thee,
  Though you've wandered so far from
    His presence, come to-day,
  Hear His loving voice calling still...
      Call..ing now for thee,..
      Oh ! wea..ry prodigal, come...
      Call..ing now for thee,..
      Oh ! wea..ry prodigal, come..

2 Patient, loving, and tenderly still the
    Father pleads,
  Hear, oh, hear Him calling, calling
    now for thee,
  Oh ! return while the Spirit in mercy
    intercedes,
  Hear His loving voice calling still...

3 Come, there's bread in the house of
    thy Father, and to spare,
  Hear, oh, hear Him calling, calling
    now for thee,
  Lo ! the table is spread and the feast
    is waiting there,
  Hear His loving voice calling still...

126 THE love that Jesus had for me,
          To suffer on the cruel tree,
    That I a ransomed soul might be,
      Is more than tongue can tell !
        His love is more than tongue can tell !..
        His love is more than tongue can tell !..
        The love that Jesus had for me
        Is more than tongue can tell !

2 The bitter sorrow that He bore,
  And oh, that crown of thorns He
    wore,
  That I might live for evermore,
    Is more than tongue can tell.

3 The peace I have in Him, my Lord,
  Who pleads before the throne of God,
  The merit of His precious blood,
    Is more than tongue can tell !

4 The joy that comes when He is near,
  The rest He gives, so free from fear,
  The hope in Him, so bright and clear,
    Is more than tongue can tell !

127 O SWEET is the story of Jesus,
          The wonderful Saviour of men,
    Who suffered and died for the sinner—
      I'll tell it again and again !
        Oh, won..derful, wonderful sto..ry,
        The dea..rest that ever was told...
        I'll repeat it in glo..ry, the wonderful sto..ry,
        Where I..shall His beauty behold...

2 He came from the brightest of glory ;
    His blood as a ransom He gave,
  To purchase eternal redemption,
    And oh, He is mighty to save !

3 His mercy flows on like a river,
    His love is unmeasured and free ;
  His grace is for ever sufficient,
    It reaches and purifies me.

128 THERE'S a song my heart is
singing ;
In my soul its tones are ringing,
Peace and rest and joy 'tis bringing :
Jesus Christ has power to save !

..Sing it over and over again to me..
In its wonderful sweet simplicity ;
Tell it o'er...the ocean wave,
Jesus Christ..has power to save !

2 Oh, that song my soul is thrilling !
Jesus saves the soul that's willing,
Precious truth my heart 'tis filling :
Jesus Christ has power to save !

3 Sinner come ! if thou'lt receive Him,
Look to Jesus and believe Him ;
All your life and service give Him :
Jesus Christ has power to save !

129 COME, sing the gospel's joyful
sound,
Salvation full and free ;
Proclaim to all the world around,
The year of jubilee !

Salvation, salvation, the grace of God
doth bring :
Salvation, salvation thro' Christ our Lord
and King.

2 Ye mourning souls aloud rejoice ;
Ye blind, your Saviour see !
Ye prisoners sing with thankful
voice,
The Lord hath made you free ;

3 With rapture swell the song again,
Of Jesus' dying love ;
'Tis peace on earth, good will to men,
And praise to God above.

130 WE can tell it as we journey to-
ward the mansion built above,
The grand old story of salvation ;
We sing it out with gladness, in the
melodies of love,
The grand old story of salvation.

Ring it out..ring it out,..
Ring to every tribe and nation,...
Ring it out,.. ring it out,...
The grand old story of salvation.

2 His hand can lift the fallen and His
blood can make them white,
The grand old story of salvation ;
His love can pierce the darkness
with a never-fading light,
The grand old story of salvation.

3 We'll sing it in the battle, and its
notes shall victory be,
The grand old story of salvation;
We'll sing it in our trials, till the
passing shadows flee,
The grand old story of salvation.

4 The angels look with wonder, yet
their harps can never tell
The grand old story of salvation ;
His ransomed, clothed with beauty,
shall the praise of Jesus swell,
The grand old story of salvation.

131 COME, ye sinners, poor and
needy,
Weak and wounded, sick and sore,
Jesus ready stands to save you,
Full of pity, love, and power.
Now, ye needy, come and welcome,
God's free bounty glorify,
True belief and true repentance,
Every grace that brings you nigh.

2 Let not conscience make you linger
Nor of fitness fondly dream,
All the fitness He requireth
Is to feel your need of Him.
Come, ye weary, heavy laden,
Bruised and mangled by the fall :
If you tarry till you're better,
You will never come at all.

132 TELL me the old, old story
Of unseen things above,
Of Jesus and His glory,
Of Jesus and His love.
Tell me the story simply,
As to a little child ;
For I am weak and weary,
And helpless and defiled.

Tell me the old, old story,
Tell me the old, old story,
Tell me the old, old story
Of Jesus and His love.

2 Tell me the story slowly,
That I may take it in—
That wonderful redemption,
God's remedy for sin.
Tell me the story often,
For I forget so soon !
The " early dew " of morning
Has passed away at noon.

3 Tell me the story softly,
With earnest tones, and grave;
Remember ! I'm the sinner
Whom Jesus came to save.

Tell me the story always,
If you would really be
In any time of trouble
A comforter to me.

4 Tell me the same old story,
When you have cause to fear
That this world's empty glory
Is costing me too dear.
Yes, and when that world's glory
Is dawning on my soul,
Tell me the old, old story,
" Christ Jesus makes thee whole."

133 JESUS is tenderly calling thee
home—
Calling to-day! calling to-day!
Why from the sunshine of love wilt
thou roam—
Farther and farther away ?

Call..ing to-day,..call..ing to-day,...
Jesus is calling, is tenderly calling to-day !

2 Jesus is calling the weary to rest—
Calling to-day! calling to-day!
Bring Him thy burden and thou
shalt be blest—
He will not turn thee away.

3 Jesus is waiting, oh, come to Him
now—
Waiting to-day! waiting to-day!
Come with thy sins—at His feet
lowly bow—
Come and no longer delay.

4 Jesus is pleading, oh, list to His
voice—   [day !
Hear Him to-day ! hear Him to-
They who believe on His name shall
rejoice— ·
Quickly arise, come away.

134 'TWAS Jesus, my Saviour, who
died on the tree,   [me,
To open a fountain for sinners like
His blood is the fountain that pardon
bestows,   [flows.
And cleanses the foulest wherever it
For the conquering Saviour shall break every
chain,
And give us the victory again and again.

2 And when I was willing with all
things to part,   [my heart,
He gave me my bounty, His love in
So now I am joined with the con-
quering band,   [command.
Who are marching to glory at Jesus'

3 Though round me the storms of
adversity roll,
And the waves of destruction encom-
pass my soul.
In vain this frail vessel the tempest
shall toss.   [the Cross.
My hopes rest secure on the blood of

4 And when with the ransomed of
Jesus, my Head,
From fountain to fountain I then
shall be led,
I'll fall at His feet and His mercy
adore,   [evermore.
And sing of the blood of the Cross

5 Come, sinners, to Jesus ! no longer
delay !
A full free salvation He offers to-day,
Arouse your dark spirits, awake
from your dream,
And Christ will support you in
coming to Him.

135 REPEAT the story o'er and o'er,
Of grace so full and free ;
I love to hear it more and more,
Since grace has rescued me.

The half....was never told,....
The half....was never told ;....
Of grace divine, so wonderful,
The half was never told.

2 Of peace I only knew the name,
Nor found my soul its rest,
Until the sweet-voiced angel came,
To soothe my weary breast.

The half....was never told,....
The half....was never told ;....
Of peace divine, so wonderful,
The half was never told.

3 My highest place is—lying low
At my Redeemer's feet ;
No real joy in life I know
But in His service sweet.

The half....was never told,....
The half....was never told ;....
Of joy divine, so wonderful,
The half was never told.

4 And oh, what rapture will it be
With all the host above,
To sing through all eternity
The wonders of His love.

The half....was never told,....
The half....was never told ;....
Of love divine, so wonderful,
The half was never told.

136 WHILE Jesus whispers to you,
  Come, sinner, come !
While we are praying for you,
  Come, sinner, come !
Now is the time to own Him,
  Come, sinner, come !
Now is the time to know Him,
  Come, sinner, come !

2 Are you too heavy laden ?
    Come, sinner, come !
  Jesus will bear your burden,
    Come, sinner, come !
  Jesus will not deceive you,
    Come, sinner, come !
  Jesus will now receive you,
    Come, sinner, come !

3 Oh, hear His tender pleading,
    Come, sinner, come !
  Oh, now receive the blessing !
    Come, sinner, come !
  While Jesus whispers to you,
    Come, sinner, come !
  While we are praying for you,
    Come, sinner, come !

137 THERE is a fountain filled
    with blood,
  Drawn from Immanuel's veins ;
And sinners plunged beneath that
    flood
  Lose all their guilty stains !

  I do believe, I will believe,
    That Jesus died for me !
  That on the Cross He shed His blood,
    From sin to set me free.

2 The dying thief rejoiced to see
    That fountain in His day ;
  And there may I, though vile as he,
    Wash all my sins away.

3 Dear dying Lamb ! Thy precious
    blood
  Shall never lose its power,
  Till all the ransomed church of God
    Be saved to sin no more.

4 E'er since by faith I saw the stream
    Thy flowing wounds supply,
  Redeeming love has been my theme,
    And shall be till I die.

  The following chorus may be substituted :—
  Hallelujah, to the Lamb,
    Who died on Mount Calvary ;
  Hallelujah ! Hallelujah !
    Hallelujah ! Amen.

138 OH, how dark the night that
    wrapt my spirit round !
  Oh, how deep the woe my Saviour
    found
  When He walked across the waters
    of my soul,
  Bade my night disperse and made
    me whole !

  All the way to Calvary He went for me,
    He went for me, He went for me,
  All the way to Calvary He went for me,
    He died to set me free.

2 Trembling a sinner bowed before
    His face,
  Naught I knew of pardon—God's
    free grace,
  Heard a voice so melting, " Cease
    thy wild regret,
  Jesus bought thy pardon, paid thy
    debt."

3 Oh, 'twas wondrous love the Saviour
    showed for me,
  When He left His throne for Calvary,
  When He trod the wine-press, trod
    it all alone,
  Praise His name for ever, make it
    known.

139 PRAISE be to Jesus, His mercy
    is free ;
  Mercy is free, mercy is free ;
  Sinner, that mercy is flowing for
    thee,
  Mercy is boundless and free.
  If thou art willing on Him to believe,
  Mercy is free, mercy is free,
  Life everlasting thy soul may receive,
  Mercy is boundless and free.

  Jesus, the Saviour, is looking for thee,
    Looking for thee, looking for thee ;
  Lovingly, tenderly calling for thee,
    Calling and looking for thee.

2 Why on the mountains of sin wilt
    thou roam ?
  Mercy is free, mercy is free ;
  Gently the Spirit is calling " Come
    home,"
  Mercy is boundless and free.
  Thou art in darkness, oh, come to
    the light,
  Mercy is free, mercy is free.
  Jesus is waiting, He'll save thee
    to-night,
  Mercy is boundless and free.

3 Think of His goodness, and patience
      and love ;
   Mercy is free, mercy is free ;
Pleading thy cause with His Father
      above,
   Mercy is boundless and free.
Come and repenting, oh, give Him
      thy heart,
   Mercy is free, mercy is free.
Grieve Him no longer, but come as
      thou art,
   Mercy is boundless and free.

4 Yes, there is pardon for all who
      believe ;
   Mercy is free, mercy is free ;
Come and this moment a blessing
      receive,
   Mercy is boundless and free.
Jesus is waiting, oh, hear Him
      proclaim
   Mercy is free, mercy is free !
Cling to His mercy, believe on His
      name,
   Mercy is boundless and free.

140 SHE only touched the hem of
         His garment
      As to His side she stole,
   Amid the crowd that gathered
         around Him,
      And straightway she was whole.

      Oh, touch the hem of His garment,
      And thou, too, shalt be free !
      His saving power this very hour
      Shall give new life to thee.

2 She came in fear and trembling
      before Him,
   She knew her Lord had come ;
She felt that from Him virtue had
      healed her,
   The mighty deed was done.

3 He turned with, " Daughter, be of
      good comfort,
   Thy faith hath made thee whole;"
And peace that passeth all under-
      standing
   With gladness filled her soul.

141 IN tenderness He sought me,
      Weary and sick with sin,
   And on His shoulders brought me
      Back to His fold again ;
   While angels in His presence sang
      Until the courts of heaven rang.

      Oh, the love that sought me !
      Oh, the blood that bought me !
      Oh, the grace that brought me to the fold.
      Wondrous grace that brought me to the fold !

2 He washed the bleeding sin-wounds,
      And poured in oil and wine ;
   He whispered to assure me,
      " I've found thee, thou art Mine;"
   I never heard a sweeter voice,
      It made my aching heart rejoice.

3 He pointed to the nail-prints ;
      For me His blood was shed,
   A mocking crown so thorny,
      Was placed upon His head :
   I wonder what He saw in me
      To suffer such deep agony.

4 I'm sitting in His presence,
      The sunshine of His face,
   While with adoring wonder
      His blessings I retrace.
   It seems as if eternal days
   Are far too short to sound His praise.

5 So while the hours are passing,
      All now is perfect rest ;
   I'm waiting for the morning,
      The brightest and the best,
   When He will call us to His side,
      To be with Him, His spotless bride.

142 I STAND all amazed at the
         love Jesus offers me,
   Confused at the grace that so fully
         He proffers me ;
   I tremble to know that for me He
         was crucified,
   That for me a sinner, He suffered,
         He bled, and died.

   Oh! it is wonderful that He should care for me,
      Enough to die for me.
   Oh ! it is wonderful, wonderful to me !

2 I marvel that He would descend
      from His throne divine,
   To rescue a soul so rebellious and
      proud as mine ;
   That He should extend His great
      love unto such as I,   [justify.
   Sufficient to own, to redeem and to

3 I think of His hands pierced and
      bleeding to pay the debt !
   Such mercy, such love and devotion
      can I forget ?   [mercy seat,
   No, no, I will praise and adore at the
   Until at the glorified throne I kneel
      at His feet.

143 ON the golden streets of heaven
    all men hope to walk some day,
Yet so many are not willing to accept
    the living way ;
But while others build on good works
    or opinions if they may,
Hallelujah ! hallelujah ! I'm de-
    pending on the blood.

In the soul-cleansing blood of the Saviour,
I've been washed in the crimson flood ;
Tho' the world may say there is hope some other
I'm depending on the blood. [way.

2 Some will tell us that God's mercy is
    their only hope and plea,
That a soul He could not punish
    throughout all eternity ;
But I read that my dear Saviour
    died for sinners just like me,
Hallelujah ! hallelujah ! I'm de-
    pending on the blood.

3 As we look back through the ages
    where the kings and prophets trod,
We may see their altars reeking with
    the sacrifice and blood,
But those types were only pointing
    to the Paschal Lamb of God,
Hallelujah ! hallelujah ! I'm de-
    pending on the blood.

4 'Tis the burden of that chorus over
    on the streets of light,
That the blood from Calvary's
    mountain hath washed all their
    garments white ;
So I'll shout along life's pathway till
    I reach that land so bright :
" Hallelujah ! hallelujah ! I'm de-
    pending on the blood."

144 OH, now I see the cleansing wave,
    The fountain deep and wide !
Jesus, my Lord, mighty to save,
    Points to His wounded side.

The cleansing stream I see. I see !
I plunge, and oh, it cleanseth me !
Oh, praise the Lord ! it cleanseth me ;
It cleanseth me, yes, cleanseth me.

2 I see the new creation rise ;
    I hear the speaking blood !
It speaks polluted nature dies !
    Sinks 'neath the cleansing flood.

3 I rise to walk in heaven's own light,
    Above the world and sin, [white,
With heart made pure and garment
    And Christ enthroned within.

4 Amazing grace ! 'tis heaven below
    To feel the blood applied ;
And Jesus, only Jesus know,
    My Jesus crucified.

145 GOD calling yet ! shall I not
    hear ?   [dear ?
Earth's pleasures shall I still hold
Shall life's sweet passing years all fly,
And still my soul in slumber lie ?

Call...ing yet ! oh, hear Him !
Call...ing yet ! oh, hear Him !
God is calling yet! oh, hear Him ! calling, calling !
Call...ing yet ! oh, hear Him !
Call...ing yet ! oh, hear Him !
God is calling yet ! oh, hear Him calling yet !

2 God calling yet ! shall I not rise ?
Can I His loving voice despise,
And basely His kind care repay ?
He calls me still : can I delay ?

3 God calling yet ! and shall He knock,
And I my heart the closer lock ?
He still is waiting to receive ;
And shall I dare His Spirit grieve ?

4 God calling yet ! and shall I give
No heed but still in bondage live ?
I wait ; but He does not forsake ;
He calls me still : my heart, awake !

5 God calling yet ! I cannot stay ;
My heart I yield without delay :
Vain world, farewell ! from thee I
    part ;   [heart.
The voice of God has reached my

146 WHY do you wait, dear brother?
    Oh, why do you tarry so long ?
Your Saviour is waiting to give you
    A place in His sanctified throng.

Why not ? why not ?
Why not come to Him now ?

2 What do you hope, dear brother,
    To gain by a further delay ?
There's no one to save you but
    Jesus,
There's no other way but His way.

3 Do you not feel, dear brother,
    His spirit now striving within ?
Oh, why not accept His salvation,
    And throw off your burden of sin ?

4 Why do you wait, dear brother ?
    The harvest is passing away,
Your Saviour is longing to bless you,
    There's danger and death in delay.

147 SOWING the seed by the day-
    light fair,   [glare,
Sowing the seed by the noon-day
Sowing the seed by the fading light,
Sowing the seed in the solemn night ;
    Oh, what shall the harvest be ?

Sown..in the dark..ness or sown..in the light..
Sown..in our weak..ness or sown..in our might,...
    Gather'd in time or eternity,
    Sure, ah, sure will the harvest be...

2 Sowing the seed by the wayside high,
Sowing the seed on the rocks to die,
Sowing the seed where the thorns will
    spoil,
Sowing the seed in the fertile soil ;
    Oh, what shall the harvest be ?

3 Sowing the seed of a lingering pain,
Sowing the seed of a maddened brain,
Sowing the seed of a tarnished name,
Sowing the seed of eternal shame ;
    Oh, what shall the harvest be ?

4 Sowing the seed with an aching
    heart,   [start,
Sowing the seed while the teardrops
Sowing in hope till the reapers come
Gladly to gather the harvest home :
    Oh, what shall the harvest be ?

148 TO-DAY the Saviour calls ;
    Ye wanderers come ;
O ye benighted souls,
    Why longer roam ?

2 To-day the Saviour calls ;
    O hear Him now ;
Before your day is gone,
    To Jesus bow.

3 To-day the Saviour calls :
    For refuge fly ;
The storm of vengeance falls ;
    Ruin is nigh.

4 The Spirit calls to-day :
    Yield to His power ;
O grieve Him not away ;
    'Tis mercy's hour.

149 TO-DAY Thy mercy calls me,
    To wash away my sin ;
However great my trespass,
    Whate'er I may have been.
However long from mercy
    I may have turned away,
Thy blood, O Christ, can cleanse me,
    And make me white to-day.

2 To-day Thy gate is open,
    And all who enter in
Shall find a Father's welcome,
    And pardon for their sin ;
The past shall be forgotten,
    A present joy be given,
A future grace be promised—
    A glorious crown in heaven.

3 To-day the Father calls me ;
    The Holy Spirit waits ;
The blessed angels gather
    Around the heavenly gates.
No question will be asked me,
    How often I have come :
Although I oft have wandered,
    It is my Father's home.

4 O all-embracing mercy,
    Thou ever-open door !
What shall I do without thee,
    When heart and eyes run o'er ?
When all things seem against me,
    To drive me to despair,
I know one gate is open,
    One ear will hear my prayer.

150 COME, contrite one, and seek
    His grace,
    Jesus is passing by ;
See in His reconciled face
    The sunshine of the sky.

Pass...ing by,...pass...ing by...
Hasten to meet Him on the way,
Jesus is passing by to-day,
Pass...ing by,...pass...ing by....

2 Come, hungry one, and tell your
    Jesus is passing by ;   [need,
The Bread of Life your soul will feed,
    And fully satisfy.

3 Come, weary one, and find sweet rest,
    Jesus is passing by ;
Come where the longing heart is
    blessed,
    And on His bosom lie.

4 Come, burdened one, bring all your
    care,
    Jesus is passing by ;
The love that listens to your prayer
    Will " no good thing " deny.

151 THE Gospel bells are ringing,
    Over land, from sea to sea :
Blessed news of free salvation
    Do they offer you and me.

" For God so loved the world
That His only Son He gave,
Whosoe'er believeth in Him
Everlasting life shall have."

Gospel bells,...how they ring ;...
Over land from sea to sea ;
Gospel bells, ..freely bring...
Blessed news to you and me.

2 The Gospel bells invite us
To a feast prepared for all ;
Do not slight the invitation,
Nor reject the gracious call.
" I am the Bread of life ;
Eat of Me, thou hungry soul,
Though your sins be red as crimson
They shall be as white as wool."

3 The Gospel bells give warning
As they sound from day to day,
Of the fate which doth await them
Who for ever will delay.
" Escape thou for thy life ;
Tarry not in all the plain,
Nor behind thee look, oh, never,
Lest thou be consumed in pain."

4 The Gospel bells are joyful,
As they echo far and wide,
Bearing notes of perfect pardon,
Through a Saviour crucified.
" Good tidings of great joy
To all people do I bring,
Unto you is born a Saviour,
Which is Christ the Lord and
King."

152 ART thou weary, art thou
languid,
Art thou sore distressed ?
" Come to Me," saith One, " and
coming,
Be at rest."

2 Hath He diadem as monarch,
That His brow adorns ?
Yes, a crown of very surety,
But of thorns.

3 If I ask Him to receive me,
Will He say me nay ?
Not till earth, and not till heaven,
Pass away.

4 Finding, following, keeping, strug-
Is He sure to bless ? [gling,
Angels, martyrs, saints, and pro-
Answer, " Yes ! " [phets

153 ON Calvary's brow my Saviour
died,
"Twas there my Lord was crucified ;
'Twas on the Cross He bled for me,
And purchased there my pardon free.

O Calvary ! dark Calvary !
Where Jesus shed His blood for me,...
O Calvary ! blest Calvary !
"Twas there my Saviour died for me.

2 'Mid rending rocks and darkening
skies,
My Saviour bows His head and dies ;
The opening veil reveals the way
To heaven's joys and endless day.

3 O Jesus, Lord, how can it be,
That Thou shouldst give Thy life for
me,
To bear the Cross and agony
In that dread hour on Calvary !

154 THERE'S a royal highway
leading
To the King's sublime abode ;
And I seek a home in glory,
Walking in that royal road.

Oh, the bless...ed royal road,...
Oh, the bless...ed royal road,...
Will you go...with me to glo...ry,
Walking in...that royal road ?

2 O'er the highway Jesus travelled,
Up the hill of Calvary trod,
That He might a path make open,
Leading to the throne of God.

3 As I journey o'er the highway
To the country of my King,
Oft by faith I hear the echo
From the land where angels sing.

4 Oft a glad, entrancing vision
To my spirit is bestowed ;
'Tis the city, bright, eternal,
Whither leads the royal road.

155 TENDERLY the Shepherd,
O'er the mountains cold,
Goes to bring His lost one
Back to the fold.

Seeking to save, seeking to save,
Lost one, 'tis Jesus, seeking to save.

2 Patiently the owner
Seeks with earnest care,
In the dust and darkness
Her treasure rare.

3 Lovingly the Father
  Sends the news around :
  " He once dead now liveth—
  Once lost is found."

156   LORD Jesus, I long **to** be
    perfectly whole,
I want Thee for ever to live in my
  soul ;   [every foe—
Break down every idol, cast out
Now wash me, and I shall be whiter
  than snow.

Whiter than snow ; yes, whiter than snow ;
Now wash me, and I shall be whiter than
  snow.

2 Lord Jesus, let nothing unholy
  remain,
Apply Thine own blood and extract
  every stain ;   [forgo—
To get this blest cleansing I all things
Now wash me, and I shall be whiter
  than snow.

3 Lord Jesus, look down from Thy
  throne in the skies,
And help me to make a complete
  sacrifice ;   [know—
I give up myself and whatever I
Now wash me, and I shall be whiter
  than snow.

4 Lord Jesus, for this I most humbly
  entreat,   [feet ;
I wait, blessed Lord, at Thy crucified
By faith, for my cleansing I see Thy
  blood flow—
Now wash me, and I shall be whiter
  than snow.

5 Lord Jesus, Thou seest I patiently
  wait ;   [heart create ;
Come now, and within me a new
To those who have sought Thee Thou
  never saidst, " No "—
Now wash me, and I shall be whiter
  than snow.

157   THE whole world was lost in
    the darkness of sin,
  The Light of the world is Jesus ;
Like sunshine at noon-day His glory
  shone in,
  The Light of the world is Jesus.

Come to the Light, 'tis shining for thee ;
Sweetly the Light has dawn'd upon me.
Once I was blind, but now I can see :
  The Light of the world is Jesus.

2 No darkness have we who in Jesus
  abide,
  The Light of the world is Jesus ;
We walk in the light when we follow
  our guide,
  The Light of the world is Jesus.

3 Ye dwellers in darkness, with sin-
  blinded eyes,
  The Light of the world is Jesus ;
Go, wash at His bidding, and light
  will arise,
  The Light of the world is Jesus.

4 No need of the sunlight in heaven,
  we're told,
  The Light of the world is Jesus ;
The Lamb is the Light in the City
  of Gold,
  The Light of the world is Jesus.

158   IF you could see Christ stand-
    ing here to-night—
  His thorn-crowned head and
    pierced hands could view ;
Could see those eyes that beam with
  heaven's own light,
  And hear Him say, " Beloved,
    'twas for you : "

Would you believe,...and Jesus receive,...
If He were stand...ing here ?...

2 If you could see that face so calm
  and sweet,
  Those lips that spake words only
    pure and true ;
Could see the nail prints in His
  tender feet,
  And hear Him say, " Beloved,
    'twas for you : '

3 He whispers to your heart, turn not
  away,
  For He's beside you in your
    narrow pew ;
If you will listen, you will hear Him
  say,
  In loving tones, " Beloved, 'twas
    for you : "

Will you believe,..and Jesus receive,..
For He is stand...ing here?..

159   I WAS drifting away on life's
    pitiless sea,
  And the angry waves threatened
    my ruin to be,

When away at my side, there I
  dimly descried
A stately old vessel, and loudly I
  cried—
  " Ship, a-hoy !
  Ship, a-hoy ! "
  And loudly I cried,
  " Ship, a-hoy ! "

2 'Twas the " old ship of Zion," thus
  sailing along,
All aboard her seemed joyous, I
  heard their sweet song ;
And the Captain's kind ear, ever
  ready to hear,
Caught my wail of distress, as I
  cried out in fear—
  " Ship, a-hoy !
  Ship, a-hoy ! "
  As I cried out in fear,
  " Ship, a-hoy."

3 The good Captain commanded a
  boat to be low'red,
And with tender compassion, He
  took me on board ;
And I'm happy to-day, all my sins
  washed away
In the blood of my Saviour ; and
  now I can say—
  " Bless the Lord !
  Bless the Lord ! "
  From my soul I can say,
  " Bless the Lord ! "

4 O soul, sinking down 'neath sin's
  merciless wave,
The strong arm of our Captain is
  mighty to save ;
Then trust Him to-day, no longer
  delay ;
Board the old ship of Zion, and
  shout on your way—
  " Jesus saves !
  Jesus saves ! "
  Shout and sing on your way,
  " Jesus saves ! "

160 JESUS the water of life will give
  Freely, freely, freely ;
Jesus the water of life will give
  Freely to those who love Him.
Come to that fountain, oh, drink and
  live !
  Freely, freely, freely ;   [live !
Come to that fountain, oh, drink and
  Flowing for those that love Him !

The Spirit and the Bride say, Come,
  Freely, freely, freely :
And he that is thirsty let him come,
  And drink of the water of life.

The fountain of life is flowing,
  Flowing, freely flowing ;
The fountain of life is flowing,
  Is flowing for you and for me.

2 Jesus has promised a home in heaven,
                      (Repeat),
  Treasures unfading will there be
    given,   (Repeat).

3 Jesus has promised a robe of white,
                      (Repeat),
  Kingdoms of glory and crowns of
    light,   (Repeat).

4 Jesus has promised eternal day,
                      (Repeat),
  Pleasures that never shall pass away,
                      (Repeat).

161 O CHRIST, what burdens
          bowed Thy head !
  Our load was laid on Thee ;
Thou stoodest in the sinner's stead,
  Didst bear all ill for me.
A Victim led, Thy blood was shed,
  Now there's no load for me.

2 Death and the curse were in our cup,
  O Christ, 'twas full for Thee !
But Thou hast drained the last dark
  drop,
'Tis empty now for me.
That bitter cup, love drank it up,
  Now blessing's draught for me.

3 The tempest's awful voice was
    heard,
  O Christ, it broke on Thee !
Thy open bosom was my ward,
  It braved the storm for me :
Thy form was scarred, Thy visage
  marred,
  Now cloudless peace for me.

4 For me, Lord Jesus, Thou hast died,
  And I have died in Thee :
Thou'rt risen—my bands are all
  untied ;
  And now Thou liv'st in me ;
When purified, made white and
  Thy glory then for me !   [tried ;

162 THE gospel of Thy grace
     My stubborn heart has won,
For God so loved the world,
     He gave His only Son,
That " Whosoever will believe,
Shall everlasting life receive."

2 The serpent " lifted up,"
     Could life and healing give ;
So Jesus on the Cross
     Bids me to look and live ;
For " Whosoever will believe,
Shall everlasting life receive ! "

3 " The soul that sinneth dies : "
     My awful doom I heard ;
I was for ever lost,
     But for Thy gracious word
That " Whosoever will believe,
Shall everlasting life receive ! "

4 " Not to condemn the world "
     The " Man of Sorrows " came ;
But that the world might have
     Salvation through His name ;
For " Whosoever will believe,
Shall everlasting life receive ! "

5 " Lord, help my unbelief ! "
     Give me the peace of faith,
To rest with child-like trust
     On what Thy gospel saith,
That " Whosoever will believe,
Shall everlasting life receive ! "

163 AT even, ere the sun was set,
     The sick, O Lord, around
     Thee lay ;
O in what divers pains they met !
O with what joy they went away !

2 Once more 'tis eventide and we,
     Oppressed with various ills, draw
     near ;
What if Thy form we cannot see,
We know and feel that Thou art here.

3 O Saviour Christ, our woes dispel :
     For some are sick, and some are sad,
And some have never loved Thee
     well,   [had.
And some have lost the love they

4 And some are pressed with worldly
     care,   [doubt,
     And some are tried with sinful
And some such grievous passions
     tear,   [out.
That only Thou canst cast them

5 And some have found the world is
     vain,
     Yet from the world they break not
     free ;
And some have friends who give
     them pain ;
     Yet have not sought a friend in
     Thee.

6 O Saviour Christ ! Thou too art Man;
     Thou hast been troubled, tempted,
     tried ;   [scan,
Thy kind but searching glance can
     The very wounds that shame
     would hide !

7 Thy touch has still its ancient power,
     No word from Thee can fruitless
     fall ;
Hear in this solemn evening hour,
And in Thy mercy heal us all.

164 ROCK of Ages, cleft for me,
     Let me hide myself in Thee !
Let the water and the blood,
From Thy riven side which flow'd,
Be of sin the double cure ;
Cleanse me from its guilt and pow'r.

2 Not the labour of my hands
Can fulfil Thy law's demands ;
Could my zeal no respite know,
Could my tears for ever flow,
All for sin could not atone ;
Thou must save, and Thou alone.

3 Nothing in my hand I bring,
Simply to Thy Cross I cling ;
Naked, come to Thee for dress ;
Helpless, look to Thee for grace ;
Foul, I to the fountain fly ;
Wash me, Saviour, or I die.

4 While I draw this fleeting breath,
When my eyelids close in death ;
When I soar to worlds unknown,
See Thee on Thy judgment throne,
Rock of Ages, cleft for me,
Let me hide myself in Thee.

165 OH, this uttermost salvation !
     'Tis a fountain full and free,
Pure, exhaustless, ever flowing,
     Wondrous grace ! it reaches me !

It reaches me ! it reaches me !
Wondrous grace ! it reaches me !
Pure, exhaustless, ever flowing :
Wondrous grace ! it reaches me !

2 How amazing God's compassion,
    That so vile a worm should prove
This stupendous bliss of heaven,
    This unmeasured wealth of love !

3 Jesus, Saviour, I adore Thee !
    Now Thy love I will proclaim !
I will tell the blessed story,
    I will magnify Thy name !

166   OH ! we are going to wear a
      crown,
Oh, we are going to wear a crown,
Oh, we are going to wear a crown,
    To wear a starry crown.

Away over Jordan, with our blessed Jesus,
Away over Jordan, to wear a starry crown.

2 You must be saved to wear a crown.

3 You must be cleansed, to wear that
    crown.

4 You must live upright, to wear that
    crown.

5 You must fight the fight, to wear
    that crown.

6 You must bear the cross, to win
    that crown.

167   WE know there's a bright and
      a glorious home,
    Away in the heavens high,
Where all the redeem'd shall with
      Jesus dwell,
    Will you be there, and I ?

Will you be there and I ? (Repeat.)
Where all the redeemed shall with Jesus
Will you be there, and I ?   [dwell.

2 In robes of white, o'er streets of gold,
    Beneath a cloudless sky,
They'll walk in the light of their
      Father's love.
    Will you be there, and I ?

Will you be there and I ? (Repeat.)
They'll walk in the light of their Father's
Will you be there and I ?   [love.

3 If we find the loving Saviour now,
    And follow Him faithfully,
When He gathers His children in
      that bright home,
    Then you'll be there, and I !

Yes, you'll be there and I (Repeat)
When He gathers His children in that bright
home,
    Yes, you'll be there and I.

4 If we are sheltered by the Cross,
    And through the blood brought
      nigh ;
Our utmost gain we'll count but loss,
    Since you'll be there, and I.

Since you'll be there and I (Repeat),
Our utmost gain we'll count but loss,
Since you'll be there and I.

168   HARK ! there comes a whisper,
      Stealing on thine ear ;
'Tis the Saviour calling,
    Soft, soft and clear.

" Give thy heart to Me,.....,
   Once I died for thee....."
Hark ! hark ! thy Saviour calls ;
   Come, sinner, come ! .

2 With that voice so gentle,
    Dost thou hear Him say ?
Tell Me all thy sorrows ;
    Come, come away ! "

3 Wouldst thou find a Refuge
    For thy soul opprest ?
Jesus kindly answers,
    " I am thy rest."

4 At the Cross of Jesus,
    Let thy burden fall ;
While He gently whispers,
    " I'll bear it all."

169   THERE is life for a look at the
      Crucified One,
    There is life at this moment for
      thee ;
Then look, sinner, look unto Him
    and be sav'd,   [tree.
    Unto Him who was nail'd to the

Look ! look ! look and live !
There is life for a look at the crucified One,
There is life at this moment for thee.

2 It is not thy tears of repentance nor
    pray'rs,   [soul ;
But the blood that atones for the
On Him then believe, and a pardon
    receive,
    For His blood now can make thee
    quite whole.

3 We are healed by His stripes ;
    wouldst thou add to the word ?
And He is our righteousness made ;
The best robe of heaven He bids
    thee to wear,   [arrayed ?
    Oh, couldst thou be better

4 Then doubt not thy welcome, since
        God has declared   [done :
    There remaineth no more to be
    That once in the end of the world
        He appeared,   [begun.
    And completed the work He'd

5 But take, with rejoicing, from
        Jesus at once,
    The life everlasting He gives ;
    And know with assurance thou never
        canst die,   [lives.
    Since Jesus thy righteousness

170   SEEKING the lost, yes, kindly
            entreating   [astray ;
        Wanderers on the mountains
    " Come unto Me." His message
            repeating,   [day.
        Words of the Master speaking to-

    Going afar....upon the mountain,.....
    Bringing the wand'rer back again....
    Into the fold....of my Redeemer,....
    Jesus the Lamb for sinners slain....

2 Seeking the lost, and pointing to Jesus,
    Souls that are weak, and hearts
        that are sore ;   [salvation,
    Leading them forth in ways of
    Showing the path to life evermore.

3 Thus I would go on missions of
        mercy,   [day ;
    Following Christ from day unto
    Cheering the faint, and raising the
        fallen ;
    Pointing the lost to Jesus the way.

171   HAVE you been to Jesus for
            the cleansing pow'r ?
        Are you washed in the blood of the
            Lamb ?   [this hour ?
        Are you fully trusting in His grace
        Are you washed in the blood of
            the Lamb ?

    Are you wash'd...in the blood,...
        In the soul-cleansing blood of the Lamb ?...
    Are your garments spotless ? are they white
        as snow ?
        Are you wash'd in the blood of the Lamb ?

2 Are you walking daily by the
        Saviour's side ?
    Are you washed in the blood of
        the Lamb ?   [Crucified ?
    Do you rest each moment in the
    Are you washed in the blood of
        the Lamb ?

3 When the Bridegroom cometh will
        your robes be white—
    Pure and white in the blood of the
        Lamb ?
    Will your soul be ready for the
        mansions bright,
    And be washed in the blood of the
        Lamb ?

4 Lay aside the garments that are
        stain'd by sin,   [Lamb :
    And be washed in the blood of the
    There's a fountain flowing for the
        soul unclean,   [Lamb.
    Oh. be washed in the blood of the

172   THERE'S a wonderful story
            I've heard long ago.
        'Tis called " The sweet story of
            old,"
    I hear it so often, wherever I go.
        That same old story is told ;
    And I've thought it was strange that
        so often they'd tell
    That story, as if it were new ;
    But I've found out the reason they
        loved it so well,
    That old, old story is true.

        That old, old story is true,....
        That old, old story is true.....
    But I've found out the reason they lov'd
        it so well,
        That old, old story is true.....

2 They told of a Saviour so lovely and
        pure,
    That came to the earth to dwell ;
    To seek for His lost ones, and make
        them secure
    From death and the power of hell.
    That He was despised, and with
        thorns He was crowned, [view;
    On the cross was extended to
    But oh, what sweet peace in my
        heart since I've found
    That old, old story is true !

        That old, old story is true,....
        That old, old story is true.....
    But oh, what sweet peace in my heart
        since I've found
        That old, old story is true.....

3 He arose and ascended to heaven,
        we're told,
    Triumphant o'er death and hell ;
    He's preparing a place in that city
        of gold,.   [dwell ;
    Where lov'd ones for ever may

Where our kindred we'll meet, and
we'll never more part,
And oh, while I tell it to you,
It is peace to my soul, it is joy to
my heart,
That old, old story is true.

That old, old story is true,....
That old, old story is true.....
It is peace to my soul, it is joy to my heart,
That old, old story is true.....

4 Oh, that wonderful story, I love to
repeat,
Of peace and good-will to men ;
There's no story to me that is half
so sweet,
As I hear it again and again.
He invites you to come—He will
freely receive, [you :
And this message He sendeth to
"There's a mansion in glory for all
who believe,"
That old, old story is true.

That old, old story is true,....
That old, old story is true.....
"There's a mansion in glory for all who
believe,"
That old, old story is true....

173 O WHAT a Saviour that He
died for me !
From condemnation He hath made
me free ; [saith He,
"He that believeth on the Son,"
"*Hath* everlasting life."

Verily, verily, I say unto you,
Verily, verily, message ever new :
"He that believeth on the Son," 'tis true !
"Hath everlasting life."

2 All my iniquities on Him were laid,
All my indebtedness by Him was
paid ; [hath said,
All who believe on Him, the Lord,
"*Have* everlasting life."

3 Tho' poor and needy, I can trust my
Lord ; [Word ;
Tho' weak and sinful, I believe His
O glad message ! ev'ry child of God,
"*Hath* everlasting life."

4 Tho' all unworthy, yet I will not
doubt, [cast out ;
For him that cometh He will not
"He that believeth," Oh, the good
news shout,
"HATH everlasting life."

174 I HEARD the voice of Jesus say,
"Come unto Me and rest;
Lay down, thou weary one, lay
down
Thy head upon My breast."

2 I came to Jesus as I was—
Weary, and worn, and sad ;
I found in Him a resting place,
And He has made me glad.

3 I heard the voice of Jesus say,
"Behold, I freely give
The living water—thirsty one,
Stoop down, and drink, and live."

4 I came to Jesus and I drank
Of that life-giving stream ;
My thirst was quench'd, my soul
revived,
And now I live in Him.

5 I heard the voice of Jesus say,
"I am this dark world's Light ;
Look unto Me, thy morn shall rise,
And all thy day be bright."

6 I looked to Jesus, and I found
In Him my Star, my Sun ;
And in that Light of Life I'll walk
Till travelling days are done.

175 O WORD, of words the sweetest,
O word, in which there lie
All promise, all fulfilment,
And end of mystery !
Lamenting, or rejoicing,
With doubt or terror nigh,
I hear the "Come !" of Jesus,
And to His Cross I fly.

"Come ! oh, come to Me !....
Come ! oh, come to Me !"....
"Weary, heavy-laden,
Come ! oh, come to Me !"

2 O soul ! why shouldst thou wander
From such a loving Friend ?
Cling closer, closer to Him,
Stay with Him to the end ;
Alas ! I am so helpless,
So very full of sin,
For I am ever wand'ring,
And coming back again.

3 Oh, each time draw me nearer,
That soon the "Come" may be
Nought but a gentle whisper,
To one close, close to Thee ;

Then, over sea and mountain,
Far from or near my home,
I'll take Thy hand and follow,
At that sweet whisper, "Come!"

176 OH, turn ye, oh, turn ye, for
why will ye die,
When God in great mercy is drawing
so nigh?
Now Jesus invites you, the Spirit
says, "Come,"
And angels are waiting to welcome
you home.

2 How vain the delusion, that while
you delay,
Your hearts may grow better by
staying away!
Come wretched, come thirsty, come
just as you be,
While streams of salvation are
flowing so free.

3 In riches, in pleasures, what can you
obtain,
To sooth your affliction, or banish
your pain,
To bear up your spirits when
summon'd to die,
Or take you to Christ in the clouds
of the sky?

177 SING them over again to me,
Wonderful words of life!
Let me more of their beauty see,
Wonderful words of life!
Words of life and beauty,
Teach me faith and duty!
Beautiful words! wonderful words!
Wonderful words of life!

2 Christ, the blessed One gives to all,
Wonderful words of life!
Sinner list to the loving call,
Wonderful words of life!
All so freely given,
Wooing us to heaven!

3 Sweetly echo the gospel call,
Wonderful words of life!
Offer pardon and peace to all.
Wonderful words of life!
Jesus, only Saviour,
Sanctify for ever!

178 SOUND the gospel of grace
abroad,
There's life in the risen Lord!

Spread the news of the gift of God,
There's life in the risen Lord.
God above desires it!
Sinful man requires it!
Tell it around, let it abound,
There's life in the risen Lord!

2 All by nature are doomed to die,
So saith the Holy Word;
Welcome, therefore, the joyful cry,
There's life in the risen Lord!
Welcome news of gladness—
Antidote of sadness.

3 Saints, apostles, and prophets, all
Published with one accord,
This deliverance from the fall—
This life in the risen Lord!
Glory be to Jesus,
Who from bondage freed us.

4 Pardon, power, and perfect peace
The words of this life afford;
Never, then, let the tidings cease,
Of life in the risen Lord.
Open wide the portal,
Unto every mortal.

179 HAVE thy affections been
nailed to the Cross?
Is thy heart right with God?
Dost thou count all things for Jesus
but loss?
Is thy heart right with God?
Is thy heart right with God,
Washed in the crimson flood,
Cleansed and made holy, humble and lowly,
Right in the sight of God?....

2 Hast thou dominion o'er self and
o'er sin?
Is thy heart right with God?
Over all evil without and within?
Is thy heart right with God?

3 Is there no more condemnation for
sin?
Is thy heart right with God?
Does Jesus rule in the temple
within?
Is thy heart right with God?

4 Are all thy powers under Jesus'
control?
Is thy heart right with God?
Does He each moment abide in thy
soul?
Is thy heart right with God?

5 Art thou now walking in heaven's
   pure light ?
Is thy heart right with God ?
Is thy soul wearing the garment of
   white ?
Is thy heart right with God ?

180 WILL your anchor hold in the
   storms of life,
When the clouds unfold their wings
   of strife ?
When the strong tide lifts, and the
   cables strain,   [remain ?
Will your anchor shift, or firm
We have an anchor that keeps the soul
Steadfast and sure while the billows roll,
Fasten'd to the Rock which cannot move,
Grounded firm and deep in the Saviour's love.

2 It is safely moor'd, 'twill the storm
   withstand,
For 'tis well secured by the Saviour's
   hand ;
And the cables, pass'd from His
   heart to mine,   [divine.
Can defy the blast, thro' strength

3 It will firmly hold in the straits of
   fear,
When the breakers have told the
   reef is near ;
Tho' the tempest rave, and the wild
   winds blow,   [o'erflow.
Not an angry wave shall our barque

4 It will surely hold in the floods of
   death,   [breath ;
When the waters cold chill our latest
On the rising tide it can never fail,
While our hopes abide within the
   veil !

5 When our eyes behold, thro' the
   gathering night,
The city of gold, our harbour bright,
We shall anchor fast by the heav'nly
   shore,   [more.
With the storms all past for ever-

181 THERE were ninety and nine
   that safely lay
In the shelter of the fold,
But one was out on the hills away,
Far off from the gates of gold ;
Away on the mountains wild and
   bare,   [care.
Away from the tender Shepherd's

2 " Lord, Thou hast here Thy ninety
   and nine,
Are they not enough for Thee ? "
But the Shepherd made answer :
   " This of Mine
Has wandered away from Me ;
And, although the road be rough
   and steep,
I go to the desert to find My sheep."

3 But none of the ransomed ever
   knew
How deep were the waters cross'd ;
Nor how dark was the night that the
   Lord pass'd through,   [lost.
Ere He found His sheep that was
Out in the desert He heard its cry—
Sick, and helpless, and ready to die.

4 " Lord, whence are those blood-
   drops all the way,   [track ? "
That mark out the mountain's
" They were shed for one who had
   gone astray   [back."
Ere the Shepherd could bring him
" Lord, whence are Thy hands so
   rent and torn ? "
" They are pierced to-night by
   many a thorn."

5 But all through the mountains
   thunder-riven,
And up from the rocky steep,
There arose a cry to the gate of
   heaven :   [sheep ! "
" Rejoice ! I have found My
And the angels echoed around the
   throne,   [His own ! "
" Rejoice ! for the Lord brings back

182 WHEN tossed on Galilee's
   rough wave,   [oppressed,
And fear their anxious hearts
The Master's voice spoke firm and
   clear,   [rest.
And calm'd the angry waves to
It was His voice that still'd the wave,
His healing touch new vision gave ;
His might has triumph'd o'er the grave,
Our Christ alone has power to save.

2 When he who sight had never
   known,   [voice,
Came to the Lord with pleading
That word and touch made darkness
   flee,
And bade the sorrowful rejoice.

3 When crucified on Calvary,
    And in the tomb was laid away,
  He rose triumphant o'er the grave,
    And lives and reigns with bound-
        less sway.

4 When trials thick my path surround,
    When hope departs and gloom
        descends,
  A gentle voice speaks from above,
    And ev'ry dark foreboding ends.

183 IN the soul's bright home
        beyond the sky,   [die,
  In a land where the ransomed never
  There will be a royal banquet by and
        by—   [the Lamb.
    'Tis the great marriage supper of

> Are you going to be there,
> Are you going to be there,
> At the great marriage supper of the Lamb?
> With your wedding garments on,
> Will you meet the lov'd ones gone?
> At the great marriage supper of the Lamb?

2 Oh, the bride shall shine in bright
        array;   [away;
  With her tears all for ever wiped
  There will be a great rejoicing on
        that day—   [the Lamb.
    At the great marriage supper of

3 From all sin for evermore released,
  They will come from the west and
        from the east,
  For all nations will be gathered at
        the feast,   [the Lamb.
    Of the great marriage supper of

4 We shall praise Him by the crystal
        tide,   [glorified,
  When the Lamb that was slain is
  And the ransomed Church of God
        shall be the bride,
    At the great marriage supper of
        the Lamb.

184 A GLORIOUS invitation
        Now calls you to the feast;
  Each soul is now invited,
    The greatest and the least.
  Come, all ye heavy burdened,
    With sorrow or with care—
  To-day you are invited,
    Your burden Christ will bear.

> The Spirit says come, the Bride says come;
> Let him that heareth say, come, let him that
>   thirsteth come.   [of life freely.
> And whosoever will, let him take of the water

2 That blessed invitation
    Oh, hear to-day and heed!
  The Spirit now is calling,
    Why longer dwell in need?
  Thy soul to-day is fainting
    For Christ, the living bread;
  Accept the invitation,
    Come while the feast is spread.

3 Repeat the invitation!
    Pass on the blessed news;
  Let none forsake His mercy,
    Or pardon now refuse.
  'Tis Jesus that is calling—
    All things are ready, come—
  The Spirit will direct you,
    The Bride will welcome home.

185 WHEN none was found to
        ransom me,
    He was found worthy.
  To set a world of sinners free,
    He was found worthy.

> Oh, the bleeding Lamb!
> He was found worthy.

2 To take the book and loose the seal,
  To bruise the head that bruised His
        heel.

3 To bridge the gulf 'twix man and
        God,
  And save the rebels by His blood.

4 To open wide the gates of heaven,
  To Him all majesty be given!

5 To reign o'er all the ransomed race,
  I've tasted of His saving grace.

6 His blood has washed me white as
        snow,
  And all His fulness I shall know.

186 FREE from the law, oh, happy
        condition,   [mission;
  Jesus hath bled, and *there* is re-
  Curs'd by the law and bruised by
        the fall,
  Grace hath redeemed us once for all.

> Once for all, oh, sinner, receive it,
> Once for all, oh, brother believe it;
> Cling to the Cross, the burden will fall,
> Christ hath redeemed us once for all.

2 Now are we free—there's no con-
        demnation,
  Jesus provides a perfect salvation;
  " Come unto *Me*," oh, hear His
        sweet call!
  Come, and He saves us once for all.

3 " Children of God," oh, glorious
    calling !
Surely His grace will keep us from
    falling ;
Passing from death to life at His call,
Blessed salvation once for all.

187 O MY brother, do you know
    the Saviour,
Who is wondrous kind and true ?
" He's the Rock of your salvation ! "
There's Honey in the Rock for you.

Oh, there's Honey in the Rock, my brother,...
There's Honey in the Rock for you ;...
Leave your sins for the blood to cover,
There's Honey in the Rock for you....

2 Have you " tasted that the Lord is
    gracious " ?   [new ?
Do you walk in the way that's
Have you drunk from the living
Fountain ?   [you.
There's Honey in the Rock for

3 Do you pray unto God the Father,
"What wilt Thou have me to do?"
Never fear, He will surely answer ;
There's Honey in the Rock for you.

4 Then go out thro' the streets and
    bye-ways,   [few ;
Preach the Word to the many or
Say to ev'ry fallen brother,
There's Honey in the Rock for you.

188 HEAR the Saviour at the door,
    Let Him in,...let Him in,...
    let Him in.
He has often knocked before,
    Let Him in,...let Him in,... let
    Him in.

'Tis the Saviour standing at the door,....
He's been watching, waiting there before ;....
Open wide the heart of sin,
Let the blessed Saviour in ;
Let Him in,...let Him in.

2 He's your best and truest Friend,
One who always will defend.

3 Do not let Him knock in vain,
He may never come again.

4 Hear His gentle, loving voice,
Bid Him welcome, and rejoice.

189 JESUS is waiting, oh sinner ! for
    thee,   [Me ; "
Calling so tenderly, " Come unto

Waiting His mercy and peace to
    impart,   [thy heart.
Come then, oh wanderer, give Him

Come to Him now, He's waiting for thee,
Turn not away from His mercy so free,
Jesus is waiting, waiting for thee,
Calling so tenderly, " Come unto Me."

2 Come from the path that seems
    pleasant and wide.
Narrow the way if thou walk by
    His side—
Narrow, yet brighten'd with bless-
    ings untold,   [gold.
Leading thee home to the city of

3 Come to the Saviour whose grace is
    so free,   [for thee ;
Come to Him now while He calleth
Enter the fold by the only true door,
Come, quickly come, lest He call
thee no more.

190 WHEN the sinner turns from sin,
    How they sing up yonder !
Come to Christ sweet peace to win,
    How they sing up yonder !
Asks for cleansing in the blood,
Sinks beneath the healing flood,
Rises, cleansed and owned of God,
    How they sing up yonder !

2 When the wanderer seeks his home,
    How they sing up yonder !
Just a servant to become,
    How they sing up yonder !
Leave the byways cold and bare,
Seeks again a Father's care,
All His wealth of love to share,
    How they sing up yonder !

3 Brother, would you join the song,
    In the home up yonder ?
Sing while ages roll along,
    In the home up yonder ?
Then forsake the paths so cold,
Fly to Jesus and His fold,
That your name may be enrolled,
    In the home up yonder !

191 OH, why thus stand with
    reluctant feet,   [sweet,
Just on the verge of this rest so
While God invites and your steps
    will greet ?
    Come away to Jesus now.

Come away....to Jesus,....
Come away to Jesus now.

2 The Spirit strives, and yet there you
    stand,
  In sight of bliss and the glory land ;
  Retreat is death in the sinking sand,
    Come away to Jesus now.

3 Your loved ones gone to the other
    shore,   [o'er ;
  With unseen hands seem to beckon
  Their voices hush'd, yet they still
    implore,
    Come away to Jesus now.

192 DOWN at the Cross where my
        Saviour died,
  Down where for cleansing from sin
    I cried,   [applied ;
  There to my heart was the blood
    Glory to His name !

      Glory to His name !
      Glory to His name !
  There to my heart was the blood applied ;
      Glory to His name !

2 I am so wondrously sav'd from sin,
  Jesus so sweetly abides within,
  There at the Cross where He took
    me in :
    Glory to His name !

3 Oh, precious fountain, that saves
    from sin !
  I am so glad I have enter'd in ;
  There Jesus saves me and keeps me
    clean :
    Glory to His name !

4 Come to this fountain, so rich and
    sweet,
  Cast thy poor soul at the Saviour's
    feet ;   [complete.
  Plunge in to-day, and be made
    Glory to His name !

193 THIS is the day the Lord hath
        made,
  He calls the hours His own ;
  Let heaven rejoice, let earth be glad,
  And praise surround the throne.

2 To-day He rose and left the dead,
  And Satan's empire fell :
  To-day the saints His triumph spread,
  And all His wonders tell.

3 Hosanna to the anointed King,
  To David's holy Son !
  Help us, O Lord ! descend and bring
  Salvation from Thy throne.

4 Blest be the Lord, who comes to
    men,
  With messages of grace ;
  Who comes in God H_s Father's
    name,
  To save our sinful race.

5 Hosanna ! in the highest strains,
  The Church on earth can raise ;
  The highest heavens in which He
    reigns
  Shall give Him nobler praise.

194 IS there a heart that is waiting,
      Longing for pardon to-day ?
  Hear the glad message proclaiming,
    Jesus is passing this way.

      Jesus is passing this way,....
      This way,....to-day ;.... ◁
      Jesus is passing this way,....
      Is passing this way to-day.

2 Is there a heart that has wandered ?
    Come with thy burden to-day ;
  Mercy is tenderly pleading,
    Jesus is passing this way.

3 Is there a heart that is broken ?
    Weary and sighing for rest ?
  Come to the arms of thy Saviour,
    Pillow thy head on His breast.

4 Come to thy only Redeemer,
    Come to His infinite love ;
  Come to the gate that is leading
    Homeward to mansions above.

195 DEAR to the heart of the
        Shepherd,
  Dear are the sheep of His fold ;
  Dear is the love that He gives them,
    Dearer than silver or gold.
  Dear to the heart of the Shepherd,
    Dear are His " other " lost sheep ;
  Over the mountains He follows,
    Over the waters so deep.

      Out in the desert they wander,
        Hungry and helpless and cold ;
      Off to the rescue He hastens,
        Bringing them back to the fold.

2 Dear to the heart of the Shepherd,
    Dear are the lambs of His fold ;
  Some from the pastures are straying,
    Hungry, and helpless, and cold.
  See, the good Shepherd is seeking,
    Seeking the lambs that are lost ;
  Bringing them in with rejoicing,
    Saved at such infinite cost.

3 Dear to the heart of the Shepherd,
    Dear are the " ninety and nine,"
Dear are the sheep that have
      wandered
    Out in the desert to pine.
Hark ! He is earnestly calling,
    Tenderly pleading to-day ;
" Will you not seek for My lost ones,
    Far from My shelter astray ? "

196 COME, ev'ry soul by sin
      oppress'd,
    There's mercy with the Lord,
And He will surely give you rest,
    By trusting in His word.

    Only trust Him ! Only trust Him !
    Only trust Him now !
    He will save you ! He will save you !
    He will save you now !

2 For Jesus shed His precious blood,
    Rich blessings to bestow ;
Plunge now into the crimson flood,
    That washes white as snow.

3 Yes, Jesus is the Truth, the Way,
    That leads you into rest ;
Believe in Him without delay,
    And you are fully blest.

4 Come, then, and join this holy band,
    And on to glory go ;
To dwell in that celestial land,
    Where joys immortal flow.

197 O TELL me o'er and o'er again
    the tale I love so well,
Of how the King of Glory left
    His throne,
And came a humble man among our
    sinful race to dwell,
    That He might save and claim us
    for His own.

Oh, tell the sweet old story once again,....
Of how the Saviour loved the sons of men,....
He loved them, oh, so well, He came on earth
    to dwell,
    Oh, tell the sweet old story once again.

2 I am both weak and sinful, but one
    thing I surely know,
    That Jesus fills my heart with
    grace and love ;
That He will guide me safely thro'
    my journey here below,
    And then will take me to Himself
    above.

3 O tell again the story of His mercy
    and His grace,
    The story that is told of Him
    alone ;
Of how He died in torment, in the
    helpless sinner's place,
    And conquered, and is now upon
    His throne.

198 I HEAR the Saviour say,
    " Thy strength indeed **is**
    small ;
Come to Me—I'll be thy stay,
    Find in Me thine all in all."

    Jesus paid it all,
    All to Him I owe—
    Sin had left a crimson stain,
    He washed it white as snow.

2 For nothing good have I
    Whereby Thy grace to claim ;
Jesus died my soul to save,
    And blessed be His name.

3 When from my dying bed
    My ransomed soul shall rise,
" Jesus died my soul to save,"
    Shall rend the vaulted skies.

4 And when before the throne,
    I stand, in Him complete :
" Jesus died my soul to save,"
    My lips shall still repeat.

199 TELL it ! let the people hear
    it,
" Jesus saves from sin ! "
Let the breezes bear the message,
    " Jesus makes men clean ;
That He shed His blood to save us ! "
    Tell it far and wide,
" In no other is redemption
    Save the Crucified ! "

    Tell it far and wide,
    Tell it far and wide,
    " In no other is redemption,
    Save the Crucified ! "

2 Tell it to the lone and weary,
    To the blithe and gay ;
To the aged with their burdens,
    To the child at play.
" There is full and free salvation ! "
    Here the blessed word,
    " There is mercy and true healing
    In the Saviour's blood ! "

3 **Free** the mercy, full of pardon,
Jesus died to give!
Sweet the welcome that the sinner
Surely will receive.
Weary, weak, and heavy laden,
Come to Him to-day;
Let the cleansing blood of Jesus
Wash your sins away.

200 WE have heard a joyful sound,
Jesus saves! Jesus saves!
Spread the gladness all around,
Jesus saves! Jesus saves!
Bear the news to ev'ry land,
Climb the steeps and cross the waves,
Onward! 'tis our Lord's command,
Jesus saves! Jesus saves!

2 Waft it on the rolling tide,
Jesus saves! Jesus saves!
Tell to sinners far and wide,
Jesus saves! Jesus saves!
Sing, ye islands of the sea,
Echo back, ye ocean caves,
Earth shall keep her Jubilee,
Jesus saves! Jesus saves!

3 Sing above the battle's strife,
Jesus saves! Jesus saves!
By His death and endless life,
Jesus saves, Jesus saves!
Sing it softly thro' the gloom,
When the heart for mercy craves;
Sing in triumph o'er the tomb,
Jesus saves! Jesus saves!

4 Give the wind a mighty voice,
Jesus saves! Jesus saves!
Let the nations now rejoice,
Jesus saves! Jesus saves!
Shout salvation full and free,
Highest hills and deepest caves,
This our song of victory,
Jesus saves! Jesus saves!

201 WHOEVER receiveth the Crucified One,
Whoever believeth on God's only Son,
A free and a perfect salvation shall have,
For He is abundantly able to save.

My brother, the Mas..ter is calling for thee;...
His grace and His mer..cy are wondrously free;..
His blood as a ran..som for sinners He gave,...
And He is abun..dantly able to save.

2 Whoever receiveth the message of God,
And trusts in the pow'r of the soul-cleansing blood,
A full and eternal redemption shall have, [save.
For He is both able and willing to

3 Whoever repents and forsakes ev'ry sin, [come in,
And opens his heart for the Lord to
A present and perfect salvation shall have, [save.
For Jesus is ready this moment to

202 FAIREST of all the earth beside,
Chiefest of all unto Thy bride,
Fulness divine in Thee I see,
Wonderful Man of Calvary!

That Man of Calvary
Has won my heart from me,
And died to set me free,
Blest Man of Calvary!

2 Granting the sinner life and peace,
Granting the captive sweet release;
Shedding His blood to make us free,
Merciful Man of Calvary!

3 Giving the gifts obtained for men,
Pouring out love beyond our ken,
Giving us spotless purity,
Bountiful Man of Calvary!

4 Comfort of all my earthly way,
Jesus, I'll meet Thee some sweet day;
Centre of glory, Thee I'll see,
Wonderful Man of Calvary!

203 SHOUT the tidings of salvation
To the aged and the young,
Till the precious invitation
Waken ev'ry heart and tongue.

Send the sound the earth around,
From the rising to the setting of the sun,
Till each gath'ring crowd shall proclaim aloud,
" The glorious work is done."

2 Shout the tidings of salvation
North and south and east and west,
Till each gath'ring congregation
With the gospel sound is blest.

3 Shout the tidings of salvation
Mingling with the ocean's roar,
Till the ships of ev'ry nation
Bear the news from shore to shore.

4 Shout the tidings of salvation
   O'er the islands of the sea,
Till, in humble adoration,
   All to Christ shall bow the knee.

204 AS when the Hebrew prophet
      rais'd
   The brazen serpent high,
The wounded look'd and straight
     were cur'd,
   The people ceased to die :

2 So from the Saviour on the Cross
   A healing virtue flows ;
Who looks to Him with lively faith
   Is saved from endless woes.

3 For God gave up His Son to death,
   So generous was His love,
That all the faithful might enjoy
   Eternal life above.

4 Not to condemn the sons of men
   The Son of God appeared !
No weapons in His hand are seen,
   Nor voice of terror heard.

5 He came to raise our fallen state,
   And our lost hopes restore ;
Faith leads us to the mercy-seat,
   And bids us fear no more.

6 But vengeance just for ever lies
   Upon the rebel race,
Who God's eternal Son despise,
   And scorn His offered grace.

205 FATHER of peace and God
      of love !
We own Thy power to save,
That power by which our Shepherd
     rose
   Victorious o'er the grave.

2 Him from the dead Thou brought'st
     again,
When by His sacred blood,
Confirmed and sealed for evermore,
   Th' eternal covenant stood.

3 Oh, may Thy Spirit seal our souls,
   And mould them to Thy will,
That our weak hearts no more may
     stray,
   But keep Thy precepts still.

4 That to perfection's sacred height
   We nearer still may rise ;
And all we think, and all we do,
   Be pleasing in Thine eyes.

206 BEHOLD th' amazing gift of
      love
   The Father hath bestow'd
On us, the sinful sons of men,
   To call us sons of God !

2 Conceal'd as yet this honour lies
   By this dark world unknown,
A world that knew not when He
     came,
   Ev'n God's eternal Son.

3 High is the rank we now possess,
   But higher we shall rise ;
Though what we shall hereafter be
   Is hid from mortal eyes.

4 Our souls, we know, when He
     appears,
   Shall bear His image bright ;
For all His glory, full disclos'd,
   Shall open to our sight.

5 A hope so great, and so divine,
   May trials well endure ;
And purge the soul from sense and sin,
   As Christ Himself is pure.

207 HO ! ev'ry one that is thirsty
      in spirit.
   Ho ! ev'ry one that is weary and
     sad :
Come to the fountain, there's fulness
     in Jesus,
   All that you're longing for, come
     and be glad.

" I will pour water on him that is thirsty,
I will pour floods upon the dry ground ;
Open your heart for the gift I am bringing ;
   While ye are seeking Me, I will be found."

2 Child of the world, are you tired of
     your bondage ?
   Weary of earth-joys, so false, so
     untrue ?
Thirsting for God and His fulness of
     blessing ?
   List to the promise, a message for
     you.

3 Child of the kingdom, be filled with
     the Spirit !
   Nothing but fulness thy longing
     can meet ;
'Tis the induement for life and for
     service ;
   Thine is the promise, so certain,
     so sweet.

208 IN evil long I took delight,
　　Unawed by shame or fear,
Till a new object met my sight,
　　And stopp'd my wild career.

　Oh, the Lamb ! the bleeding Lamb !
　　The Lamb upon Calvary !
　The Lamb that was slain,
　　That liveth again
　　　To intercede for me !

2 I saw One hanging on a tree
　　In agonies and blood,
Who fixed His languid eyes on me,
　　As near His Cross I stood.

3 My conscience felt and owned my
　　guilt,
　　And plunged me in despair ;
I saw my sins His blood had spilt,
　　And help'd to nail Him there.

4 A second look He gave, which said,
　　" I freely all forgive ;
This blood is for thy ransom paid ;
　　I die that thou may'st live."

5 Thus while His death my sin displays
　　In all its blackest hue
(Such is the mystery of grace),
　　It seals my pardon, too.

209 HAVE you found the Saviour
　　precious,
More than all on earth beside,
He who gave His life to save you,
　　Who for your transgressions died ?

　Have you found...the Saviour precious ?
　　Can you slight...such love as this ?
　Surely there...can be no greater !
　　Would you give...your life for His ?

2 Have you found the Saviour
　　precious,　　　　[grave,
　　Who for you passed thro' the
Broke the bonds of death asunder,
　　Have you " prov'd His power to
　　save " ?

3 Have you found the Saviour
　　precious ?
Do you know the peace and rest
That doth fill each soul that trusts
　　Him,
　　Who in His deep love is blest ?

4 Have you found the Saviour
　　precious ?
　　Seek Him then without delay,
Taste the sweetness of His pardon,
　　He will take your sins away.

210 WHEN sorrows and trouble
　　like sea billows roll,
Tell me the story of Jesus ;
When evil assails me and doubts
　　fill my soul,
Tell me the story of Jesus.

　　Tell....it to me,....
　　Tell....it to me,....
　　Tell me the story of Jesus :
　　Tell....it to me.....

2 When weary from labour I rest by
　　the way,
　　It strengthens my purpose and
　　brightens the day.

3 In times of affliction, when suff'ring
　　from pain,
　　It softens my pillow, revives me
　　again.

4 When life here is over, and time i
　　no more,
　　Oh, tell it again on the beautifu
　　shore.

211 JESUS died for you and me ;
　　Is it not good news ?
Now there's pardon full and free ;
　　Is it not good news ?
On the Cross our sins He bore,
That on heav'n's eternal shore
We might live for evermore ;
　　Is it not good news ?

　　Is it not good news ?
　　Is it not good news ?
　On the Cross our sins He bore ;
　　Oh, is it not good news ?

2 " It is finished," Jesus said ;
　　Is it not good news ?
Sin and death are captive led ;
　　Is it not good news ?
In the grave our Lord was laid,
And the last great tribute paid,
Free the sacrifice He made ;
　　Is it not good news ?

　　Is it not good news ?
　　Is it not good news ?
　Free the sacrifice He made ;
　　Oh, is it not good news ?

3 From the grave the Saviour rose ;
　　Is it not good news ?
Gain'd the vict'ry o'er His foes ;
　　Is it not good news ?

Christ the law did satisfy,
Christ ascended up on high,
We shall meet Him by and bye ;
Is it not good news ?

> Is it not good news ?
> Is it not good news ?
> We shall meet Him by and bye ;
> Oh, is it not good news ?

4 Now He pleads for us on high ;
Is it not good news ?
Pleads that we may never die;
Is it not good news ?
Soon He'll come to claim His own,
All who trust in Him alone,
We shall gather round His throne ;
Is it not good news ?

> Is it not good news ?
> Is it not good news ?
> We shall gather round His throne ;
> Oh, is it not good news ?

212 HARK ! the gospel news is sounding,
Christ has suffered on the tree ;
Streams of mercy are abounding,
Grace for all is rich and free.
Now poor sinner,
Come to Him who died for thee.

2 Oh ! escape to yonder mountain,
Refuge find in Him to-day ;
Christ invites you to the fountain,
Come and wash your sins away.
Do not tarry,
Come to Jesus while you may.

3 Grace is flowing like a river,
Millions there have been supplied ;
Still it flows as fresh as ever
From the Saviour's wounded side.
None need perish,
All may live, for Christ hath died.

4 Christ alone shall be our portion,
Soon we hope to meet above ;
Then we'll bathe in the full ocean
Of the great Redeemer's love ;
All His fulness
We shall then for ever prove.

213 COME unto Jesus, all ye that labour,
All that are weary, sad, and oppressed ;
Still He is calling, oh, friend and neighbour, [you rest."
" Come unto Me, and I will give

Down thro' the ages, sweetly 'tis ringing,
This word of Jesus, come and be blest ;
Sweeter than carols angels are singing.
" Come unto Me, and I will give you rest."

2 Bring Him the burden, heavily pressing, [breast ;
Tell Him the sorrow hid in your
Sin and transgression freely confessing, [you rest.
Come unto Him and He will give

3 Lose not a moment, haste to your Saviour,
Ere the bright day-beams fade in the west ; [favour,
Asking His mercy, seeking His
Come unto Him and He will give you rest.

4 Come unto Jesus, Saviour and Brother, [best ;
Surely you need Him, purest and
Truer than father, fonder than mother, [you rest.
Come unto Him and He will give

214 " GIVE Me thy heart," says the Father above,
No gift so precious to Him as our love ; [art,
Softly He whispers wherever thou
" Gratefully trust Me, and give Me thy heart."

" Give Me thy heart, give Me thy heart,"
Hear the soft whisper, wherever thou art ;
From this dark world He would draw you apart,
Speaking so tenderly, " Give Me thy heart."

2 " Give Me thy heart," says the Saviour of men,
Calling in mercy again and again ;
" Turn now from sin, and from evil depart,
Have I not died for thee ? give Me thy heart."

3 " Give Me thy heart," says the Spirit divine, [resign ;
" All that thou hast to My keeping
Grace more abounding is Mine to impart, [heart."
Make full surrender, and give Me thy

215 THERE'S no one like my Saviour,
No friend can be like Him ;
My never-failing sunshine
When earthly lights grow dim ;

When summer flow'rs are blooming,
 The brightness of my joy,
Oh, may His happy service
 My heart and life employ!

No one, no one like my precious Saviour,
 No one, no one such a friend can be;
No one, no one like my precious Saviour.
 Glory! glory! Jesus cares for me.

2 There's no one like my Saviour;
 In seasons of distress,
He draws me closer to Him,
 To comfort and to bless;
He gives me, in temptation,
 The strength of His right arm;
His angels camp around me,
 To keep me from all harm.

3 There's no one like my Saviour,
 He pardons all my sin;
And gives His Holy Spirit,
 A springing well within;
He leads me out to service,
 With gentle touch and mild;
Oh, wonder of all wonders,
 That I should be His child!

4 There's no one like my Saviour,
 Come now, and find it true,
He gave His life a ransom,
 His blood was shed for you;
Then, when we reach the city
 Of everlasting light,
We'll sing with saints and angels,
 All honour, pow'r, and might.

216 I HEAR the words of love,
  I gaze upon the blood,
I see the mighty sacrifice,
 And I have peace with God.

2 'Tis everlasting peace!
 Sure as Jehovah's name;
'Tis stable as His steadfast throne,
 For evermore the same.

3 The clouds may go and come,
 And storms may sweep my sky—
This blood-sealed friendship changes not,
 The Cross is ever nigh.

4 My love is oft-times low,
 My joy still ebbs and flows;
But peace with Him remains the same—
 No change Jehovah knows.

5 I change, He changes not,
 The Christ can never die;
His love, not mine, the resting place,
 His truth, not mine, the tie.

217 NOT all the blood of beasts
  On Jewish altars slain
Could give the guilty conscience peace
 Or wash away the stain.

2 But Christ, the heavenly Lamb,
 Takes all our sins away;
A sacrifice of nobler name
 And richer blood than they.

3 My faith would lay her hand
 On that dear head of Thine,
While like a penitent I stand
 And there confess my sin.

4 My soul looks back to see
 The burdens Thou didst bear,
When hanging on the cursed tree,
 And knows her guilt was there.

5 Believing, we rejoice
 To see the curse remove;
We bless the Lamb with cheerful voice
 And sing His bleeding love!

218 HEAR the promise of the Lord,
  As recorded in His Word,
"Unto you is everlasting life!"
Heavy laden and distress'd,
Come, and I will give you rest;
 "Unto you is everlasting life!"

"Everlasting life," the promise reads,
While at God's right hand the Saviour pleads;
Will you come to-day, making Christ your stay?
For with Him is everlasting life.

2 Weary pilgrim on the road
 To the judgment seat of God,
  "Unto you is everlasting life!"
If on Jesus you believe,
And His blessed Word receive,
  "Unto you is everlasting life!"

3 Cast on Jesus all your care,
 And your burden He will bear,
  "Unto you is everlasting life!"
In the strait and narrow way,
He will lead you day by day!
  "Unto you is everlasting life!"

219 THERE's nothing like the old,
   old story,
  Grace is free, grace is free !
Which saints and martyrs tell in
   glory,
  Grace is free, grace is free !
It brought them thro' the flood and
   flame,
By it they fought and overcame,
And now they cry thro' His dear
   name,
  Grace is free, grace is free !

  There's nothing like the old, old story,
    Grace is free, Grace is free !
  Which saints and martyrs tell in glory,
    Grace is free, Grace is free !

2 There's only hope in trusting Jesus,
  Grace is free, grace is free !
From sin that doomed He died to
   free us.
  Grace is free, grace is free !
Who would not tell the story sweet
Of love so wondrous, so complete,
And fall in rapture at His feet !
  Grace is free, grace is free !

3 From age to age the theme is telling,
  Grace is free, grace is free !
From shore to shore the strains are
   swelling.
  Grace is free, grace is free !
And when that time shall cease to be,
And faith is crowned with victory,
'Twill sound thro' all eternity,
  Grace is free, grace is free !

220 WOULD I know Him if He
   stood here
  By my side, by my side ?
Do the cruel, cruel nail-prints
  Yet abide, yet abide ?
Would He show to me His beauty,
  So divine, so divine,
That in rapture I would feel Him
  To be mine, to be mine ?

2 When to Satan thou dost answer,
  " Flee from me, flee from me ! "
When between thee and the Master
  Naught shall be, naught shall be ;
On thine eyes shall flash a vision,
  Wondrous fair, wondrous fair—
Lo ! a pierced and thorn-crowned
   Saviour,
  Standeth there, standeth there.

3 Could I hear Him if He called me,
  Waiting here, waiting here ?
Would His words of magic sweetnes
  Pierce my ear, pierce my ear ?
Could the world with all its lurings,
  Drown that tone, drown that tone
And He pass me by and leave me
  All alone, all alone ?

4 When thou criest in thine anguish,
  " Saviour, hear ; Saviour, hear ! "
It will reach Him thro' the clamour,
  Never fear, never fear !
Tho' sometimes thine ears are
   deafened
  By the din, by the din,
He is list'ning for the summons,
  " Lord, come in ; Lord, come in ! "

221 I HAD wander'd far away
   In the land of mighty foes,
And my soul had felt the bitterness
   of sin ;
  I was marching with the hosts
  That the truth of God oppose,
And among the sav'd I was not
   counted in.

  Counted in.... Counted in,....
Whosoever will believe is counted in ;....
What a jubilee of joy in the heavens then is
   heard,
When a soul among the saved is counted in !

2   But I found it written down,
    Whosoever will believe
  In the Son of God is sav'd from
     ev'ry sin ;
    And I bless His holy name
    That the promise I receive—   [in.
  In that " whosoever " I am counted

3   When the pardon full and free,
    That is promised in His Word,
  Is received by faith, and Jesus enters in;
    What a jubilee of joy
    In the heavens then is heard,
  And a soul among the sav'd is
     counted in.

4   Oh, my sinner friend, beware !
    A revealing day is near,
  That will show the secrets of thy
     heart within ;
    Have it cleansed by grace divine,
    And when Jesus shall appear,
  He will then among His jewels count
     you in.

222 THEY nail'd my Lord upon
  the tree,
And left Him, dying, there ;
Thro' love He suffered there for me,
'Twas love beyond compare.

Crucified ! Crucified !
And nailed upon the tree !
With pierced hands and feet and side !
  For you !...For me !....

2 Upon His head a crown of thorns,
  Upon His heart my shame ;
For me He prayed, for me He died,
  And, dying, spoke my name.

3 "Forgive him, O forgive!" He cried,
  Then bow'd His sacred head ;
" O Lamb of God ! my sacrifice ! "
  For me Thy blood was shed.

4 His voice I hear, His love I know ;
  I worship at His feet ;
And kneeling there, at Calvary's
  Cross,
  Redemption is complete.

223 O MOURNER in Zion, how
  blessed art thou,
For Jesus is waiting to comfort thee
  now ;   [God ;
Fear not to rely on the Word of thy
Step out on the promise—get under
  the blood.

2 O ye that are hungry and thirsty,
  rejoice !
For ye shall be filled ; do you hear
  that sweet voice   [God ?
Inviting you now to the banquet of
Step out on the promise—get under
  the blood.

3 Who sighs for a heart from iniquity
  free ?
  O, poor troubled soul ; there's a
    promise for thee.
There's rest, weary one, in the bosom
  of God ;
Step out on the promise—get under
  the blood.

4 Step out on this promise, and Christ
  thou shalt win.
  " The blood of His Son cleanseth us
    from all sin ; "   [God !
It cleanseth me now, hallelujah to
I rest on His promise—I'm under
  the blood.

224 SOULS of men ! why will ye
  scatter
Like a crowd of frightened sheep ?
Foolish hearts, why will ye wander
From a love so true and deep ?

2 Was there ever kindest shepherd
  Half so gentle, half so sweet,
As the Saviour, who would have us
  Come and gather round His feet ?

3 There's a wideness in God's mercy,
  Like the wideness of the sea ;
There's a kindness in His justice,
  Which is more than liberty.

4 For the love of God is broader
  Than the measures of man's mind ;
And the heart of the Eternal
  Is most wonderfully kind.

5 There is plentiful redemption
  In the blood that has been shed ;
There is joy for all the members
  In the sorrows of the Head.

6 Pining souls ! come nearer Jesus,
  And oh, come not doubting thus,
But with faith that trusts more
  bravely
  His great tenderness for us.

7 If our love were but more simple,
  We should take Him at His Word ;
And our lives would be all sunshine
  In the sweetness of our Lord.

225 A FRIEND I have called
  Jesus,
Whose love is strong and true,
And never fails howe'er 'tis tried,
  No matter what I do.
I've sinn'd against this love of His,
  But when I knelt to pray,
Confessing all my guilt to Him,
  The sin clouds rolled away.

It's just like Jesus to roll the clouds away,
It's just like Jesus to keep me day by day,
It's just like Jesus all along the way,
  It's just like His great love.

2 Sometimes the clouds of trouble
  Bedim the sky above ;
I cannot see my Saviour's face,
  I doubt His wondrous love.
But He, from heaven's mercy-seat,
  Beholding my despair,
In pity bursts the clouds between,
  And shows me He is there.

3 When sorrow's clouds o'ertake me,
And break upon my head,
When life seems worse than useless,
And I were better dead ;
I take my grief to Jesus then,
Nor do I go in vain,
For heav'nly hope He gives that cheers,
Like sunshine after rain.

4 O, I could sing for ever
Of Jesus' love divine,
Of all His care and tenderness,
For this poor life of mine.
His love is in and over all,
And winds and waves obey
When Jesus whispers ," Peace, be
still ! "
And rolls the clouds away.

226 COME to the Saviour, come to
the Saviour,
Thou sin-stricken offspring of man ;
He left His throne above,
To reveal His wondrous love,
And to open a fountain for sin.

I do believe it ! I do believe it !
I'm saved thro' the blood of the Lamb
My happy soul is free,
For the Lord has pardoned me,
Hallelujah to His blessed name !

2 Pardon is offer'd, pardon is offer'd,
A pardon, full, present, and free ;
The mighty debt was paid,
When on Calvary Jesus died,
To atone for a rebel like me.

3 Plunge in the fountain, plunge in the
fountain, [soul ;
The fountain which cleanses the

'Tis cleansing far and near,
And its streams are flowing here,
Oh, believe it, and thou art made
whole.

227 LISTEN to the blessed in-
vitation,
Sweeter than the notes of angel song,
Chiming softly with a heav'nly
cadence,
Calling to the passing throng.

Him that cometh unto Me,....
Him that cometh unto Me,....
Him that cometh unto Me,....
I will in no wise cast out.

2 Weary toiler, sad and heavy laden,
Joyfully the great salvation see ;
Close beside thee stands the Burden-
Bearer,
Strong to bear thy load and thee.

3 Come, ye thirsty, to the living
waters,
Hungry, come, and on His bounty
feed ; [Him,
Not thy fitness is the plea to bring
But thy pressing utmost need.

4 Whoso cometh, blind, or maimed, or
sinful,
Cometh for his healing to the Lord,
Claims the cleansing of the blood so
precious,
Proves anew this gracious word.

5 Coming humbly daily to this Saviour,
Breathing all the heart to Him in
pray'r ; [mansions,
Coming some day to the heav'nly
He will give thee welcome there.

WARNING AND ENTREATY

228 OH, why not say Yes to the
Saviour to-night ?
He's tenderly pleading with thee
To come to Him now with thy sin-
burden'd heart,
For pardon so full and so free....

Why not say Yes to-night ?....
Why not ? Why not ?
While He so gently, so tenderly pleads,
Oh, accept Him to-night !....

2 For with you the Spirit will not
always plead—
O do not reject Him to-night !

To-morrow may bring you the
darkness of death,
Unbroken by heavenly light....

3 Take Christ as your Saviour, then
all shall be well,
The morrow let bring what it may;
His love shall protect you, His Spirit
shall guide,
And safely keep you in His way....

229 DRIFTING away from the
Saviour,
Drifting to lands unknown,

Drifting away by night and by day,
  Drifting, yes, drifting alone.

Drifting away from the Saviour,
  Drifting away from His love;
While the Saviour is tenderly calling,
  You are drifting away from God.

2 Drifting away from the Saviour,
    He who would bear your load;
  Drifting away by night and by day,
    Drifting, yes, drifting from God.

3 Drifting away from the Saviour,
    Fearlessly on you go;
  Drifting away by night and by day,
    Drifting to regions of woe.

4 Drifting away from the Saviour,
    Even the angels weep;
  Still you drift on with mirth and
      with song,
    Out on the fathomless deep.

230 O SINNER, the Saviour is
          calling for thee,   [vain;
  Long, long has He called thee in
  He called thee when joy lent its
    'crown to thy days,
  He called thee in sorrow and pain.

Oh, turn, while the Saviour in mercy is waiting,
  And steer for the harbour light;
For how do you know but your soul may be
    drifting
  Over the dead-line to-night?

2 O sinner, thine ears have been deaf
      to His voice,
    Thine eyes to His glory been dim;
  The calls of thy Saviour have so
      wearied thee,   [Him?
    Oh, what if they should weary

3 O sinner, the Spirit is striving with
      thee;   [more,
    What if He should strive never
  But leave thee alone in thy darkness
      to dwell,
    In sight of the heavenly shore?

4 O sinner, God's patience may weary
      some day,
    And leave thy sad soul in the
      blast;   [away
  By wilful resistance you've drifted
    Over the dead-line at last.

231 LIFE at best is very brief,
          Like the falling of a leaf,
  Like the binding of a sheaf,
    Be in time.

Fleeting days are telling fast
That the die will soon be cast,
And the fatal line be passed,
    Be in time.

Be in time,....Be in time,....
While the voice of Jesus calls you,
    Be in time.....
If in sin you longer wait
You may find no open gate,
And your cry be just too late.
    Be in time.

2 Fairest flowers soon decay,
  Youth and beauty pass away,
  Oh, you have not long to stay,
    Be in time.
  While God's Spirit bids you come,
  Sinner, do no longer roam,
  Lest you seal your hopeless doom,
    Be in time.

3 Time is gliding swiftly by,
  Death and judgment draweth nigh,
  To the arms of Jesus fly,
    Be in time.
  Oh, I pray you, count the cost,
  Ere the fatal line be crossed,
  And your soul in hell be lost,
    Be in time.

4 Sinner, heed the warning voice,
  Make the Lord your final choice,
  Then all heaven will rejoice,
    Be in time.
  Come from darkness into light,
  Come, let Jesus make you right,
  Come, and start for heaven to-night,
    Be in time.

232 ON the happy golden shore,
          Where the faithful part no
            more,
  When the storms of life are o'er,
    Meet me there;
  When the night dissolves away,
  Into pure and perfect day,
  I am going home to stay.
    Meet me there.

Meet me there,....meet me there,....
Where the tree of life is blooming,
    Meet me there.....
When the storms of life are o'er,
On the happy golden shore,
Where the faithful part no more,
    Meet me there.

2 Here our fondest hopes are vain,
  Dearest links are rent in twain,
  But in heaven no throb of pain—
    Meet me there;

By the river sparkling bright,
In the city of delight,
Where our faith is lost in sight,
Meet me there.

3 Where the harps of angels ring,
And the blest for ever sing,
In the palace of the King,
Meet me there ;
Where in sweet communion blend,
Heart with heart, and friend with
friend,
In a world that ne'er shall end,
Meet me there.

233 YOU are drifting far from
shore, leaning on an idle oar,
You are drifting, slowly drifting,
drifting down ;
You are drifting with the tide, to
the ocean wild and wide,
You are drifting, slowly drifting,
drifting down.

You are drift..ing..down,..drift..ing..down
  To the dark and awful sea ;
You are drift..ing..down,
  From a Father's loving care,
  To the blackness of despair ;
You are drifting, slowly drifting, drifting down.

2 Lights upon the homeland shore give
you warning o'er and o'er,
You are drifting, slowly drifting,
drifting down.
Soon beyond the harbour bar will
your boat be carried far.
You are drifting, slowly drifting,
drifting down.

3 Voices from the homeland shore
fainter grow as they implore ;
You are drifting, slowly drifting,
drifting down.
O my brother, do not wait ! heed
them ere it be too late,
Ere for ever you have drifted,
drifted down.

234 STILL out of Christ, when so
oft He has call'd you,
Why will you longer refuse to
believe ?
What can you hope from the world
or its pleasure ?
How can you trust them when
both will deceive ?

Come, come to Jesus, weary, heavy-hearted,
  Come, come to Jesus while you may ;
Now He is waiting, waiting to receive you,
  Hark ! He is calling you to-day.

2 Still out of Christ, and the moments
so precious,
Night is approaching, oh, what
will you do ?
Still out of Christ, yet there's room
at the fountain,
Free are its waters, and flowing
for you.

3 Still out of Christ, yet for you there
is mercy,
If you are willing to turn from
your sin ;
Yonder He stands at the door of
salvation,
Waiting to pardon and welcome
you in.

4 Still out of Christ, and the love He
has promised ;
How you are longing that love
to receive !
Haste where the star of your faith
is directing,
Haste, and this moment repent
and believe.

235 NO beautiful chamber,
No soft cradle bed,
No place but a manger,
Nowhere for His head ;
No praises of gladness,
No thought of their sin,
No glory, but sadness,
No room in the inn.

No room, no room for Jesus !
  Oh, give Him welcome free,
Lest you should hear at heaven's gate,
  There is no room for thee !

2 No sweet consecration,
No seeking His part,
No humiliation,
No place in the heart ;
No thought of the Saviour,
No sorrow for sin,
No prayer for His favour,
No room in the inn.

3 No one to receive Him,
No welcome while here,
No balm to relieve Him,
No staff but a spear ;
No seeking His treasure,
No weeping for sin,
No doing His pleasure,
No room in the inn.

36 OVER the river faces I see,
Fair as the morning, looking
for me ;
Free from their sorrow, grief, and
despair,   [there.
Waiting and watching patiently

Looking this way, yes, looking this way ;
Loved ones are waiting, looking this way ;
Fair as the morning, bright as the day,
Dear ones in glory looking this way.

2 Father and mother safe in the vale,
Watch for the boatman, wait for
the sail,
Bearing the loved ones over the tide,
Into the harbour, near to their side.

3 Brother and sister, gone to that clime,
Wait for the others, coming some-
time ;
Safe with the angels, whiter than
snow,   [below.
Watching for dear ones waiting

4 Sweet little darling, light of the
home,
Looking for someone, beckoning
come ;   [dew,
Bright as a sunbeam, pure as the
Anxiously looking, mother, for you.

5 Jesus the Saviour, bright morning
star,
Looking for lost ones straying afar ;
Hear the glad message, why will you
roam ?   [home."
Jesus is calling, " Sinner, come

237 OH, come, sinner come, 'tis
mercy's call ;
Here at Jesu's feet !
Oh, come, and repenting, lay thy all
Down at Jesu's feet !

Oh, lay it down, lay it down,
Lay thy weary burden down ;
Oh, lay it down, lay it down,
Down at Jesu's feet.

2 Oh come, and believing, seek thy rest
Here, at Jesu's feet !
Thy heart, with its heavy weight
opprest,
Lay at Jesu's feet.

3 Oh come where thy faith can make
thee whole,
Here at Jesu's feet !   [soul
Oh come, and thy weary, troubled
Lay at Jesu's feet !

c

4 Oh come ! bless the Lord, there's
room for thee,
Here at Jesu's feet !
Thy burden of sin, whate'er it be,
Lay at Jesu's feet !

238 BEHOLD a Stranger at the
door,
He gently knocks, has knock'd
before ;
Has waited long—is waiting still :
You treat no other friend so ill !

Oh, let the dear Saviour come in,....
He'll cleanse the heart from sin !....
Oh, keep Him no more out at the door,
But let the dear Saviour come in !....

2 Oh, lovely attitude, He stands
With melting heart and open hands :
Oh, matchless kindness ! and He
shows
That matchless kindness to His foes.

3 But will He prove a Friend indeed ?
He will—the very Friend you need !
The Friend of sinners ?   Yes, 'tis
He,
With garments dyed on Calvary !

4 Rise, touch'd with gratitude divine,
Turn out His enemy and thine,
That soul-destroying monster, sin,
And let the Heav'nly Stranger in.

5 Admit Him ere His anger burn ;
His feet departed, ne'er return ;
Admit Him ! or the hour's at hand
You'll at His door rejected stand.

239 ONCE I heard a sound at my
heart's dark door,
And was roused from the slumber
of sin ;
It was Jesus knock'd, He had
knock'd before ;
Now I said, " Blessed Master,
come in ! "

Then open ! open ! open ! let the Master in....
For the heart will be bright with a heav'nly
light,
When you let the Master in.

2 Then He spread a feast of redeeming
love,   [guest ;
And He made me His own happy
In my joy I thought that the saints
above   [blest.
Could be hardly more favour'd or

3 In the holy war with the foes of
   truth,
He's my shield; He my table
   prepares.   [youth,
He restores my soul, He renews my
And gives triumph in answer to
   pray'rs.

4 He will feast me still with His
   presence dear,
And the love He so freely hath
   giv'n;   [Him here,
While His promise tells, as I serve
Of the banquet of glory in heav'n.

240 OUT of Christ, without a
     Saviour,
Oh! can it, can it be?
Like a ship without a rudder,
On a wild and stormy sea!

   Oh, to be without a Saviour,
     With no hope nor refuge nigh!
   Can it be, O blessed Saviour,
     One without Thee dares to die?

2 Out of Christ, without a Saviour,
Lonely and dark the way;
With no light, no hope in Jesus,
Making bright the cheerless day.

3 Out of Christ, without a Saviour,
No help nor refuge nigh;
How can you, my friend and brother,
Dare to live, or dare to die?

4 Out of Christ, without a Saviour,
Dark will the voyage be;
Clouds will gather, storms surround
   you,
Oh, to Christ for refuge flee!

5 Out of Christ, without a Saviour,
Give to Him now your heart,
Ere the door of mercy closes,
And you hear His word, "Depart."

241 THERE'S a great day coming,
     a great day coming,
There's a great day coming by
   and by,
When the saints and the sinners
   shall be parted right and left.
Are you ready for that day to
   come?

   Are you ready, are you ready,
     Are you ready for the judgment day?
   Are you ready, are you ready
     For the judgment day?

2 There's a bright day coming,
   bright day coming,
There's a bright day coming by
   and by,
But its brightness shall only come to
   them that love the Lord,
Are you ready for that day to come?

3 There's a sad day coming, a sad day
   coming,   [by
There's a sad day coming by and
When the sinner shall hear his doom
   "Depart, I know you not."
Are you ready for that day to
   come?

242 SINNERS, whither will you
     wander?
Whither will you stray?
Oh, remember, life is slender,
'Tis but a short day.

   Death is coming, coming, coming,
     And the judgment day;
   Hasten sinner, hasten sinner,
     Seek the narrow way.

2 Satan has resolv'd to have you
For his lawful prey;
Jesus Christ has died to save you;
Haste, oh, haste away!

3 Listen to the invitation,
Whilst He's crying, "Come!"
If you miss the great salvation,
Hell will be your doom.

4 Would you 'scape the awful sentence,
From destruction flee;
Seek the Lord by true repentance,
Haste to Calvary.

243 WILL you open the door of
     your heart to-night?
Outside Jesus patiently stands;
He is graciously waiting, how can
   you Him slight?   [hands.
He's knocking with nail-pierced

   Just open the door of your heart to-night,
     For Jesus now seeks you to win;
   He is waiting outside, swing the door open wide,
     And gladly He'll enter in.

2 Will you open the door of your
   heart to-night?
Oh, soul, will you longer delay?
When the Saviour can free you from
   sin's awful blight,   [way.
There is danger and death in your

3 Will you open the door of your heart
      to-night ?
  God's Spirit is striving within ;
  He may never again with your
      stubborn will fight,
  But leave you to perish in sin.

4 Will you open the door of your
      heart to-night ?   [away ;
  Do not send the dear Saviour
  Lest He leave you for ever con-
      demned in God's sight,
  On the awful reckoning day.

244 IS there any sad heart that
      is heavy laden ?
  Any one here ? Any one here ?
  Is there any poor soul who would
      love the Saviour ?
  Come and we will help you on
      your way !

Just as you are, the Lord will save you,
    Come without delay !
Is there any poor soul who would follow Jesus ?
Come, and we will help you on your way !

2 Is there any who thirst for the living
      water ?
  Any one here ? Any one here ?
  Is there any who sigh for the
      crimson fountain ?
  Come and we will help you on
      your way !

3. Is there any who long to be own'd
      by Jesus ?
  Any one here ? Any one here ?
  Is there any will say, " I believe
      this moment " ?
  Come and we will help you on
      your way !

245 IF you are tired of the load
      of your sin,
  Let Jesus come into your heart ;
  If you desire a new life to begin,
      Let Jesus come into your heart.
      Just now, your doubtings give o'er ;
      Just now, reject Him no more ;
      Just now, throw open the door ;
      Let Jesus come into your heart.

2 If 'tis for purity now that you sigh,
  Fountains for cleansing are flowing
      near by.

3 If there's a tempest your voice
      cannot still,   [can fill.
  If there's a void this world ne'er

4 If friends, once trusted, have proven
      untrue,   [you.
  Find what a friend He will be unto
5 If you would join the glad songs of
      the blest,   [rest.
  If you would enter the mansions of

      Just now, my doubtings are o'er ;
      Just now, rejecting no more ;
      Just now, I open the door
      And Jesus comes into my heart.

246 DRIFTING away from Christ
      in thy youth,
  Drifting away from mercy and truth,
  Drifting to sin in tenderest youth,
      Drifting away from God.

Brother, the Saviour has called you before ;
See ! you are nearing eternity's shore !
Soon you may perish, be lost evermore,
    Jesus now calls for you.

2 Drifting away from mother and home,
  Drifting away in sorrow to roam,
  Drifting where peace and rest cannot
      come,
      Drifting away from God.

3 Drifting away on sin's treach'rous
      tide,
  Drifting where death and darkness
      abide,   [pride,
  Drifting from heav'n away in your
      Drifting away from God.

4 Drifting away from hope's blessed
      shore,   [roar,
  Drifting away where wild breakers
  Drifting and   stranded, wreck'd,
      evermore
      Far from the light of God.

5 Why will ye drift on billows of shame,
  Spurning His grace again and again ?
  Soon you'll be lost ! in sin to remain,
      Ever away from God.

247 DOST thou know at thy
      bolted heart's door to-night,
  The Saviour in meekness doth
      stand,
  And longs for admission ? Pray
      listen now   [hand.
  To the knock of the nail-pierced

Heed the knock of the nail-pierced hand,....
Heed the knock of the nail-pierced hand ;....
Swing the door open wide, bid Him enter
    and abide,
Heed the knock of the nail-pierced hand.....

2 You turn not away when a friend's
at your door,
Here's One there's none like in
the land,
Who asks to come in and for ever
abide,
Heed the knock of the nail-
pierced hand.

3 All the pain and the shame of His
death on the tree,
A welcome from you should
command,
Since the weight of your sins in His
body He bore,
Heed the knock of the nail-
pierced hand.

248 PASSING onward, quickly
passing ;
But I ask thee, Whither bound ?
Is it to the many mansions,
Where eternal rest is found ?
Passing onward, passing onward,
Tell me, sinner, whither bound ?

2 Passing onward, quickly passing ;
Nought the wheels of time can
stay ; [going
Sweet the thought that some are
To the realms of perfect day.
Passing onward, passing onward,
Christ their Leader, Christ their
Way.

3 Passing onward, quickly passing,
Many on the downward road ;
Careless of their souls immortal,
Heeding not the call of God.
Passing onward, passing onward,
Trampling on the Saviour's blood.

4 Passing onward, quickly passing ;
Time its course will swiftly run ;
Still we hear the fond entreaty
Of the ever gracious One :
" Come and welcome, come and
welcome,
'Tis by Me that life is won."

249 HARK ! sinner, while God from
on high doth entreat thee,
And warning with language of
mercy doth blend ;
Attend to His voice, lest in judgment
He meet thee ;
" The harvest is passing, the
summer will end."

2 How oft of thy danger and guilt P
hath told thee !
How oft still the message of merc
doth send !
Haste, haste, while He waits in H
arms to enfold thee !
" The harvest is passing, th
summer will end."

3 Despised and rejected, at length H
may leave thee ;
What anguish and horror th
bosom will rend !
Then haste thee, O sinner, while H
will receive thee :
" The harvest is passing, th
summer will end."

4 Ere long and Jehovah will come i
His power !
Our God will arise with His foe
to contend ;
Haste, haste thee, O sinner ! prepar
for that hour :
" The harvest is passing, th
summer will end."

5 The Saviour will call thee in judg-
ment before Him,
O, let all thy sins go, and make
Him thy friend !
Now yield Him thy heart, and make
haste to adore Him !
" Thy harvest is passing, thy
summer will end."

250 ONCE again the gospel message
From the Saviour you have
heard :
Will you heed the invitation ?
Will you turn and seek the Lord ?
Come believing !...come believing !...
Come to Jesus ! look and live !...
Come believing !...come believing !...
Come to Jesus ! look and live !

2 Many summers you have wasted,
Ripened harvests you have seen,
Winter snows by spring have melted,
Yet you linger in your sin.

3 Jesus for your choice is waiting ;
Tarry not ; at once decide !
While the Spirit now is striving,
Yield and seek the Saviour's side.

4 Cease of fitness to be thinking ;
Do not longer try to feel ;
It is *trusting*, and not *feeling*,
That will give the Spirit's seal.

5 Let your will to God be given,
　　Trust in Christ's atoning blood ;
　Look to Jesus now in heaven,
　　Rest on His unchanging Word.

251 " ALMOST persuaded " now
　　to believe ;
　" Almost persuaded," Christ to
　　receive ;
　Seems now some soul to say ?—
　" Go, Spirit, go Thy way :
　Some more convenient day,
　　On Thee I'll call."

2 " Almost persuaded : " come, come
　　to-day !　　　　　　　[away !
　" Almost persuaded : " turn not
　　Jesus invites you here,
　Angels are ling'ring near,
　Pray'rs rise from hearts so dear,
　　O wanderer, come !

3 " Almost persuaded : " harvest is
　　past !　　　　　　　　[at last !
　" Almost persuaded : " doom comes
　" Almost " cannot avail ;
　" Almost " is but to fail ;
　Sad, sad, that bitter wail—
　　" Almost "—*but lost.*

252 A VOICE is heard in the dewy
　　dawn,
　And the call is sweet and low ;
　Come now, My child, to the Shep-
　　herd's fold,
　Where the living waters flow ;
　But the gay heart answers in careless
　　tones,
　　As light as the morning chime :
　" Let me live for the world just a
　　little while,
　I will turn to God—sometime."

Beware ! beware ! At the pearly gate
God may answer your " Sometime," " Too
　late ! Too late ! "

2 The day is nearing the noontide glow,
　　And the voice is heard again ;
　It calls the soul to a nobler life,
　'Tis a patient, kind refrain ;
　Enter now the Master's broad
　　harvest field,
　　In the strength of your early
　　prime ;
　Come, and bring to His work service
　　good and true—
　Still the same reply—" Sometime!"

3 The feet are treading the western
　　slope,
　And the air is growing chill ;
　Oh, can it be God is waiting yet,
　　That His voice is pleading still ?
　That He'll flood with beauty the
　　sunset sky,　　　　　　[Clime ?
　Bright rays from the Golden
　But the sinner, long-harden'd, has
　　turn'd away,
　　With the fatal word—"Sometime."

4 O soul, take heed, ere the shadows
　　fall,
　And the day of grace be past,
　For how shall a trembling sinner
　　stand
　By the gates of death at last ?
　Hear the Saviour's call ; at the
　　Cross lay down
　　Thy burden of guilt and crime ;
　And the angels shall sing thee a
　　sweeter song
　　Than the sad refrain, " Sometime."

253 AFTER the storm that sweeps
　　the sea ;
　After the drifting to the lee,
　After the rocks and sands are passed,
　Cometh the joy of home at last.

　　After all that here we see,
　　　What will there be, what will there be ?
　　After all that here we see,
　　　After all, eternity.

2 After the winter long and drear ;
　After the snow-clouds disappear ;
　After the winds sweet odours bring,
　Cometh the ever-welcome spring.

3 After the long and toilsome day ;
　After the sun's fierce burning ray ;
　After the toiler homeward goes,
　Cometh the night and sweet repose.

4 After the march of time shall cease,
　After earth-strife shall end in peace,
　After the changeful disappears,
　Cometh the long eternal years.

254 COME, soul, and find thy rest,
　　No longer be distressed ;
　Come to thy Saviour's breast ;
　　O, don't stay away.

　　Pray'rs are ascending now,
　　Angels are bending now ;
　　Both worlds are blending now ;
　　Oh, don't stay away.

2 Dark is the world and cold,
Her cares cannot be told ;
Come to thy Saviour's fold ;
  Oh, don't stay away.

3 Come with thy load of sin,
Christ died thy soul to win ;
Now He will take thee in ;
  Oh, don't stay away.

4 Time, here, will soon be past,
Moments are flying fast ;
Judgment will come at last ;
  Oh, don't stay away.

5 Come, oh ! we pray thee, come,
Come, and no longer roam ;
Come, now, and start for home ;
  Oh, don't stay away.

255 RETURN, O wand'rer, to thy
          home,
Thy Father calls for thee :
No longer now in exile roam,
  In guilt and misery.
    Return, return.

2 Return, O wand'rer, to thy home,
'Tis Jesus calls for thee ;
The Spirit and the Bride say "Come,"
  Oh, now for refuge flee.
    Return, return.

3 Return, O wand'rer, to thy home,
'Tis madness to delay ;
There are no pardons in the tomb,
  And brief is mercy's day.
    Return, return.

256 WHAT means this eager,
          anxious throng,
Which moves with busy haste along ;
These wondrous gatherings day by
    day ?   [pray ?
What means this strange commotion,
In accents hushed the throng reply:
" Jesus of Nazareth passeth by."

2 Who is this Jesus ? Why should He
The city move so mightily ?
A passing stranger, has He skill
To move the multitude at will ?
Again the stirring notes reply :
" Jesus of Nazareth passeth by."

3 Jesus ! 'tis He who once below
Man's pathway trod, 'mid pain and
    woe ;

And burdened ones, where'er He
    came,   [and lame ;
Brought out their sick, and deaf,
The blind rejoiced to hear the cry :
" Jesus of Nazareth passeth by."

4 Again He comes ! From place to place
His holy footprints we can trace.
He pauseth at our threshold—nay,
He enters—condescends to stay,
Shall we not gladly raise the cry :
" Jesus of Nazareth passeth by ? "

5 Ho ! all ye heavy laden, come !
Here's pardon, comfort, rest, and
    home.
Ye wanderers from a Father's face,
Return, accept His proffered grace.
Ye tempted ones, there's refuge nigh,
" Jesus of Nazareth passeth by."

6 But if you still this call refuse,
And all His wondrous love abuse,
Soon will He sadly from you turn,
Your bitter prayer for pardon spurn.
"Too late! too late!" will be the cry—
" *Jesus of Nazareth has passed by.*"

257 THO' only a line, just a line
          intervenes
Between your salvation and you,
Your soul will be lost if the line is
    not crossed,
  God's Word to the sinner is true.
Oh, won't you step over, step over it now ?
 Believing His Word to be true ;
Come then at the foot of the Cross humbly bow;
 And let the dear Saviour save you.

2 You may have gone far in the dark
    and the cold,
  Like one in the wilderness lost ;
But would you come back to the
    true Shepherd's fold,
  There's only a line to be crossed.

3 You may have been drifting the
    world's stormy main, [tossed ;
  By billow and tempest been
But would you return to the home-
    port again,
  There's only a line to be crossed.

4 Has sin sown the seed of despair in
    your soul ?
  O come without money or cost !
The Saviour is waiting to say, " Be
    thou whole ; "
  There's only a line to be crossed.

258 THE Saviour is bending above
    thee,
To hear what thy spirit will say,
    To the tender embrace,
    Of His mercy and grace,
Will the answer be " Yea, Lord,"
    or " Nay."
" I died for thee," sweetly He
    whispers,   [hands,"
" See, here are the wounds in My
    Thy finger bring near
    And touch without fear
The nail-prints as o'er thee He
    stands.
The Saviour is bending above thee,
  To hear what thy spirit will say,
To the tender embrace of His mercy and grace,
  Will the answer be "Yea, Lord," or "Nay" ?

2 Look up in the face of the Saviour,
    The thorn-crown'd yet beautiful
    brow ;
    He waits the reply
    Of thy tear-dimming eye,
Oh, what wilt thou answer Him now?
The Saviour is bending above thee,
He asks for thy heart in return
    For the heart that He gave,
    To ransom and save ;
Oh, will not thy glad spirit burn ?

3 Thou hearest His offers of mercy,
    The promise of pardon and peace ;
    Come, wilt thou not say
    To His voice a glad " Yea,"
And bid all thy waverings cease ?
The Saviour is bending above thee,
His quick ear awaits the glad word:
    " Lord Jesus, to-day,
    I whisper my ' Yea,'
And know that my answer is heard."

259 A FEW more years shall roll,
    A few more seasons come,
And we shall be with those that rest
    Asleep within the tomb.
    Then, oh, my Lord, prepare
      My soul for that great day ;
    Oh, wash me in Thy precious blood,
      And take my sins away.

2 A few more suns shall set
    O'er these dark hills of time,
And we shall be where suns are not,
    A far serener clime.
    Then, oh, my Lord, prepare
      My soul for that blest day
    Oh, wash me in Thy precious blood,
      And take my sins away.

3 A few more storms shall beat
    On this wild rocky shore,
And we shall be where tempests
    cease,
    And surges swell no more.
    Then, oh, my Lord, prepare
      My soul for that calm day ;
    Oh, wash me in Thy precious blood,
      And take my sins away.

260 WHERE will you spend eter-
    nity ?
This question comes to you and me !
Tell me, what shall your answer be ?
Where will you spend eternity ?
    Eternity ! Eternity !
    Where will you spend eternity ?

2 Many are choosing Christ to-day,
Turning from all their sins away ;
Heav'n shall their happy portion be.
Where will you spend eternity ?
    Eternity ! Eternity !
    Where will you spend eternity ?

3 Leaving the strait and narrow way,
Going the downward road to-day,
Sad will their final ending be—
Lost thro' a long eternity !
    Eternity ! Eternity !
    Lost thro' a long eternity !

4 Repent, believe, this very hour,
Trust in the Saviour's grace and
    power,
Then will your joyous answer be,
Saved thro' a long eternity !
    Eternity ! Eternity !
    Saved thro' a long eternity !

261 NOW He will save you, now
    He will bless,
If all your vileness you but confess ;
He will receive you home to His
    breast,
If you are weary He'll give you rest.

2 Now is God's mercy offer'd to thee ;
Now His salvation, precious and free;
Will you not take it ?   Turn not
    aside
From the love offer'd and Him who
    died.

3 Now He beseeches you to believe ;
Now He is longing you to receive ;
Now light and darkness, heaven and
    hell,   [well.
Lie each before you, now choose ye

262 TIME is earnest, passing by;
 Death is earnest, drawing nigh;
Sinner, wilt thou trifling be?
Time and death appeal to thee.

2 Life is earnest; when 'tis o'er,
 Thou returnest never more;
Soon to meet eternity,
Wilt thou never serious be?

3 God is earnest; kneel and pray,
 Ere thy season pass away;
Ere be set His judgment throne—
Vengeance ready, mercy gone.

4 Oh, be earnest; death is near;
 Thou wilt perish, ling'ring here;
Sleep no longer, rise and flee,
Lo, thy Saviour waits for thee.

REPENTANCE AND DECISION

263 LIKE a wayward child I
 wandered
From my Father's house away,
But I hear His voice entreating,
And I'm coming home to-day.

Coming....home, coming....home,
For I can no longer roam;....
I am sad and broken-hearted,
And I'm coming, coming home !....

2 I have wandered in the darkness,
 All my path was lone and drear;
But my Father did not leave me,
He was watching ever near.

3 O the rapture that awaits me
 When I reach my Father's door!
Once within its blest enclosure,
I am safe for evermore.

4 I will ask Him to forgive me
 For the wrong that I have done,
To receive, accept, and bless me,
Through His well-beloved Son.

264 OH, tender and sweet was the
 Master's voice,
As He lovingly called to me,
"Come over the line, it is only a step:
I am waiting, my child, for thee."

" Over the line," hear the sweet refrain,
Angels are chanting the heavenly strain;
" Over the line "—Why should I remain
With a step between me and Jesus?

2 But my sins are many, my faith is
 small, [clear;
Lo! the answer came quick and
" Thou needst not trust in thyself
 at all,
Step over the line, I am here."

3 " But my flesh is weak," I tearfully
 said,
" And Thy way I cannot see;
I fear if I try I may sadly fail,
And thus may dishonour Thee."

4 Ah, the world is cold, and I cannot
 go back,
Press forward I surely must;
I will place my hand in His wounded
 palm,
Step over the line, and *trust*.

" Over the line," hear the sweet refrain,
Angels are chanting the heavenly strain :
" Over the line "—I *will not* remain,
I'll cross it and go to Jesus.

265 OH, hear my cry, be gracious
 now to me,
Come, great Deliv'rer, come!
My soul, bow'd down, is longing
 now for Thee,
Come, great Deliv'rer, come!

I've wander'd far away o'er mountains cold,
I've wander'd far away from home;
Oh, take me now, and bring me to Thy fold,
Come, great Deliv'rer, come!

2 I have no place, nor shelter from the
 night,
Come, great Deliv'rer, come!
One look from Thee would give me
 life and light,
Come, great Deliv'rer, come!

3 My path is lone, and weary are my
 feet,
Come, great Deliv'rer, come!
Mine eyes look up Thy loving smile
 to meet!
Come, great Deliv'rer, come!

4 Thou wilt not spurn contrition's
 broken sigh,
Come, great Deliv'rer, come!
Regard my prayer, and hear my
 humble cry,
Come, great Deliv'rer, come!

266 HE tells me to trust and not
 fear,
He bids me each promise believe;

His presence and glory seem **near,**
I open my heart to receive.

> I am ra som'd I know,
> For His Word tells me so,
> So I trust, trust, trust !

2 My need He is pledged to supply,
    I trust for each breath that I
    breathe ;
And since I take *life* at His hands,
    Why not *all* He wishes to give ?

> Lord, I yield evermore,
> For Thy promise is sure,
> So I trust, trust, trust !

3 He offers me pardon and peace,
    He offers me cleansing from sin ;
The fountain once open'd I see,
    Dear Jesus, I dare to plunge in.

> Now I know I am free,
> For Thy blood cleanseth me,
> While I trust, trust, trust !

4 Praise God, it is done—I am His !
    The blood covers body and soul ;
I am pardon'd and cleans'd, I am
    healed,
All glory, I'm ev'ry whit whole !

> Praise His name, I believe,
> And this moment receive,
> While I trust, trust, trust !

267 THERE'S a gentle voice within calls away,....
'Tis a warning I have heard o'er
and o'er ;....
But my heart is melted now, oh,
obey,....   [more.
From my Saviour I will wander no

> Yes, I will go ; Yes, I will go ;
> To Jesus I will go and be saved.
> Yes, I will go ; Yes, I will go ;
> To Jesus I will go and be saved.

2 He has promised all my sins to
    forgive,....
If I ask in simple faith for His
    love,....
In His holy Word I learn how to live,
And to labour for His kingdom
    above.

3 I will try to bear the Cross in my
    youth,....
And be faithful in its cause till I
    die ;....
If with cheerful step I walk in the
    truth,....   [by.
I shall wear a starry crown by and

4 Still the gentle voice within calls
    away,....
And its warning I have heard o'er
    and o'er ;....
But my heart is melted now, I
    obey,....   [more.
From my Saviour I will wander no

268 I'VE wandered far away from
God,
Now I'm coming home ;
The path of sin too long I've trod,
Lord, I'm coming home.

> Coming home, coming home,
> Never more to roam ;
> Open wide Thine arms of love,
> Lord, I'm coming home.

2 I've wasted many precious years,
    Now I'm coming home ;
I now repent with bitter tears,
    Lord, I'm coming home.

3 I'm tired of sin and straying, Lord,
    Now I'm coming home ;
I'll trust Thy love, believe Thy Word,
    Lord, I'm coming home.

4 My soul is sick, my heart is sore,
    Now I'm coming home ;
My strength renew, my hope restore,
    Lord, I'm coming home.

269 I HEAR Thy welcome voice,
That calls me, Lord, to Thee,
For cleansing in Thy precious blood,
That flowed on Calvary.

> I am coming, Lord,
> Coming now to Thee !
> Trusting only in the blood
> That flowed on Calvary.

2 Though coming weak and vile,
    Thou dost my strength assure ;
Thou dost my vileness fully cleanse,
    Till spotless all and pure.

3 All hail, atoning blood !
    All hail, redeeming grace !
All hail, the gift of Christ, our Lord,
    Our strength and righteousness !

270 THERE are angels hov'ring
'round,
There are angels hov'ring 'round,
There are angels, angels hov'ring
'round.

2 To carry the tidings home, etc.

3 To the new Jerusalem, etc.
4 Poor sinners are coming home, etc.
5 And Jesus bids them come, etc.
6 And children, too, may come, etc.
7 For Jesus loves to save, etc.
8 There's glory all around, etc.

271 CHRIST is knocking at my sad
heart,
Shall I let Him in ?   [heart,
Patiently pleading with my sad
Oh ! shall I let Him in ?
Cold and proud is my heart with sin ;
Dark and cheerless is all within ;
Christ is bidding me turn unto Him,
Oh ! shall I let Him in ?

2 Shall I greet Him with loving word ?
Shall I let Him in ?
Meekly accepting my gracious Lord,
Oh ! shall I let Him in ?
He can infinite love impart ;
He can pardon this rebel heart ;
Shall I bid Him for ever depart,
Or shall I let Him in ?

3 Yes, I'll open this heart's proud door,
Yes, I'll let Him in ;
Gladly I'll welcome Him evermore,
Oh ! yes, I'll let Him in !
Blessed Saviour, abide with me,
Cares and trials will lighter be ;
I am safe, if I'm only with Thee,
O blessed Lord, come in !

272 JESUS is pleading with my
poor soul,
Shall I be saved to-night ?
If I believe, He will make me whole,
Shall I be saved to-night ?
Tenderly, sadly, I hear Him say,
" How can you grieve Me from
day to day ? "
Shall I go on in the old, old way,
Or shall I be saved to-night ?

2 Jesus was nail'd to the Cross for me,
Shall I be saved to-night ?
How can my heart so ungrateful be ?
Shall I be saved to-night ?
Now He will save me by grace
divine,
Now, if I will, I may call Him mine.
Can I the pleasures of earth resign ?
Oh, shall I be saved to-night ?

3 Jesus is knocking at my poor heart,
Shall I be saved to-night ?
What if His Spirit should now depart,
Shall I be saved to-night ?
Over and over His voice I hear,
Sweetly it falls on my list'ning ear ;
Shall I reject Him, a Friend so dear ?
Oh, shall I be saved to-night ?

4 What if that voice I should hear no
more ?
Shall I be saved to-night ?
Quickly I'll open this bolted door,
Save me, O Lord, to-night !
Blessed Redeemer, come in, come in,
Pity my sorrow, forgive my sin !
Now let Thy work in my soul begin,
For I will be saved to-night !

273 ONLY a step to Jesus !
Then why not take it now ?
Come, and thy sin confessing,
To Him thy Saviour bow.

Only a step, only a step ;
Come ! He waits for thee ;
Come, and thy sin confessing,
Thou shalt receive a blessing ;
Do not reject the mercy
He freely offers thee.

2 Only a step to Jesus !
Believe, and thou shalt live ;
Lovingly now He's waiting,
And ready to forgive.

3 Only a step to Jesus !
A step from sin to grace ;
What has thy heart decided ?
The moments fly apace.

4 Only a step to Jesus !
O why not come, and say,
Gladly to Thee, my Saviour,
I give myself away.

274 'TIS the promise of God full
salvation to give
Unto Him who on Jesus His Son
will believe.

Hallelujah ! 'tis done,
I believe on the Son ;
I am saved by the blood of the Crucified One.

2 Tho' the pathway be lonely and
dangerous, too,
Surely Jesus is able to carry me
through.

3 Many loved ones have I in yon
  heavenly throng,
  They are safe now in glory, and this
    is their song :

4 There are prophets and kings in
  that throng I behold,
  And they sing while they march
    through the streets of pure gold :

5 There's a part in that chorus for you
  and for me,
  And the theme of our praises for
    ever will be :

275 ONE sweetly solemn thought
      Comes to me o'er and o'er :
  I'm nearer home to-day, to-day,
    Than I have been before.

      Nearer my home, nearer my home.
      Nearer my home to-day, to-day,
      Than I have been before.

2 Nearer my Father's house,
    Where many mansions be :
  Nearer the great white throne to-day
    Nearer the crystal sea.

3 Nearer the bound of life,
    Where burdens are laid down ;
  Nearer to leave the cross to-day.
    And nearer to the crown.

4 Be near me when my feet
    Are slipping o'er the brink ;
  For I am nearer home to-day.
    Perhaps, than now I think.

276 LORD, thro' the blood of the
      Lamb that was slain,
  Cleansing for me, cleansing for me !
  From all the guilt of my sins now
    I claim
  Cleansing from Thee, cleansing
    from Thee !
  Sinful and black tho' the past may
    have been,
  Many the crushing defeats I have
    seen,   [lean,
  Yet on Thy promise, O Lord, now I
  Cleansing for me, cleansing for me !

2 From all the doubts that have filled
    me with gloom,
  Cleansing for me !
  From all the fears that would point
    me to doom,
  Cleansing for me !

Jesus, although I may not under-
    stand,   [my hand,
  In childlike faith now I put forth
  And through Thy Word and Thy
    grace I shall stand,
  Cleansed by Thee !

3 From all the care of what men
    think or say,
  Cleansing for me !
  From ever fearing to speak, sing,
    or pray,
  Cleansing for me !
  Lord, in Thy love and Thy power
    make me strong,
  That all may know that to Thee I
    belong ;   [song—
  When I am tempted, let this be my
  Cleansing for me !

277 LORD, I hear of show'rs of
      blessing,
    Thou art scattering full and free—
  Show'rs the thirsty land refreshing.
    Let some droppings fall on me—
      Even me, even me,
    Let some droppings fall on me.

2 Pass me not, O God, my Father,
    Sinful though my heart may be :
  Thou might'st leave me, but the rather
    Let Thy mercy light on me—
      Even me.

3 Pass me not, O mighty Spirit,
    Thou canst make the blind to see ;
  Witnesser of Jesus' merit,
    Speak the word of power to me—
      Even me.

4 Love of God, so pure and changeless,
    Blood of Christ, so rich and free ;
  Grace of God, so rich and boundless,
    Magnify it all in me—
      Even me.

5 Pass me not, Thy lost one bringing ;
    Bind my heart, O Lord, to Thee,
  Whilst the streams of life are
    springing,
    Blessing others, oh, bless me !
      Even me.

278 DEPTH of mercy ! can there be
      Mercy still reserved for me ?
  Can my God His wrath forbear ?—
  Me, the chief of sinners, spare ?

2 I have long withstood His grace,
   Long provoked Him to His face ;
   Would not hearken to His calls,
   Grieved Him by a thousand falls.

3 Whence to me this waste of love ?
   Ask my Advocate above !
   See the cause in Jesus' face,
   Now before the throne of grace.

4 There for me the Saviour stands,
   Shows His wounds, and spreads His
      hands ;
   God is love, I know, I feel ;
   Jesus lives and loves me still.

5 If I rightly read Thy heart,
   If Thou all compassion art,
   Bow Thine ear, in mercy bow,
   Pardon and accept me now !

279 O JESUS, Thou art standing
         Outside the fast closed door,
      In lowly patience waiting
         To pass the threshold o'er.

2 O Jesus, Thou art knocking,
   And lo ! that hand is scarred,
   And thorns Thy brow encircle,
   And tears Thy face have marred !

3 Oh, love that passeth knowledge,
   So patiently to wait !
   Oh, sin that hath no equal,
   So fast to bar the gate !

4 O Jesus, Thou art pleading
   In accents meek and low—
   " I died for you, My children,
   And will you treat Me so ? "

5 O Lord, with shame and sorrow,
   We open now the door ;
   Dear Saviour, enter, enter,
   And leave us nevermore !

280 PASS me not, O gentle Saviour,
         Hear my humble cry ;
      While on others Thou art calling,
         Do not pass me by.

      Saviour, Saviour,
         Hear my humble cry ;
      While on others Thou art calling,
         Do not pass me by.

2 Let me at Thy throne of mercy
   Find a sweet relief ;
   Kneeling there in deep contrition,
   Help my unbelief.

3 Trusting only in Thy merits
   Would I seek Thy face ;
   Heal my wounded, broken spirit,
   Save me by Thy grace.

4 Thou, the spring of all my comfort,
   More than life to me—
   Whom have I on earth beside Thee ?
   Whom in heav'n but Thee ?

281   I LAY my sins on Jesus,
            The spotless Lamb of God ;
         He bears them all, and frees us
            From the accursed load.
         I bring my guilt to Jesus,
            To wash my crimson stains
         White in His blood most precious,
            Till not a spot remains.

2 I lay my wants on Jesus,
      All fulness dwells in Him ;
   He heals all my diseases,
      He doth my soul redeem.
   I lay my griefs on Jesus,
      My burdens and my cares ;
   He from them all releases,
      He all my sorrows shares.

3 I rest my soul on Jesus,
      This weary soul of mine ;
   His right hand me embraces,
      I on His breast recline.
   I love the name of Jesus,
      Immanuel, Christ, the Lord ;
   Like fragrance on the breezes
      His name abroad is poured.

4 I long to be like Jesus,
      Meek, loving, lowly, mild ;
   I long to be like Jesus,
      The Father's Holy Child ;
   I long to be with Jesus,
      Amid the heav'nly throng,
   To sing with saints His praises,
      To learn the angels' song.

282 ALL my doubts I give to Jesus !
         I've His gracious promise heard ;
      I shall never be confounded,
         I am trusting in that Word.
      I am trusting, fully trusting,
         Sweetly trusting to His Word.
      I am trusting, fully trusting,
         Sweetly trusting to His Word.

2 All my sins I lay on Jesus !
      He doth wash me in His blood ;
   He will keep me pure and holy,
      He will bring me home to God.

3 All my fears I give to Jesus !
  Rests my weary soul on Him ;
  Though my way be hid in darkness,
  Never can His light grow dim.

4 All my joys I give to Jesus !
  He is all I want of bliss ;
  He of all the worlds is Master,
  He has all I need in this.

5 All I am I give to Jesus !
  All my body, all my soul !
  All I have, and all I hope for,
  While eternal ages roll.

283 I WILL go, I cannot stay
  From the arms of love away ;
  O for strength of faith to say,
  Jesus died for me.

  Can it be, O can it be,
  There is hope for one like me ?
  I will go with this my plea,
  Jesus died for me.

2 Tho' I long have tried in vain,
  Tried to break the tempter's chain,
  Yet to-day I'll try again,
  Jesus, help Thou me.

3 I am lost, and yet I know
  Earth can never heal my woe ;
  I will rise at once and go,
  Jesus died for me.

4 Something whispers in my soul,
  Tho' my sins like mountains roll,
  Jesus' blood will make me whole,
  Jesus died for me.

284 MY life, my love, I give to
  Thee,
  Thou Lamb of God, who died for me:
  O may I ever faithful be,
  My Saviour and my God !

  I'll live for Thee, I'll live for Thee,
  And O how glad my soul should be,
  That Thou didst give Thyself for me,
  My Saviour and my God !

2 I now believe Thou dost receive,
  For Thou hast died that I might
  live ;   [Thee,
  And now henceforth I'll trust in
  My Saviour and my God !

3 O Thou who died on Calvary,
  To save my soul, and make me free ;
  I consecrate my life to Thee,
  My Saviour and my God !

285 RING the bells of heaven !
  there is joy to-day,
  For a soul returning from the wild ;
  See ! the Father meets him out upon
  the way,   [child.
  Welcoming His weary, wand'ring

  Glory ! Glory ! how the angels sing !
  Glory ! Glory ! how the loud harps ring !
  'Tis the ransomed army, like a mighty sea,
  Pealing forth the anthem of the free !

2 Ring the bells of heaven ! there is
  joy to-day,
  For the wand'rer now is reconciled ;
  Yes, a soul is rescued from his sinful
  way,   [child.
  And is born a new, a ransom'd

3 Ring the bells of heaven ! spread
  the feast to-day !
  Angels swell the glad, triumphant
  strain !   [away !
  Tell the joyful tidings ! bear it far
  For a precious soul is born again.

286 SAVIOUR, hear me, while
  before Thy feet
  I the record of my sins repeat,
  Stained with guilt, myself abhorring,
  Fill'd with grief, my soul out-
  pouring,   [me,
  Canst Thou still in mercy think of
  Stoop to set my shackled spirit free ;
  Raise my sinking heart, and bid me be
  Thy child forgiven ?

  Grace...there is my ev'ry debt to pay,
  Blood...to wash my ev'ry sin away,
  Pow'r...to keep me spotless day by day,
  In Christ for me.

2 Back with all the guilt my spirit bears
  Past the haunting memories of years ;
  Self and shame and fear despising,
  Foes and taunting fiends surprising ;
  Saviour, to Thy cross I press my way,
  And a broken heart before it lay ;
  Ere I leave, oh let me hear Thee say
  I am forgiven.

3 Yet why should I fear ? Hast Thou
  not died   [denied ?
  That no seeking soul should be
  To that heart, its sins confessing,
  Canst Thou fail to give a blessing ?
  By the love and pity Thou hast shown,
  By the blood that did for me atone,
  Boldly will I kneel before thy throne,
  A pleading soul.

4 All the rivers of Thy grace I claim,
Over ev'ry promise write my name ;
As I am I come believing,
As Thou art Thou dost, receiving,
Bid me rise, a freed and pardoned
slave,   [grave,
Master o'er my sin, the world, the
Charging me to preach Thy power
to save
     To sin-bound souls.

287 LOVING Saviour, hear my cry,
    Hear my cry, hear my cry ;
Trembling to Thine arms I fly,
    Oh, save me at the Cross.
I have sinn'd, but Thou hast died,
Thou hast died, Thou hast died ;
In Thy mercy let me hide,
    Oh, save me at the Cross.

    Lord Jesus, receive me,
    No more would I grieve Thee.
    Now, blessed Redeemer,
    Oh, save me at the Cross.

2 Though I perish I will pray,
    I will pray, I will pray ;
Thou of Life the Living Way,
    Oh, save me at the Cross.
Thou hast said Thy grace is free,
Grace is free, grace is free ;
Have compassion, Lord, on me,
    Oh, save me at the Cross.

3 Wash me in Thy cleansing blood,
Cleansing blood, cleansing blood ;
Plunge me now beneath the flood,
    Oh, save me at the Cross.
Only faith will pardon bring,
Pardon bring, pardon bring ;
In that faith to Thee I cling,
    Oh, save me at the Cross.

288 LONG I have wandered afar
    from my Lord,
    Now I am coming home ;
Longing to be to His favour restored
Now I am coming home.

    Yes, I am coming, dear Lord, I'm coming,
      Just now I'm coming home ;
    Yes, I am coming, dear Lord, I'm coming,
      Just now I'm coming home.

2 Tired of the world with its folly and sin,
    Now I am coming home ;
Believing the Saviour will welcome
    me in,
    Now I am coming home.

3 Knowing my Saviour can give me
    His rest,
    Now I am coming home ;
Longing to anchor my soul on His
    breast,
    Now I am coming home.

4 Humbly I crave but a poor servant's
    place,
    Now I am coming home ;
Only desiring to taste of His grace,
    Now I am coming home.

5 Oh, bless the Lord, my dear Saviour
    I see,
    Now I am coming home ;
Waiting to welcome a sinner like me,
    Now I am coming home.

289 I AM coming to the Cross,
    I am poor, and weak, and blind;
I am counting all but dross,
    I shall full salvation find.

    I am trusting, Lord, in Thee,
    Blest Lamb of Calvary ;
    Humbly at Thy Cross I bow,
    Save me, Jesus, save me now.

2 Long my heart has sighed for Thee,
    Long has evil reigned within ;
Jesus sweetly speaks to me,
    " I will cleanse you from all sin."

3 Here I give my all to Thee,   [store ;
    Friends, and time, and earthly
Soul and body Thine to be—
    Wholly Thine for evermore.

290 YES, there is room for Jesus
    Within this contrite heart !
Dear Saviour, wait no longer,
    But grace divine impart.

    Room, O blessed Saviour,
    In my poor wand'ring heart ;
    Come in and reign for ever,
    New life and peace impart.

2 Yes, there is room for Jesus—
    The Guest of heav'nly birth ;
His life He gave a ransom
    For all the sons of earth.

3 Yes, there is room for Jesus,
    Oh enter, Lord, and reign ;
The King and mighty Conqueror
    O'er death and sin and pain.

4 I'll sing aloud the praises
    Of Him who saves from doom ;
Dear Lord, through coming ages
    My heart shall give Thee room.

291 THE great Physician now is near,
The sympathising Jesus ;
He speaks the drooping heart to cheer,
Oh, hear the voice of Jesus.

> Sweetest note in seraph song,
> Sweetest name on mortal tongue ;
> Sweetest carol ever sung,
> Jesus, blessed Jesus.

2 Your many sins are all forgiv'n,
Oh, hear the voice of Jesus :
Go on your way in peace to heav'n,
And wear a crown with Jesus.

3 All glory to the dying Lamb !
I now believe in Jesus ;
I love the blessed Saviour's name,
I love the name of Jesus.

4 His name dispels my guilt and fear,
No other name but Jesus :
Oh ! how my soul delights to hear
The precious name of Jesus.

292 JUST as I am, without one plea,
But that Thy blood was shed for me,
And that Thou bidst me come to Thee,
O Lamb of God, I come, I come.

2 Just as I am, and waiting not
To rid my soul of one dark blot ;
To Thee, whose blood can cleanse each spot,
O Lamb of God, I come, I come.

3 Just as I am, Thou wilt receive,
Wilt welcome, pardon, cleanse, relieve ;
Because Thy promise I believe,
O Lamb of God, I come, I come.

4 Just as I am—Thy love unknown
Has broken ev'ry barrier down ;
Now to be Thine, yea, Thine alone,
O Lamb of God, I come, I come.

293 JESUS, see me at Thy feet,
Nothing but Thy blood can save me ;
Thou alone my need canst meet,
Nothing but Thy blood can save me.

> No ! No ! Nothing do I bring,
> But by faith I'm clinging
> To Thy Cross, O Lamb of God !
> Nothing but Thy blood can save me.

2 See my heart, Lord, torn with grief,
Nothing but Thy blood can save me ;
Me unpardoned do not leave,
Nothing but Thy blood can save me.

3 Dark, indeed, the past has been.
Nothing but Thy blood can save me.
Yet in mercy take me in,
Nothing but Thy blood can save me.

4 As I am, oh, hear me pray,
Nothing but Thy blood can save me ;
I can come no other way,
Nothing but Thy blood can save me.

5 All that I can do is vain,
Nothing but Thy blood can save me ;
I can ne'er remove a stain,
Nothing but Thy blood can save me.

6 Lord, I cast myself on Thee,
Nothing but Thy blood can save me ;
From my guilt, oh, set me free,
Nothing but Thy blood can save me.

294 O SPOTLESS Lamb, I come to Thee,
No longer can I from Thee stay ;
Break ev'ry chain, now set me free,
Take all my sins away !

> Take all my sins away !
> Take all my sins away !
> O spotless Lamb, I come to Thee,
> Take all my sins away !

2 My hungry soul cried out for Thee,
Come, and for ever seal my breast ;
To Thy dear arms at last I flee,
There only can I rest.

3 I plunge beneath Thy precious blood,
My hand in faith takes hold of Thee ;
Thy promises just now I claim—
Thou art enough for me.

CHRISTIAN LIFE AND SERVICE

295 TRYING to walk in the steps of the Saviour,
Trying to follow our Saviour and King ;   [example,
Shaping our lives by His blessed
Happy, how happy, the songs that we bring.

How beautiful to walk in the steps of the Saviour,
Stepping in the light, stepping in the light ;
How beautiful to walk in the steps of the Saviour,
Led in paths of light.

2 Pressing more closely to Him who is leading,
When we are tempted to turn from the way ;
Trusting the arm that is strong to defend us,
Happy, how happy, our praises each day.

3 Walking in footsteps of gentle forbearance,
Footsteps of faithfulness, mercy, and love ;
Looking to Him for the grace freely promised,   [above.
Happy, how happy, our journey

4 Trying to walk in the steps of the Saviour,   [our Guide ;
Upward, still upward, we'll follow
When we shall see Him, " the King in His beauty,"
Happy, how happy, our place at His side.

296 DO you ever feel downhearted or discouraged ?
Do you ever think your work is all in vain ?
Do the burdens thrust upon you make you tremble,
And you fear that you shall ne'er the vict'ry gain ?....

Have faith in God,...the sun will shine..
Tho' dark the cloud..may be to-day ;..
His heart hath planned..your path and mine!..
Have faith in God,..have faith alway...

2 Darkest night will always come before the dawning,
Silver linings shine on God's side of the cloud :

All your journey He has promised to be with you,
Nought has come to you but what His love allowed.....

3 God is mighty ! He is able to deliver ;   [hour ;
Faith can victor be in ev'ry trying
Fear and care, and sin, and sorrow be defeated,
By our faith in God's almighty, conqu'ring pow'r.....

297 I CAN hear my Saviour calling,
I can hear my Saviour calling,
I can hear my Saviour calling,
" Take thy cross and follow, follow Me."

Where He leads me I will follow,
Where He leads me I will follow,
Where He leads me I will follow,
I'll go with Him, with Him all the way.

2 I'll go with Him thro' the garden,
I'll go with Him, with Him all the way.

3 I'll go with Him thro' the judgment,
I'll go with Him, with Him all the way.

4 He will give me grace and glory,
And go with me, with me all the way.

298 A TREMBLING soul, I sought the Lord,
My sin confessed, my guilt deplored ;
How soft and sweet His word to me,
"I took thy place, and died for thee."

No other hope,..no other plea ;..
He took my place,..and died for me ;..
O precious Lamb..of Calvary !..
He took my place,...and died for me....

2 Here rests my heart ; assurance sweet,
His blessed work He will complete,
Since in His love so great and free,
He took my place, and died for me.

3 When sorrow veils the smiling day,
When evil foes beset my way,
Abundant grace in Him I see,
He took my place, and died for me.

4 No room for doubt, no room for fears,
When to my view the Cross appears ;
My joyful song shall ever be,
He took my place, and died for me.

299 SOLDIERS of Zion, on we go,
   Brave are the hearts that face
      the foe ;
Vict'ry awaits us, for we know
  We follow the Lord our King.
Not by the might of human arm,
Not by the pow'r of earth to harm,
But by the Spirit's holy charm,
  Shall we the triumph sing.

   Soldiers of Zion, on we go,
     Brave are the hearts that face the foe.
   Vict'ry awaits us, for we know
     We follow the Lord our King.

2 Hark to the trump that sounds for
    war,
  See how the flag goes on before,
  Look how the ranks swell more and
    more,
    As Jesus the King leads on.
Strong are the hosts of Sin and Death,
Stronger the might of Him who
  saith,   [breath ! "
" I will consume them with My
  Then will the field be won.

3 Sure as the Truth will dawn the day
  When giant Wrong will end his sway ;
  Bondage and error flee away,
    And earth to the Lord belong.
Courage, ye souls who fight and plod,
This is the path that worthies trod ;
Gird up your loins, elect of God :
  Soon comes the victor's song.

300 JESUS comes with pow'r to
    gladden,
  When love shines in,
Ev'ry life that woe can sadden,
  When love shines in.
Love will teach us how to pray,
Love will drive the gloom away,
Turn our darkness into day,
  When love shines in.

   When love shines in,...when love shines in,
   How the heart is tuned to singing when love
     shines in ;
   When love shines in, when love shines in,
   Joy and peace to others bringing, when love
     shines in.

2 How the world will glow with beauty
  When love shines in,
And the heart rejoice in duty,
  When love shines in.
Trials may be sanctified,
And the soul in peace abide,
Life will all be glorified,
  When love shines in.

3 Darkest sorrows will grow brighter,
  When love shines in,
And the heaviest burden lighter,
  When love shines in.
'Tis the glory that will throw
Light to show us where to go ;
O the heart shall blessing know
  When love shines in.

4 We may have unfading splendour,
  When love shines in,
And a friendship true and tender,
  When love shines in.
When earth's vict'ries shall be won,
And our life in heav'n begun,
There will be no need of sun,
  For love shines in.

301 O CHRIST, in Thee my soul
    hath found,
  And found in Thee alone,
The peace, the joy I sought so long
  The bliss till now unknown.

   Now none but Christ can satisfy,
    None other name for me,....
   There's love and life and lasting joy,
    Lord Jesus, found in Thee.

2 I sigh'd for rest and happiness,
  I yearned for them, not Thee ;
But while I pass'd my Saviour by,
  His love laid hold on me.

3 I tried the broken cisterns, Lord,
  But, ah ! the waters failed !
E'en as I stooped to drink, they fled,
  And mock'd me as I wail'd.

4 The pleasures lost I sadly mourn'd,
  But never wept for Thee,
Till grace the sightless eyes receiv'd,
  Thy loveliness to see.

302 I SHALL see them again in
    the light of the morning,
When the night has pass'd by with
  its tears and its mourning,
Where the light of God's love is the
  sun ever shining,   [rest.
In the land where the weary ones

2 I shall know them again though ten
  thousand surround them,
I shall hear their dear voice 'midst
  the blessed ones round them ;
And the love that was theirs on the
  earth shall detect them,
In the land where the weary ones
  rest.

3 'Twas their lives in the past helped
   to fill me with gladness ;
   And the future is heaven, the home
   with no sadness,
   Where I see them to-day clad in
   bright robes of whiteness,
   In the land where the weary ones
   rest.

4 Would I wish for them back from
   their bright home in heaven ?
   No ! in patience I'll wait till the veil
   shall be riven,
   And the Saviour restores me the
   friends He has given,
   In the land where the weary ones
   rest.

303 OH ! the sowing time seems
        weary,
   And full oft the workers cry,
   To the Lord who rules the harvest,
   For the reaping by and by.

   What a reap..ing...reap..ing,
   What a reaping it will be by and by...
   Ev'ry sorrow we have known,
   Ev'ry tear that we have sown,
   What a reaping it will be by and by !...

2 In the sorrow and the suff'ring,
   When each breath is but a sigh ;
   Tho' we sow in tears, remember
   There's a reaping by and by.

3 When our hearts are strained to
   breaking,
   Comfort other suff'rers nigh ;
   And our harvest will be doubled
   In the reaping by and by.

4 For the love of Christ is flowing
   In a stream that's never dry ;
   He will water all our sowing,
   For the reaping by and by.

304 THE way our fathers travelled
        is good enough for me ;
   They followed in the footsteps that
   led from Calvary ;
   It led them up to glory, that land of
   endless day ;
   I expect to get to heaven by the
   same old way.

   O this blessed old way, it is good enough for me,
   It is good enough for me, it is good enough for
   me ;   [each day ;
   My Saviour goes before me, I follow Him
   I expect to get to heaven by the same old way.

2 The world may sneer and tell me
   I'll never reach the goal,
   That good works are sufficient to
   save a human soul ;
   But while the world is talking, I still
   will watch and pray ;
   I expect to get to heaven by the
   same old way.

3 When bowers of sin entice me to rest
   my weary feet,
   I find in Christ, my Saviour, a safe,
   a sure retreat ;
   He tells me to press onward, and not
   look back, nor stay ;   [old way.
   I expect to get to heaven by the same

4 Millions are now in glory, in shining
   white arrayed,
   Who travelled this same pathway,
   and often were dismayed ;
   But happy now in glory, they sing,
   both night and day ;
   I expect to get to heaven by the
   same old way.

305 THERE'S a land that is fairer
        than day,
   And by faith we can see it afar ;
   For the Father waits over the way,
   To prepare us a dwelling-place
   there.

   In the sweet...by and by,...
   We shall meet on that beautiful shore...
   In the sweet...by and by,...
   We shall meet on that beautiful shore.

2 We shall sing on that beautiful shore
   The melodious songs of the blest,
   And our spirits shall sorrow no more,
   Not a sigh for the blessing of rest.

3 To our bountiful Father above,
   We will offer our tribute of praise,
   For the glorious gift of His love,
   And the blessings that hallow our
   days.

306 ONWARD still, and upward,
        Follow evermore
   Where our mighty Leader
   Goes in love before.
   " Looking unto Jesus,"
   Reach a helping hand
   To a struggling neighbour,
   Helping him to stand.

   Marching on...ward,...up ..ward....
   Marching steadily onward, Jesus leads the way.
   Marching on...ward.. upward,
   Onward unto glory, to the perfect...day.

2 Onward, ever onward,
    Through the pastures green,
  Where the streams flow softly,
    Under skies serene ;
  Or, if need be, upward,
    O'er the rocky steep,
  Trusting Him to guide us,
    Strong to save and keep.

3 Upward, ever upward,
    T'ward the radiant glow,
  Far above the valley,
    Where the mist hangs low.
  On, with songs of gladness,
    Till the march shall end,
  Where ten thousand thousand
    Hallelujahs blend.

307 OH, I have got good news for you
        A story wonderful and true ;
      'Twill make you happy, that I know,
      It made me glad, and now I go—
        To sing my great Redeemer's song,
        To sing my great Redeemer's song,
        To sing my great Redeemer's song,
          With the happy saints above.

2 I once was far away from God,
  On ruin's dark and fatal road,
  And little dream'd I'd see the day
  That I should tread the narrow way.

3 O'er this wild waste I loved to roam,
  My back to God and heav'n and home,
  When Jesus met me far astray,
  And beckoned me to come away.

4 He said on Calv'ry's Cross He died,
  A sacrifice for sin was made,
  And all because He loved me so :
  Then how could I do else than go ?

5 Now ev'ry one that's standing by
  Oh, 'twas for you the Christ did die;
  This moment, too, He waits for thee,
  Then just believe, and you'll be free.

6 Whene'er the record you believe,
  You life eternal shall receive,
  And soon from pain and sorrow free,
  You'll join that glorious company.

308 IN the heav'nly pastures fair,
      'Neath the tender Shepherd's
            care,   [to-day—
      Let us rest beside the living stream
      Calmly there in peace recline,
      Drinking in the truth divine,
      As His loving call we now with joy
        obey.....

Glorious streams of life eternal,
Beauteous fields of living green.....
    Though reveal'd within the Word
    Of our Shepherd and our Lord,
  By the pure in heart alone can they be seen...

2 Far from all the noise and strife,
    That disturbs our daily life,
  Let us pause awhile in silence and adore;
    Then the sound of His dear voice
    Will our waiting souls rejoice,
  As He nameth us His own for ever-
        more.....

3 Oh, how good, and true, and kind,
    Seeking His stray sheep to find,
  If they wander into danger from His
        side ;
    Ever closely may we tread
    Where His holy feet have led,
  So at last with Him in heav'n we may
        abide.....

309 FIRMLY stand for God in the
          world's mad strife,
      Tho' the bleak winds roar, and the
          waves beat high ;
      'Tis the Rock alone giveth strength
          and life,
      When the hosts of sin are nigh.
        Let us stand on the Rock !
        Firmly stand on the Rock :
        On the Rock of Christ alone ;
          If the strife we endure,
          We shall stand secure,
        'Mid the throng who surround the Throne.

2 Firmly stand for Right, with a
          motive pure,
    With a true heart bold, and a faith
      e'er strong ;   [sure,
    'Tis the Rock alone giveth triumph
    O'er the world's array of wrong.

3 Firmly stand for Truth ! it will
          serve you best,
    Tho' it waiteth long, it is sure at
      last ;   [rest.
    'Tis the Rock alone giveth peace and
    When the storms of life are past.

310 IN the dew of early youth,
          None can help like Jesus ;
      Seeking after pearls of truth,
          None can help like Jesus ;
      He's the source of living light,
      He will guide your steps aright ;
          None can help like Jesus,
          No ! none like Jesus.

2 In the midday whirl of care,
    None can help like Jesus ;
 When you heavy burdens bear,
    None can help like Jesus ;
 He will give you sweetest rest,
 All who trust in Him are blest ;
    None can help like Jesus,
    No ! none like Jesus.

3 In the twilight's fading glow,
    None can help like Jesus ;
 When your strength is ebbing slow,
    None can help like Jesus ;
 He will shield from death's alarms,
 Fold you in His loving arms ;
    None can help like Jesus,
    No ! none like Jesus.

311 ALL around this very hour,
    Falls there streams of heav'nly
        pow'r ;
 Falling now so full and free,
 Praise the Lord, it's filling me.
        Hallelujah ! feel the pow'r,
        Falling like a mighty show'r ;
        Coming now so full and free ;
        Praise the Lord, it's filling me.

2 Send us show'rs of heav'nly grace ;
 Let Thy presence fill this place ;
 Speak the word and it shall be,
 That Thy showers fall on me.

3 Thou alone this pow'r canst give ;
 Without Thee I dare not live ;
 Give me pow'r to work for Thee,
 Let the stream reach even me.

312 JESUS, Thy blood and right-
    eousness
 My beauty are, my glorious dress ;
 'Midst flaming worlds, in these
    arrayed,
 With joy shall I life up my head.

2 Bold shall I stand in Thy great day ;
 For who aught to my charge shall lay ?
 Fully absolv'd through these I am
 From sin and fear, from guilt and
    shame.

3 When from the dust of death I rise,
 To claim my mansion in the skies,
 Even then, this shall be all my plea,
 Jesus hath lived, hath died for me.

4 Jesus, be endless praise to Thee,
 Whose boundless mercy hath for me—
 For me, a full atonement made,
 An everlasting ransom paid.

5 O let the dead now hear Thy voice ;
 Now bid Thy banished ones rejoice ;
 Their beauty this, their glorious
    dress,
 Jesus, Thy blood and righteousness.

313 OVER the river they call me,
    Friends that are dear to my
        heart,....
 Soon shall I meet them in glory,
 Never, no, never to part.
        Over the river of Eden,
        Home to the mansions so fair ;
        Angels will carry me safely,
        Jesus will welcome me there.

2 Over the river they call me ;
    Hark ! 'tis their voices I hear,....
 Borne on the wings of the twilight,
 Murmuring softly and clear.

3 Over the river they call me,
    There is no sorrow nor night ;....
 There they are walking with Jesus,
 Clothed in their garments of
    white.

4 Over the river they call me,
    Watching with bright beaming
        eyes,...
 " Over the river I'm coming,"
 Gladly my spirit replies.

314 LET us sing a song that will
    cheer us by the way,
    In a little while we're going home ;
 For the night will end in the ever-
    lasting day,
    In a little while we're going home.
        In a little while,...in a little while...
        We shall cross the billow's foam ;
        We shall meet at last,
        When the stormy winds are past,
        In a little while we're going home.

2 We will do the work that our hands
    may find to do,
    In a little while we're going home ;
 And the grace of God will our daily
    strength renew,
    In a little while we're going home.

3 We will smooth the path for some
    weary, wayworn feet,
    In a little while we're going home ;
 O may loving hearts spread around
    an influence sweet !
    In a little while we're going home.

4 There's a rest beyond, there's relief
   from ev'ry care,
   In a little while we're going home ;
And no tears shall fall in that city
   bright and fair,
   In a little while we're going home.

315 ARE you heavy laden and
      with sorrow tried ?
Look in faith to Christ, your Helper,
   Friend, and Guide ;
Think of all your mercies, such a
   boundless store,
Tears will change to praises as you
   count them o'er.

Count..your mercies, such a boundless store,
Count..your mercies, pressed and running o'er,
All..your mercies, count them o'er and o'er
Lost in love and wonder at the boundless store.

2 Think of hidden dangers He has
   brought you through,
Of the cares and burdens He has
   borne for you,
Of His words of comfort in your
   deepest need,
Count the times when Jesus proved
   a Friend indeed.

3 Does your pathway darken when
   the clouds draw near ?
Count your many mercies, dry the
   flowing tear ;
Trust Him in the shadows dim and
   have no fear ;
" Heaven will be the sweeter for the
   dark down here."

4 As He looks from heaven down on
   you and me,
Know ye not He chooseth what each
   day shall be ?
Trust His loving wisdom, though the
   hot tears start,
Give to Him the incense of a grateful
   heart.

316 IT was down at the feet of
      Jesus,
   O the happy, happy day !
That my soul found peace in
   believing,
   And my sins were washed away.

Let me tell the old, old story
   Of His grace so full and free,
For I feel like giving Him the glory
   For His wondrous love to me.

2 It was down at the feet of Jesus,
   Where I found such perfect rest ;
Where the light first dawned on my
   spirit,
   And my soul was truly blest.

3 It was down at the feet of Jesus
   Where I brought my guilt and sin ;
That He cancelled all my trans-
   gressions,
   And salvation entered in.

317 BLESSED is the service of our
      Lord and King,
Precious are the jewels we may help
   to bring ;
Down the passing ages words of
   counsel ring,
   He that winneth souls is wise.

He that winneth souls is wise ;...
In the home beyond the skies...
There's a crown of glory, oh, the wondrous prize
   He that winneth souls is wise.

2 In the quiet home-life, showing
   love's bright ray,
More and more like Jesus, living
   ev'ry day,
We may guide a dear one to the
   heavenward way,
   He that winneth souls is wise.

3 Out upon the highway, going forth
   with prayer,
For the lost and straying seeking
   ev'rywhere,
Close beside the Shepherd, we His
   joy may share,
   He that winneth souls is wise.

4 Sow beside all waters, sow the
   gospel seed,
Here a word in season, there a loving
   deed ;
Sinners to the Saviour be it ours
   to lead,
   He that winneth souls is wise.

318 I'M a pilgrim, and I'm a
      stranger ;
I can tarry, I can tarry but a night !
Do not detain me, for I am going
To where the fountains are ever
   flowing.

I'm a pilgrim,..and I'm a stranger ;...
   I can tarry, I can tarry but a night ;...
I'm a pilgrim,..and I'm a stranger,...
   I can tarry, I can tarry but a night.

2 Of that city to which I journey,
My Redeemer, my Redeemer is the
light ;
There is no sorrow, nor any sighing,
Nor any tears there, nor any dying.

3 There the sunbeams are ever shining,
O my longing heart, my longing
heart is there ;
Here in this country, so dark and
dreary,
I long have wander'd forlorn and
weary.

319 THE dear old story of a
Saviour's love
Is sweeter as the days go by ;
The glad assurance of a home above
Is sweeter as the days go by.
We'll fill..the days with joy..ful praise,
We'll sing as the happy moments fly ;...
The song of love to Him above
Grows sweeter as the days go by.

2 The sunbeams shining from the
living Light
Are brighter as the days go by ;
The stars of promise cheering
sorrow's night
Are brighter as the days go by.

3 Hope's anchor, holding in the
stormy strife,
Is stronger as the days go by ;
We feel the throbbings of immortal
life
Grow stronger as the days go by.

4 The peace that Jesus gives to us
anew
Is deeper as the days go by ;
The prospects opening to the
Christian's view
Are grander as the days go by.

320 CAN it be that Jesus bought
me,
And on the hallow'd Cross atoned
for me,
Loved me, chose me ere I knew Him?
Oh, what a precious, precious
Friend is He !
Oh, it is wonderful, very, very wonderful,
All His grace so rich and free !
Oh, it is wonderful, very, very wonderful,
All His love and grace to me !

2 Praise His name, He sought and
found me,
Sav'd me from wandering and
brought me near ;
Freely now His grace bestowing,
Jesus is growing unto me more
dear.

3 It was months He had been waiting,
Waiting the dawning of the
precious hour ;
When I should at last be yielding,
Yielding to Jesus ev'ry ransom'd
pow'r.

4 From that hour He has been seeking
How He may fill me with His
precious love ;
How He may through grace trans-
form me,
Meet for the fellowship of saints
above.

5 As I think of all, I marvel
Why in such patience He my good
has sought,
And bestowed His grace upon me,
And in my spirit such a change
has wrought.

6 So I cry with love o'erflowing :
" Unto the Saviour be eternal
praise,
Who redeemed me, soul and body,
Filling with gladness all my
earthly days."

321 NOR silver nor gold hath
obtained my redemption,
No riches of earth could have
saved my poor soul ;
The blood of the Cross is my only
foundation,
The death of my Saviour now
maketh me whole.
I am redeemed,...but not with silver,...
I am bought,...but not with gold ;...
Bought with a price,...the blood of Jesus,...
Precious price of love untold.

2 Nor silver nor gold hath obtained
my redemption,
The guilt on my conscience too
heavy had grown ;
The blood of the Cross is my only
foundation,
The death of my Saviour could
only atone.

3 Nor silver nor gold hath obtained
my redemption,
The holy commandment forbade
me draw near ;
The blood of the Cross is my only
foundation
The death of my Saviour removeth
my fear.

4 Nor silver nor gold hath obtained
my redemption,
The way into heaven could not
thus be bought ;
The blood of the Cross is my only
foundation,
The death of my Saviour redemption hath wrought.

322 HOW sweet the name of
Jesus sounds
In a believer's ear ;
It soothes his sorrows, heals his
wounds,
And drives away his fear.

2 It makes the wounded spirit whole,
And calms the troubled breast ;
'Tis manna to the hungry soul,
And to the weary rest.

3 Dear Name, the Rock on which I
build,
My shield and hiding place,
My never-failing Treasury, filled
With boundless stores of grace.

4 Jesus, my Shepherd, Saviour, Friend,
My Prophet, Priest, and King,
My Lord, my Life, my Way, my
End,
Accept the praise I bring.

5 I would Thy boundless love pro-
claim
With every fleeting breath ;
So shall the music of Thy Name
Refresh my soul in death.

323 WE are trav'ling on with our
staff in hand,
Walking in the good old way ;
We are pilgrims bound for the
heav'nly land,
Walking in the good old way.
Walking in the blessedness of love untold,
Trav'ling to a country that will ne'er grow old,
Jesus, our Redeemer, we shall there behold,
Home in the realms of day.

2 We are trav'ling on through a
world of sin,
Walking in the good old way ;
Though our foes are strong, we have
peace within,
Walking in the good old way.

3 We are trav'ling on in the Master's
name,
Walking in the good old way ;
And we sing His praise with a loud
acclaim,
Walking in the good old way.

4 We are trav'ling on to the rolling
tide,
Walking in the good old way ;
But we trust in Him who is still our
Guide,
Walking in the good old way.

324 WE may lighten toil and care,
Or a heavy burden share,
With a word, a kindly deed, or
sunny smile ;
We may girdle day and night
With a halo of delight,
If we keep our hearts singing all the
while.
Keep your heart singing all the while,...
Make the world brighter with a smile,...
Keep the song ringing ! lonely hours we may
beguile,
If we keep our hearts singing all the while.

2 If His love is in the soul,
And we yield to His control,
Sweetest music will the lonely hours
beguile ;
We may drive the clouds away,
Cheer and bless the darkest day,
If we keep our hearts singing all the
while.

3 How a word of love will cheer,
Kindle hope and banish fear,
Soothe a pain, or take away the
sting of guile ;
Oh, how much we all may do,
In the world we travel through,
If we keep our hearts singing all the
while.

325 " FEAR not, I am with thee ; "
Blessed golden ray,
Light a star of glory,
Lighting up my way !

Through the clouds of midnight,
   This bright promise shone,
" I will never leave thee,
   Never will leave thee alone."
   No...never alone,...No, never alone ;
     He promised never to leave me,
   Never to leave me alone.

2 Roses fade around me,
   Lilies bloom and die,
Earthly sunbeams vanish—
   Radiant still the sky !
Jesus, Rose of Sharon,
   Blooming for His own,
Jesus, Heaven's sunshine,
   Never will leave me alone.

3 Steps unseen before me,
   Hidden dangers near ;
Nearer still my Saviour,
   Whisp'ring, " Be of cheer ; "
Joys, like birds of spring-time,
   To my heart have flown,
Singing all so sweetly,
   " He will not leave me alone."

326 PRECIOUS Saviour, Thou hast
      saved me ;
   Thine, and only Thine I am ;
Oh, the cleansing blood has reach'd
      me !
   Glory, glory to the Lamb !
   Glory, glory, hallelujah !
     Glory, glory to the Lamb !
   Oh, the cleansing blood has reach'd me !
     Glory, glory to the Lamb !

2 Long my yearning heart was
      striving
   To obtain this precious rest ;
But when all my struggles ended,
   Simply trusting, I was blest.

3 Consecrated to Thy service,
   I will live and die for Thee ;
I will witness to Thy glory,
   Of salvation, full and free.

4 Glory to the Lord who bought me !
   Glory for His saving pow'r !
Glory to the Lord who keeps me !
   Glory, glory, evermore !

327 HAVE you heard of that
      heavenly home,
Just beyond the rough wilds where
      we roam ;
   Where the angels of light,

And the saints robed in white,
   Lift their voices in song 'round the
      throne ?
   Where Je..sus is waiting for me,
   Where Je..sus is waiting for me,
In those mansions so fair, He has gone to
     prepare,
   Where Jesus is waiting for me....

2 How I long for that beautiful home,
   Just beyond the dark vale and the
      tomb !
   For my loved ones are there,
   In those palaces fair,
They are waiting for me by the
      throne.

3 I will welcome the dawn of the day,
   When the trumpet shall call me
      away,
   To the sweet peaceful rest,
   In the home of the blest,
In the light of that radiant throne.

328 COME, ye that fear the Lord,
      Unto me, unto me ;
Come ye that fear the Lord,
   Unto me !
I've something good to say
   About the narrow way :
For Christ the other day
   Saved my soul, saved my soul !
For Christ the other day
   Saved my soul !

2 He gave me first to see
   What I was, what I was ;
He gave me first to see
   What I was !
He gave me first to see
   My guilt and misery,
And then He set me free !
   Bless His Name ! bless His Name !
And then He set me free !
   Bless His Name !

3 My old companions said,
   " He's undone, he's undone ! "
My old companions said,
   " He's undone ! "
My old companions said,
   " He's surely going mad ! "
But Jesus makes me glad !
   Bless His Name ! bless His Name !
But Jesus makes me glad !
   Bless His Name !

4 Some said, " He'll soon give o'er,
    You shall see, you shall see ! "
Some said, " He'll soon give o'er,
    You shall see ! "
But time has passed away,
Since I began to pray,
And I feel His love to-day !
    Bless His Name ! bless His Name !
And I feel His love to-day !
    Bless His Name !

329 THERE'S an old-fashioned
        story,
    And an old-fashioned song,
That has gladdened the weary
    Through the ages along ;
In the old upper chamber
    It was joyfully told ;
Oh, 'tis very old-fashioned,
    But as sweet as of old.

Oh, this old-fashion'd story and this old-
    fashion'd song
Is a joy to the weary all life's journey along,
For they know, hallelujah! in the city of gold :
They will sing it for ever, this sweet story of old.

2 There's a band of old soldiers,
    That to Jesus belong,
Who have told this old story,
    And have sung this old song ;
In the heat of the battle,
    In the face of the bold,
And to-day they will tell you
    'Tis as sweet as of old.

3 Oh, the old-fashioned story
    And the old-fashioned song,
O'er the broad earth are rolling,
    Winning souls all along ;
This sweet story of Jesus,
    And this glad song so old,
Shall be heard through the ages,
    In that bright upper fold.

330 JESUS, Saviour, pilot me
        Over life's tempestuous sea ;
Unknown waves before me roll,
Hiding rock and treach'rous shoal ;
Chart and compass come from Thee ;
Jesus, Saviour, pilot me.

2 As a mother stills her child,
Thou canst hush the ocean wild ;
Boist'rous waves obey Thy will,
When Thou say'st to them, "Be still,"
Wondrous Sov'reign of the sea,
Jesus, Saviour, pilot me.

3 When at last I reach the shore,
And the fearful breakers roar
'Twixt me and the peaceful rest,
Then, while leaning on Thy breast,
May I hear Thee say to me,
" Fear not, I will pilot thee."

331 WOULD you know why Christ
        my Saviour
    Is my constant theme and song ?
Why to seek His loving favour
    Is my joy the whole day long ?

He redeem'd me,..He redeem'd me,...
    How the ransom'd choir repeat it o'er and
        o'er ;...
He redeem'd me,....He redeem'd me,...
    Glory, glory be to Him for evermore....

2 Oh, the days are full of gladness
    That I spend in His employ !
I can banish care and sadness
    In that song of heav'nly joy.

3 Come, beloved, bow before Him,
    Seek the pardon of your King,
That on earth you may adore Him,
    And with saints in glory sing.

332 MY faith has found a resting-
        place,
    Not in device nor creed ;
I trust the ever-living One,
    His wounds for me shall plead.

I need no other argument,
    I need no other plea ;
It is enough that Jesus died,
    And that He died for me.

2 Enough for me that Jesus saves,
    This ends my fear and doubt ;
A sinful soul I come to Him,
    He'll never cast me out.

3 My heart is leaning on the Word,
    The written Word of God ;
Salvation by my Saviour's name,
    Salvation through His blood.

4 My great Physician heals the sick,
    The lost He came to save ;
For me His precious blood He shed,
    For me His life He gave.

333 WHEN we have come to
        Jordan's tide,
    There'll be no dark river there ;
With Jesus standing close beside,
    There'll be no dark river there.

His boundless grace shall light the
place,
With beams of glory fair ;
And in the sunshine from His face,
There'll be no dark river there.

There'll be no dark river there,
There'll be no dark river there :
Upon His breast we'll sweetly rest,
There'll be no dark river there.

2 With angels bending from above,
There'll be no dark river there ;
In fellowship with Him we love,
There'll be no dark river there.
His word divine shall brightly shine,
His endless life we'll share ;
When all to Jesus we resign,
There'll be no dark river there.

3 And when we've crossed the mystic
tide,
There'll be no dark river there ;
When we have reached the other
side, ·
There'll be no dark river there.
And hand in hand we'll walk the
strand
With loved ones bright and fair ;
For in that happy heav'nly land,
There'll be no dark river there.

4 Let this blest thought fresh courage
give,
There'll be no dark river there ;
In that bright home of peace and
love,
There'll be no dark river there.
The gates ajar, we see afar,
Beyond this world of care ;
Though Jordan's stream may us
divide,
There'll be no dark river there.

334 OH, scatter seeds of loving
deeds
Along the fertile field,
For grain will grow from what you
sow,
And fruitful harvest yield.

Then day by day..along your way..
The seeds of pro..mise cast,..
That ripened grain..from hill and plain,..
Be gathered home..at last...

2 Tho' sown in tears thro' weary years,
The seed will surely live ;
Tho' great the cost, it is not lost,
For God will fruitage give.

3 The harvest home of God will come,
And after toil and care,
With joy untold your sheaves of gold
Will all be garner'd there.

335 IN the Christian's home in
glory,
There remains a land of rest,
Where the Saviour's gone before me,
To fulfil my soul's request.

On the other side of Jordan,
In the sweet fields of Eden,
Where the Tree of Life is blooming,
There is rest for you ;
There is rest for the weary,
There is rest for you !

2 He is fitting up my mansion,
Which eternally shall stand ;
There my stay shall not be transient
In that holy, happy land.

3 Pain nor sickness e'er can enter,
Grief nor woe my lot shall share ;
But in that celestial centre,
I a crown of life shall wear.

4 Death itself shall then be vanquished,
And its sting shall be withdrawn ;
Shout with gladness, O ye ransomed !
Hail with joy the happy morn !

5 Sing, O sing, ye heirs of glory !
Shout your triumphs as you go !
Zion's gates will open to you—
You shall find an entrance
through.

336 LOVED with everlasting love,
Led by grace that love to know;
Spirit, breathing from above,
Thou hast taught me it is so.
Oh this full and perfect peace !
Oh this transport all divine !
In a love which cannot cease,
I am His, and He is mine.

In a love, which cannot cease,
I am His, and He is mine.

2 Heaven above is softer blue,
Earth around is sweeter green !
Something lives in every hue
Christless eyes have never seen ;
Birds with gladder songs o'erflow,
Flowers with deeper beauties
Since I know as *now* I know, [shine,
I am His, and He is mine.

Since I know, as now I know,
I am His, and He is mine.

3 Things that once were wild alarms
   Cannot now disturb my rest ;
Closed in everlasting arms,
   Pillowed on the loving breast,
Oh to lie for ever here,
   Doubt and care and self resign,
While He whispers in my ear—
   I am His, and He is mine.
> While He whispers in my ear—
> I am His, and He is mine !

4 His for ever, only His ;
   Who the Lord and me shall part ?
Ah, with what a rest of bliss
   Christ can fill the loving heart !
Heaven and earth may fade and flee,
   First-born light in gloom decline ;
But, while God and I shall be,
   I am His, and He is mine.
> But, while God and I shall be,
> I am His, and He is mine !

337 BLESSED Lily of the Valley,
      oh, how fair is He !
   He is mine,....I am His ;....
Sweeter than the angels' music is
   His voice to me,
   He is mine,....I am His !....
Where the lilies fair are blooming
   by the waters calm,
There He leads me and upholds me
   by His strong right arm ;
All the air is love around me, I can
   feel no harm,
   He is mine,....I am His.....

> Lil - - y of the Valley, He..is mine !
> Lil - - y of the Valley, I am His !
> Sweeter than the angels' music is His voice to me,
> He is mine,...I am His !...

2 Let me sing of all His mercies, of
   His kindness true,
   He is mine,....I am His ;....
Fresh at morn, and in the evening,
   comes a blessing new,
   He is mine,....I am His !....
With the deep'ning shadows comes a
   whisper, " Safely rest !
Sleep in peace, for I am near thee,
   naught shall thee molest ;
I will linger till the morning, Keeper,
   Friend, and Guest,"
   He is mine,....I am His.....

3 Though He lead me through the
   valley of the shade of death,
   He is mine,....I am His ;....

Should I fear when, oh, so tenderly,
   He whispereth,
   He is mine,....I am His ;....
For the sunshine of His presence
   doth illume the night,
And He leads me through the valley
   to the mountain height ;
Out of bondage, into freedom, into
   cloudless light,
   He is mine,....I am His.....

338 SOME day, I know not when
      'twill be,
The angel of death will come to me ;
But this I know, if Christ be near,
Old Jordan's waves I will not fear.

2 My sins He long ago forgave,
And still I feel His pow'r to save ;
And if I keep the witness clear,
Old Jordan's waves I will not fear.

3 O'er me has sorrow's storm oft swept,
Safe from the danger me He's kept ;
If still I trust this Friend so dear,
Old Jordan's waves I will not fear.

4 My lov'd ones they have cross'd the tide,
But safely cross'd with Christ their
   guide ;
They sweetly whisper in my ear,
Old Jordan's waves I do not fear.

5 So, if at death's cold brink I stand,
My hand clasped in the Saviour's hand;
I, too, shall shout in tones so clear,
Old Jordan's waves I do not fear.

339 TRUE-HEARTED,   whole-
      hearted, faithful and loyal,
King of our lives, by Thy grace
   we will be !   [royal,
Under the standard exalted and
Strong in Thy strength we will
   battle for Thee.

> Peal out the watchword ! silence it never !
> Song of our spirit rejoicing and free ;
> Peal out the watchword ! loyal for ever,
> King of our lives, by Thy grace we will be !

2 True-hearted, whole-hearted, fullest
   allegiance
   Yielding henceforth to our glorious
     King :
Valiant endeavour and loving obed-
   ience,
   Freely and joyfully now would we
     bring.

3 True-hearted, whole-hearted, Saviour
  all glorious !
  Take Thy great power and reign
  there alone ;
Over our wills and affections vic-
  torious,
  Freely surrender'd and wholly
  Thine own.

340 A WORTHY soldier I would
  be
Of Christ, who gave Himself for me,
  Obeying His command ;
And with the gospel shield and sword,
For truth and right, with Christ
  my Lord,
  God helping me, I'll stand.

God helping me, I'll stand,...
With His unyielding band ;
All times and ev'rywhere for Christ,
God helping me, I'll stand.

2 When over me shall grandly wave
  The banner of the martyred brave,
  God's faithful, steadfast band ;
Beneath which none e'er fought in
  vain,
  All foes and dangers I'll disdain,
  God helping me, I'll stand.

3 Though I be weary in the fight,
  And Satan's legions, in their spite
  Attack on ev'ry hand,   [Friend,
I'll stand by Christ, my faithful
  And steadily, unto the end,
  God helping me, I'll stand.

341 IN the fight, say, does your
  heart grow weary ?
Do you find your path is rough and
  thorny,
And above the sky is dark and
  stormy ?
  Never mind : go on !
Lay aside all fear, and onward
  pressing,
Bravely fight, and God will give
  His blessing ;
Though the war at times may prove
  distressing,
  Never mind : go on.

When the road we tread is rough, let us
  bear in mind,
In our Saviour strength enough we may
  always find ;
Tho' the fighting may be tough, let our
  motto be :
Go on,..go on..to vict'ry.

2 Faithful be, delaying not to follow
  Where Christ leads, though it may
  be through sorrow ;
If the strife should fiercer grow to-
  morrow,
  Never mind : go on.
Cheerful be, it will your burden
  lighten,
One glad heart will always others
  brighten ;
Though the strife the coward's soul
  may frighten,
  Never mind : go on !

3 When down-hearted, look away to
  Jesus,
Who for you did shed His blood
  most precious ;
Let us say, though all the world
  should hate us,
  Never mind : go on !
Do your best in fighting for your
  Saviour,
For His sake, fear not to lose men's
  favour,
If beside you should a comrade
  waver,
  Never mind : go on !

342 THERE'S a place in heav'n
  prepared for me,
  When the toils of this life are o'er ;
Where the saints, robed in white,
  shall for ever be,
  Singing praises for evermore.

Jesus promised me a home over there,
Jesus promised me a home over there ;
No more sickness, sorrow, pain or death,
Jesus promised me a home over there.

2 In my Father's home are mansions
  bright,
  Jesus says it, and I know 'tis true ;
There's a home for me in that land
  of light :
  Brother, sister, there is one for
  you.

3 Many dear ones we loved are before
  the throne,
  In that happy, happy home on
  high ;
I shall walk with them through the
  streets of gold,
  I shall wear a starry crown by
  and by.

4 In that home above, beyond the skies,
   Free from sickness, pain, and
      death I'll be,
   There with Jesus to reign for evermore,
      Throughout all eternity.

343 TELL it to Jesus, He under-
      stands thee,
   Reads all the secret intents of thy
      heart ;
   Foes may misjudge and friends may
      mistake thee,
   He will not deal with thee but as
      thou art.

Tell it to Jesus, He understands thee,
  What is thy gain, and what is thy loss ;
While thou art His no harm can befall thee,
  Tell out thy heart at the foot of His Cross.

2 Tell it to Jesus, He understands thee,
   Knows all thy sorrows, and sees
      all thy tears ;
   Knows all the hidden pow'rs that
      withstand thee,
   Knows all thy tremblings, thy
      doubts and thy fears.

3 Tell it to Jesus, He understands thee,
   He can explain ev'ry mystery of
      life ;
   He can unravel tangles that try thee,
   He can speak peace 'midst thy
      turmoil and strife.

4 Tell it to Jesus, He understands thee,
   Seeks by His Spirit to perfect thy
      soul ;
   Sorrows and trials He sends to refine
      thee,
   Tell Him thy case, not in part, but
      in whole.

5 Tell it to Jesus, He understands thee,
   Hide not thy faults, and excuse
      not thy sin ;
   For in the day of account He will
      greet thee,
   Not as thou art from without, but
      within.

344 IS your life a channel of
      blessing ?   [you ?
   Is the love of God flowing thro'
   Are you telling the lost of the
      Saviour ?
   Are you ready His service to do ?

Make me a channel of blessing to-day,
Make me a channel of blessing, I pray ;
My life possessing, my service blessing,
Make me a channel of blessing to-day.

2 Is your life a channel of blessing ?
   Are you burdened for those that
      are lost ?
   Have you urged upon those who are
      straying,
   The Saviour who died on the Cross?

3 Is your life a channel of blessing ?
   Is it daily telling for Him ?
   Have you spoken the word of
      salvation
   To those who are dying in sin ?

4 We cannot be channels of blessing
   If our lives are not free from all
      sin ;
   We will barriers be and a hindrance
   To those we are trying to win.

345 THE blood has always precious
      been,
   'Tis precious now to me ;
   Through it alone my soul has rest,
   From fear and doubt set free.

Oh, wondrous is the crimson tide
  Which from my Saviour flowed ;
And still in heav'n my song shall be,
  The precious, precious blood.

2 I will remember now no more,
   God's faithful Word has said,
   The follies and the sins of him
   For whom My Son has bled.

3 Not all my well-remembered sins
   Can startle or dismay ;
   The precious blood atones for all,
   And bears my guilt away.

4 Perhaps this feeble frame of mine
   Will soon in sickness lie,
   But, resting on the precious blood,
   How peacefully I'll die.

346 SOW flowers, and flowers will
      blossom
   Around you wherever you go ;
   Sow weeds, and of weeds reap the
      harvest,
   You'll reap whatsoever you sow.

You'll reap whatsoever you sow,...
You'll reap whatsoever you sow,...
The harvest is certainly coming,
You'll reap whatsoever you sow.

2 Sow blessings, and blessings will
    ripen,
    Sow hatred, and hatred will grow;
    Sow mercy, and reap sweet com-
        passion,
    You'll reap whatsoever you sow.

3 Sow love, and its sweetness up-
    rising
    Shall fill all your heart with its glow;
    Sow hope, and receive its fruition,
    You'll reap whatsoever you sow.

4 In faith sow the Word of the Master,
    A blessing He'll surely bestow ;
    And souls shine like stars for your
        crowning,
    You'll reap whatsoever you sow.

5 Preach Christ in His wonderful
    fulness,
    That all His salvation may know;
    Reap life through the ages eternal,
    You'll reap whatsoever you sow.

347 I HAVE a Friend, a precious
        Friend,
    O how He loves me ;
    He says His love will never end,
    O how He loves me.

        O how He loves me !
        O how He loves me !
        I know not why, I only cry,
        O how He loves me !

2 Why He should come, I cannot tell,
    O how He loves me ;
    In my poor broken heart to dwell,
    O how He loves me.

3 He died to save my soul from death,
    O how He loves me ;
    I'll praise Him while He gives me
        breath,
    O how He loves me.

4 He walks with me along life's road,
    O how He loves me ;
    He carries ev'ry heavy load,
    O how He loves me.

5 He has a home prepared for me,
    O how He loves me ;
    With Him I'll spend eternity,
    O how He loves me.

348 FOR ever with the Lord !
        Amen, so let it be !
    Life from the dead is in that word ;
        'Tis immortality.
    Here in the body pent,
        Absent from Him I roam ;
    Yet nightly pitch my moving tent,
        A day's march nearer home.
            Nearer home, nearer home,
            A day's march nearer home.

2 My Father's house on high,
        Home of my soul, how near
    At times to faith's foreseeing eye,
        Thy golden gates appear !
    My thirsty spirit faints
        To reach the land I love,
    The bright inheritance of saints—
        Jerusalem above.

3 For ever with the Lord !
        Father, if 'tis Thy will,
    The promise of that faithful word,
        E'en here to me fulfil.
    Be Thou at my right hand,
        Then can I never fail ;
    Uphold Thou me, so I shall stand,
        Fight, and I must prevail.

4 So when my latest breath
        Shall rend the vail in twain,
    By death I shall escape from death,
        And life eternal gain.
    Knowing as I am known,
        How shall I love that word !
    And oft repeat before the throne,
        For ever with the Lord !

349 I'VE cast my heavy burdens
        down on Canaan's happy
            shore,
    I'm living where the healing
        waters flow ;....
    I'll wander in the wilderness of
        doubt and sin no more ;
    I'm living where the healing
        waters flow.....
    Living on the shore, I'm living on the shore,
        I'm living where the healing waters flow...

2 With Israel's trusting children I'm
        rejoicing on my way,
    I'm living where the healing
        waters flow ;....
    The cloudy, fiery pillar is my
        guiding light to-day ;
    I'm living where the healing
        waters flow.....

3 My hung'ring soul is satisfied with
    manna from above,
  I'm living where the healing
    waters flow ;....
  No more I thirst, the rock I've found,
    that fount of endless love ;
  I'm living where the healing
    waters flow.....

4 I'm singing "Hallelujah," safely
    anchored is my soul,
  I'm living where the healing
    waters flow ;....
  I'm resting on His promises, the
    blood has made me whole ;
  I'm living where the healing
    waters flow.....

350 WHEN Israel out of bondage
        came,
  A sea before them lay ;
  The Lord reach'd down His mighty
    hand,
  And rolled the sea away.
  Then forward still, 'tis Jehovah's will,
  Tho' the billows dash and spray ;
  With a conqu'ring tread we will push ahead,
  He'll roll the sea away.

2 Before me was a sea of sin,
  So great I feared to pray ;
  My heart's desire the Saviour read,
  And rolled the sea away.

3 When sorrows dark, like stormy
    waves,
  Were dashing o'er my way ;
  Again the Lord in mercy came,
  And rolled the sea away.

4 And when I reach the sea of death,
  For needed grace I'll pray ;
  I know the Lord will quickly come,
  And roll the sea away.

351 I ONCE was a stranger
        To grace and to God,
  I knew not my danger
    And felt not my load ;
  Though friends spoke in rapture
    Of Christ on the tree,
  Jehovah Tsidkenu
    Was nothing to me.

2 Like tears from the daughters
    Of Zion that roll,
  I wept when the waters
    Went over His soul ;

Yet thought not that my sins
  Had nailed to the tree,
Jehovah Tsidkenu—
  'Twas nothing to me.

3 When free grace awoke me
    By light from on high,
  Then legal fears shook me,
    I trembled to die ;
  No refuge, no safety,
    In self could I see,
  Jehovah Tsidkenu
    My Saviour must be.

4 My terrors all vanished
    Before the sweet name,
  My guilty fears banished,
    With boldness I came
  To drink at the fountain,
    Life-giving and free,
  Jehovah Tsidkenu
    Is all things to me.

5 E'en treading the valley,
    The shadow of death,
  This watchword shall rally
    My faltering breath ;
  For when from life's fever
    My God sets me free,
  Jehovah Tsidkenu
    My death-song shall be.

352 LOW in the grave He lay,
        Jesus, my Saviour !
  Waiting the coming day—
    Jesus, my Lord !
  Up from the grave He arose,...
  With a mighty triumph o'er His foes ;...
  He arose a Victor from the dark domain,
  And He lives for ever with His saints to reign;
  He arose !...He arose !...
  Hallelujah ! Christ arose !

2 Vainly they watch His bed—
    Jesus, my Saviour !
  Vainly they seal the dead—
    Jesus, my Lord !

3 Death cannot keep his prey—
    Jesus, my Saviour !
  He tore the bars away—
    Jesus, my Lord !

353 WHO can wash a sinner's
        guilt away ?
  There is no one like the Saviour,
    hallelujah !

Who can turn his darkness into day ?
   There is no one like the Saviour,
     hallelujah !

> Oh, glory, glory hallelujah !
> There is no one like the Saviour, hallelujah !
> While we live or die, in the earth or sky,
> There is no one like the Saviour, hallelujah !

2 When we're lowly bent with grief
    and care,
   There is no one like the Saviour,
     hallelujah !
He speaks and the sunbeams linger
    there,
   There is no one like the Saviour,
     hallelujah.

3 When we're tempest tossed upon
    life's deep,
   There is no one like the Saviour,
     hallelujah !
He speaks, and the wild waves
    hush to sleep,
   There is no one like the Saviour,
     hallelujah !

4 When we feel the icy touch of death,
   There is no one like the Saviour,
     hallelujah !
He will take us at our closing breath,
   There is no one like the Saviour,
     hallelujah.

5 Over in that blest home of the soul,
   There is no one like the Saviour,
     hallelujah !
This shall be our song while ages roll,
   There is no one like the Saviour,
     hallelujah.

354 WHEN I see life's golden sun-
    set lighting up the rosy west,
  When the shadows backward o'er
    my way are cast,
I shall look upon that moment as
    the one supremely blest ;
  I'm going home at last.

> I'm going home at last,...
> I'm going home at last ;....
> When my work on earth is ended and my
> race below is run,
> I'm going home at last.

2 Tho' the road at times was weary
    over which my feet have trod,
  Tho' through many tribulations
    I have passed ;
Yet I soon will reach my mansion
    in the city of our God ;
  I'm going home at last.

3 When I pass down through the
    valley and the shadow of the
    dead,
  To my blessed Saviour's hand I
    will hold fast ;
He has promised to go with me, so
    my soul will have no dread ;
  I'm going home at last.

355 WHEN the troubles gather
    And the billows roll,
  Dark the way before you,
    Cares oppress the soul ;
  There is blessed sunshine
    Just beyond your view ;
  Oft 'tis but a trial
    You are going through.

> See the sunlight, shining bright and clear ;
> Blessed sunlight drives away all fear ;
> Look above you, clouds will disappear ;
> Put your trust in Jesus, He is ever near.

2 Though you cannot fathom
    Why you're called to bear
  All the heavy burdens
    That you cannot share ;
  Keep the Cross before you
    In the darkest day ;
  Put your trust in Jesus
    All along the way.

3 Go, with faith, to conquer
    Trials that appear ;
  Know that Christ your Saviour
    With His help is near.
  Ne'er give up the battle,
    Hard though it may be,
  For your Lord has promised
    You the victory.

4 Though severe the conflict,
    And the anguish deep ;
  Though the trial's heavy
    That may o'er you sweep ;
  God is always near you,
    Giving strength to bear
  All the heavy burdens
    When they shall appear.

5 Tried and found not wanting,
    Will the Master say ;
  Tried, yet ever faithful
    All along life's way ;
  Tried as in the furnace
    Of refining fire,
  You shall see the triumph
    Of your heart's desire.

356 THEY tell me there are dangers
In the path my feet must tread,
But they cannot see the glory
That is shining round my head.
Oh, 'tis Jesus leads my footsteps,
He has made my heart His own,
For I would not dare to journey
Thro' the wide, wide world alone.

2 They tell me life has trials,
And the fairest hopes will flee,
But I trust my all to Jesus,
For I know He cares for me.

3 I know my heart is sinful,
And my love is all too small,
But with Jesus' arms around me
I shall win and conquer all.

357 COME, ye that love the Lord,
And let your joys be known;
Join in a song with sweet accord,
And thus surround the throne.
We're marching to Zion,
Beautiful, beautiful Zion;
We're marching upward to Zion,
The beautiful city of God.

2 Let those refuse to sing
Who never knew our God;
But children of the heav'nly King
Must speak their joys abroad.

3 The hill of Zion yields
A thousand sacred sweets;
Before we reach the heav'nly fields,
Or walk the golden streets.

4 Then let our songs abound
And ev'ry tear be dry;
We're marching through Immanuel's
ground,
To fairer worlds on high.

358 STANDING like a lighthouse
on the shores of time,
Looking o'er the waves of darkness,
sin, and crime,
Open up your windows, there's a
work sublime :
Let the Gospel light shine out.
Let the Gospel light shine out...
Let the Gospel light shine out...
While your lamp is burning, keep the win-
dows clean,
Let the Gospel light shine out.

2 There are human shipwrecks lying
all around !
O what moral darkness everywhere
is found !

D

Warn some other vessels off from
dang'rous ground :
Let the Gospel light shine out.

3 Do not let the bushel cover up your
light ;
Keep your lamp in order, trimmed
and burning bright ;
Try to be a blessing, brighten up
the night :
Let the Gospel light shine out.

4 Try to live for Jesus till this life is o'er,
For along this pathway you will pass
no more ;
Till He bids you welcome on the
other shore,
Let the Gospel light shine out.

359 WOULD you always cheerful be?
Let the blessed sunlight in ;
Would you bid the darkness flee ?
Let the blessed sunlight in.
Let the blessed sunlight, sunlight in,
Let the blessed sunlight in ;...
Would you never weary when the days are
dreary,
Let the blessed sunlight in...

2 Would you brighten dreary days ?
Let the blessed sunlight in ;
Would you fill your heart with praise?
Let the blessed sunlight in.

3 Would you ease a burden'd heart ?
Let the blessed sunlight in ;
Would you joy and strength impart?
Let the blessed sunlight in.

4 Would you speed the truth abroad ?
Let the blessed sunlight in ;
Would you bring the world to God ?
Let the blessed sunlight in.

360 I'VE found a Friend in Jesus,
He's everything to me,
He's the Fairest of Ten Thousand
to my soul ;   [I see
The Lily of the Valley, in Him alone
All I need to cleanse and make me
fully whole ;
In sorrow He's my comfort, in
trouble He's my stay,   [roll.
He tells me ev'ry care on Him to
He's the Lily of the Valley, the
Bright and Morning Star,
He's the Fairest of Ten Thousand
to my soul.

In sorrow He's my comfort, in trouble He's
    my stay,
He tells me ev'ry care on Him to roll.
He's the Lily of the Valley, the Bright and
    Morning Star,
He's the Fairest of Ten Thousand to my soul.

2 He all my grief has taken, and all
    my sorrows borne,
    In temptation He's my strong and
      mighty tower ;
I've all for Him forsaken, I've all my
    idols torn
    From my heart, and now He keeps
      me by His pow'r.
Though all the world forsake me,
    and Satan tempt me sore,
    Through Jesus I shall safely reach
      the goal ;
He's the Lily of the Valley, the
    Bright and Morning Star,
    He's the Fairest of Ten Thousand
      to my soul.

3 He'll never, never leave me, nor yet
    forsake me here,
    While I live by faith and do His
      blessed will ;
A wall of fire about me, I've nothing
    now to fear,
    With His manna He my hungry
      soul shall fill ;
Then sweeping up to glory I'll see
    His blessed face,   [flow ;
    Where rivers of delight shall ever
He's the Lily of the Valley, the
    Bright and Morning Star,
    He's the Fairest of Ten Thousand
      to my soul.

361   ONE little hour for watching
      with the Master,
    Eternal years to walk with Him
      in white ;
One little hour to bravely meet
    disaster,
    Eternal years to reign with Him
      in light.
Then souls, be brave, and watch until the
      morrow !
Awake ! arise ! your lamps of purpose trim !
Your Saviour speaks across the night of sorrow :
Can ye not watch one little hour with Him ?

2 One little hour to suffer scorn and
    losses,
    Eternal years beyond earth's
      cruel frowns ;

One little hour to carry heavy crosses
    Eternal years to wear unfading
      crowns.

3 One little hour for weary toils and
    trials,   [ful rest ;
    Eternal years for calm and peace-
One little hour for patient self-
    denials,   [blest.
    Eternal years of life where life is

362   SAVED by grace alone, God's
      own Word believing ;
    It is glory all the way !
Walking in the light, daily grace
    receiving :
    It is glory all the way !
Glo - - ry ! glo - - ry ! it is glory all the way...
Glo - - ry ! glo - - ry ! it is glory all the way...

2 Not a care have I since my Saviour
    It is glory all the way ! [careth ;
    Guided by His eye, while with me
      He fareth,
    It is glory all the way !

3 Sever'd from the world His dear
    name confessing :
    It is glory all the way !
Taking up the Cross, sharing in the
    blessing :
    It is glory all the way !

4 Sinner, put your trust in this loving
    Saviour :
    It is glory all the way !
Freely He forgives all our past
    behaviour :
    It is glory all the way !

363   I KNOW I love Thee better,
      Lord,
    Than any earthly joy,
For Thou hast given me the peace
    Which nothing can destroy.
The half has never yet been told,....
    Of love so full and free ;
The half has never yet been told,....
    The blood it cleanseth me.....

2 I know that Thou art nearer still
    Than any earthly throng,
And sweeter is the thought of Thee
    Than any lovely song.

3 Thou hast put gladness in my heart ;
    Then well may I be glad ;
Without the secret of Thy love
    I could not but be sad.

4 O Saviour, precious Saviour mine !
  What will Thy presence be,
If such a life of joy can crown
  Our walk on earth with Thee ?

364 WHEN my life work is ended
    and I cross the swelling tide,
When the bright and glorious
  morning I shall see ;
I shall know my Redeemer when I
  reach the other side,
And His smile will be the first to
  welcome me.

 I shall know...Him, I shall know Him,
  As redeem'd by His side I shall stand.
 I shall know...Him, I shall know Him
  By the print of the nails in His hand.

2 Oh, the soul-thrilling rapture when
  I view His blessed face
  And the lustre of His kindly beam-
   ing eye ;
How my full heart will praise Him
  for the mercy, love, and grace,
That prepares me for a mansion
  in the sky.

3 Oh, the dear ones in glory, how they
  beckon me to come,
  And our parting at the river I
   recall ;
To the sweet vales of Eden they will
  sing my welcome home,
But I long to meet my Saviour
  first of all.

4 Thro' the gates to the city in a robe
  of spotless white,
  He will lead me where no tears
   shall ever fall ;
In the glad song of ages I shall
  mingle with delight,
But I long to meet my Saviour
  first of all.

365 THE prize is set before us,
    To win, His words implore us ;
The eye of God is o'er us,
  From on high, from on high !
His loving tones are calling,
While sin is dark, appalling ;
'Tis Jesus gently calling,
  He is nigh, He is nigh.

 By-and-by we shall meet Him,
 By-and-by we shall greet Him,
 And with Jesus reign in glory, by-and-by.

2 We'll follow where He leadeth,
  We'll pasture where He feedeth,
  We'll yield to Him who pleadeth,
   From on high, from on high !
Then nought from Him shall sever,
Our hope shall brighten ever,
And faith shall fail us never,
  He is nigh, He is nigh.

3 Our home is bright above us,
  No trials dark to move us,
  But Jesus dear to love us,
   There on high, there on high !
We'll give Him best endeavour,
And praise His name for ever,
His precious ones can never,
  Never die, never die.

366 WHEN all my labours and
    trials are o'er,
And I am safe on that beautiful
  shore,
Just to be near the dear Lord I adore,
  Will thro' the ages be glory for me.

 Oh, that will be...glory for me,...
 Glory for me,...glory for me,...
 When by His grace I shall look on His face,
 That will be glory, be glory for me.

2 When by the gift of His infinite
  grace,
I am accorded in heaven a place,
Just to be there and to look on His
  face,
  Will thro' the ages be glory for me.

3 Friends will be there I have lov'd
  long ago ;
Joy like a river around me will flow ;
Yet, just a smile from my Saviour, I
  know,
  Will thro' the ages be glory for me.

367 THOU my everlasting portion,
    More than friend or life to
    me,
All along my pilgrim journey,
  Saviour, let me walk with Thee

  Close to Thee, close to Thee,
  Close to Thee, close to Thee,
  All along my pilgrim journey,
  Saviour, let me walk with Thee.

2 Not for ease or worldly pleasure,
  Nor for fame my prayer shall be ;
Gladly will I toil and suffer,
  Only let me walk with Thee.

Close to Thee, close to Thee,
Close to Thee, close to Thee,
Gladly will I toil and suffer,
Only let me walk with Thee.

3 Lead me through this vale of shadows,
Bear me o'er life's fitful sea ;
Then the gate of life eternal
May I enter, Lord, with Thee.

Close to Thee, close to Thee,
Close to Thee, close to Thee ;
Then the gate of life eternal
May I enter, Lord, with Thee.

368 SINCE Christ my soul from sin
set free,
This world has been a heav'n to me,
And 'mid earth's sorrow and its woe,
'Tis heav'n my Jesus here to know.

Oh hallelujah, yes, 'tis heav'n,
'Tis heav'n to know my sins forgiv'n ;
On land or sea, what matters where,
Where Jesus is, 'tis heav'n there.

2 Once heaven seemed a far-off place,
Till Jesus showed His smiling face ;
Now it's begun within my soul,
'Twill last while endless ages roll.

3 What matter where on earth we
dwell ?
On mountain top, or in the dell ?
In cottage or in mansion fair,
Where Jesus is, 'tis heaven there.

369 TAKE the world, but give me
Jesus,
All its joys are but a name,
But His love abideth ever,
Thro' eternal years the same.

Oh, the height and depth of mercy !
Oh ! the length and breadth of love !
Oh, the fulness of redemption,
Pledge of endless life above.

2 Take the world, but give me Jesus,
Sweetest comfort of my soul ;
With my Saviour watching o'er me
I can sing, though billows roll.

3 Take the world, but give me Jesus,
Let me view His constant smile ;
Then throughout my pilgrim journey
Light will cheer me all the while.

4 Take the world, but give me Jesus,
In His Cross my trust shall be,
Till, with clearer, brighter vision,
Face to face my Lord I see.

370 SAVIOUR, lead me, lest I
stray,....
Gently lead me all the way ;....
I am safe when by Thy side,....
I would in Thy love abide.....

Lead me, lead me,
Saviour, lead me, lest I stray ;....
Gently down the stream of time,.....
Lead me, Saviour, all the way.....

2 Thou, the refuge of my soul,....
When life's stormy billows roll,....
I am safe when Thou art nigh,....
All my hopes on Thee rely.....

3 Saviour, lead me then at last,....
When the storm of life is past,....
To the land of endless day,....
Where all tears are wiped away.....

371 A WONDERFUL Saviour is
Jesus, my Lord,
A wonderful Saviour to me ;
He hideth my soul in the cleft of the
rock,
Where rivers of pleasure I see.

He hideth my soul in the cleft of the rock,
That shadows a dry thirsty land ;
He hideth my life in the depths of His love,
And covers me there with His hand.

2 A wonderful Saviour is Jesus, my
Lord,
He taketh my burden away ;
He holdeth me up, and I shall not
be mov'd,
He giveth me strength as my day.

3 With numberless blessings each
moments He crowns
And fill'd with His fulness divine,
I sing in my rapture, oh, glory to God,
For such a Redeemer as mine !

4 When cloth'd in His brightness
transported I rise,
To meet Him in clouds of the sky,
His perfect salvation, His wonderful
love,   [high.
I'll shout with the millions on

372 JERUSALEM the golden,
With milk and honey blest,
Beneath thy contemplation
Sink heart and voice opprest ;
I know not, oh ! I know not,
What joys await us there,
What radiancy of glory,
What bliss beyond compare.

2 They stand, those halls of Zion,
  All jubilant with song ;
And bright with many an angel,
  And all the martyr throng ;
The Prince is ever in them,
  The daylight is serene,
The pastures of the blessed
  Are deck'd in glorious sheen.

3 There is the throne of David,
  And there, from care releas'd,
The shout of them that triumph,
  The song of them that feast ;
And they who, with their Leader,
  Have conquer'd in the fight,
For ever and for ever
  Are cloth'd in robes of white.

4 Oh, sweet and blessed country,
  The home of God's elect !
Oh, sweet and blessed country,
  That eager hearts expect !
Jesus, in mercy bring us
  To that dear land of rest,
Who art, with God the Father,
  And Spirit, ever blest.

373   O THE grace of God is bound-
    less,
  It is like a mighty sea,
And it rolls on through the ages,
  Bearing love to you and me ;
But the Lord's so great in goodness,
  That He opens heav'n to view,
And not only gives us mercy,
  But He gives us glory too.

    There's grace...and glory too,...
    There's grace...and glory too ;...
    There's grace below for weal or woe,
    And then there's glory too.

2 There is grace for each temptation,
  There is strength for ev'ry day,
There's a lift for ev'ry burden
  That we carry on the way,
There's a refuge from the tempest,
  There is help for all we do.
And when we shall end the journey,
  We will find there's glory too.

3 For the grace that God has given,
  I will praise Him in my song :
I will love Him and will serve Him
  While my days of life prolong ;
And when I shall get to heaven,
  And my journey I review,
Then I'll bless His name for ever,
  That there's grace and glory too.

374   IN the shadow of His wings
    There is rest, sweet rest ;
There is rest from care and labour,
  There is rest for friend and neighbour;
  In the shadow of His wings
    There is rest, sweet rest ;
  In the shadow of His wings
    There is rest.....

    There is rest ! sweet rest !
    There is peace ! sweet peace !
    There is joy, glad joy,
    In the shadow of His wings !...

2 In the shadow of His wings
  There is peace, sweet peace ;
Peace that passeth understanding,
  Peace, sweet peace, that knows no
    ending ;
  In the shadow of His wings
    There is peace, sweet peace,
  In the shadow of His wings
    There is peace.....

3 In the shadow of His wings
  There is joy, glad joy ;
There is joy to tell the story,
  Joy exceeding, full of glory ;
  In the shadow of His wings
    There is joy, glad joy,
  In the shadow of His wings
    There is joy.....

375   TO that summer land up
    yonder,
  Where the angels ever sing
Hallelujahs to the Saviour,
  Sweet hosannahs to the King :
We are marching swiftly onward,
  Guided by a Father's hand,
Thro' this world of sin and sorrow,
  To that happy summer-land.

    Oh,....the joy when we get there,...
    Golden crowns of life to wear,...
    In that happy land so fair,
    In that summer land up yonder.

2 To that summer land up yonder
  Some are going ev'ry day,
And the time is drawing nearer
  When we, too, shall go away ;
We are going straight to Jesus,
  There to join the ransom'd band,
We will praise His name for ever,
  In that happy summer land.

3 In that summer land up yonder,
  There's a place prepared for all
Who are trusting in the Saviour,
  Who will listen to His call ;

And the happy time is coming
  When the Lord shall give command,
And we'll leave this world for ever,
  For that happy summer land.

376 WHEN you start for the land
    of heavenly rest,
  Keep close to Jesus all the way ;
For He is the Guide, and He knows
    the way best,
  Keep close to Jesus all the way.
Keep close to Jesus, keep close to Jesus,
  Keep close to Jesus all the way ;
By day or by night never turn from the right,
  Keep close to Jesus all the way.

2 Never mind the storms or trials as
    you go.
  Keep close to Jesus all the way ;
'Tis a comfort and joy His favour
    to know,
  Keep close to Jesus all the way.

3 To be safe from the darts of the evil
    one,
  Keep close to Jesus all the way ;
Take the shield of faith till the
    vict'ry is won,
  Keep close to Jesus all the way.

4 We shall reach our home in heaven
    by and by,
  Keep close to Jesus all the way ;
Where to those we love we'll never
    say " good-bye,"
  Keep close to Jesus all the way.

377 WHAT a fellowship, what a
    joy divine,
  Leaning on the everlasting arms ;
What a blessedness, what a peace
    is mine,
  Leaning on the everlasting arms.
Lean - - ing, lean - - ing,
  Safe and secure from all alarms,
Lean - - ing, lean - - ing,
  Leaning on the everlasting arms.

2 Oh, how sweet to walk in this pilgrim
    way,
  Leaning on the everlasting arms ;
Oh, how bright the path grows from
    day to day,
  Leaning on the everlasting arms.

3 What have I to dread, what have I
    to fear,
  Leaning on the everlasting arms ?
I have blessed peace with my Lord
    so near,
  Leaning on the everlasting arms.

378 THERE comes to my heart
    one sweet strain,....
A glad and a joyous refrain,....
I sing it again and again,   [love.
  Sweet peace, the gift of God's
Peace, peace, sweet peace,
  Wonderful gift from above ;
Oh, wonderful, wonderful peace,
  Sweet peace, the gift of God's love.

2 By Christ on the Cross peace was
    made,....
My debt by His death was all paid,...
No other foundation is laid
  For peace, the gift of God's love.

3 When Jesus, as Lord, I had
    crown'd,....
My heart with this peace did
    abound,....
In Him the rich blessing I found,
  Sweet peace, the gift of God's
    love.

4 In Jesus for peace I abide,....
  And as I keep close to His side,....
There's nothing but peace doth
    betide,
  Sweet peace, the gift of God's love.

379 I HAVE a song I love to sing,
    Since I have been redeemed ;
Of my Redeemer, Saviour, King,
  Since I have been redeemed.
Since I...have been redeemed,...
  Since I...have been redeemed,...
  I will glory in His Name.
Since I...have been redeemed,...
  I will glory in the Saviour's Name.

2 I have a Christ that satisfies,
    Since I have been redeemed ;
To do His will my highest prize,
  Since I have been redeemed.

3 I have a witness bright and clear,
    Since I have been redeemed,
Dispelling ev'ry doubt and fear
  Since I have been redeemed.

4 I have a joy I can't express,
    Since I have been redeemed ;
All through His blood and right-
    eousness,
  Since I have been redeemed.

5 I have a home prepared for me,
    Since I have been redeemed ;
Where I shall dwell eternally,
  Since I have been redeemed.

380 TILL I learned to love Thy
name,
Lord, Thy grace denying,
I was lost in sin and shame,
Dying, dying, dying !

This is now my constant theme,
This my favourite story,
Jesus' blood avails for me,
Glory glory, glory !

2 Nothing could the world impart,
Darkness held no morrow ;
In my soul, and in my heart,
Sorrow, sorrow, sorrow !

3 When I learned to love Thy name,
O, Thou meek and lowly ;
Rapture kindled to a flame,
Holy, holy, holy !

4 Henceforth shall creation ring
With salvation's story ;
Till I rise with Thee to sing,
Glory, glory, glory !

Hallelujah ! grace is free,
I will tell the story,
Jesus' blood hath made me free,
Glory, glory, glory !

381 THERE is sunshine in my soul
to-day,
More glorious and bright,
Than glows in any earthly sky,
For Jesus is my light.

Oh, there's sun - - shine, blessed sun - - shine,
While the peaceful, happy moments roll ;...
When Jesus shows His smiling face,
There is sunshine in my soul.

2 There is music in my soul to-day,
A carol to my King,
And Jesus, listening, can hear
The song I cannot sing.

3 There is springtime in my soul
to-day,
For when the Lord is near
The dove of peace sings in my heart,
The flowers of grace appear.

4 There is gladness in my soul to-day,
And hope, and praise, and love,
For blessings which He gives me
now,
For joys " laid up " above.

382 I HAVE entered the valley of
blessing so sweet,
And Jesus abides with me there ;

And His Spirit and blood make my
cleansing complete,
And His perfect love casteth out
fear.

Oh, come to this valley of blessing so sweet,
Where Jesus will fulness bestow,
Oh, believe and receive and confess Him,
That all His salvation may know.

2 There is peace in the valley of
blessing so sweet,
And plenty the land doth impart ;
There is rest for the weary-worn
traveller's feet,
And joy for the sorrowing heart.

3 There is love in the valley of blessing
so sweet,
Such as none but the blood-
washed may feel,
When heaven comes down redeemed
spirits to greet,
And Christ sets His covenant seal.

4 There's a song in the valley of
blessing so sweet,
And angels would fain join the
strain,
As with rapturous praises we bow
at His feet,
Crying, " Worthy the Lamb that
was slain ! "

383 TO the work ! to the work !
we are servants of God,
Let us follow the path that our
Master has trod,
With the balm of His counsel our
strength to renew,
Let us do with our might what our
hands find to do.

Toiling on,...toiling on,...
Toiling on,...toiling on,...
Let us hope,...let us watch and pray,...
And labour till the Master comes.

2 To the work ! to the work ! let the
hungry be fed ;
To the Fountain of Life let the weary
be led ;
In the Cross and its banner our glory
shall be,
While we herald the tidings, " Salvation is free ! "

3 To the work ! to the work ! there
is labour for all,
For the kingdom of darkness and
error shall fall,

And the name of Jehovah exalted
shall be
In the loud swelling chorus, " Salvation is free ! "

4 To the work ! to the work ! pressing
on to the end,
For the harvest will come, and the
reapers descend ;
And the home of the ransomed our
dwelling will be,
And our chorus for ever, " Salvation
is free ! "

384 I HEAR my dying Saviour
say :
Follow Me ! come, follow Me !
For thee I gave My life away,
Follow Me ! come, follow Me !
I know how heart and flesh may fail,
I've borne the fury of the gale ;
Do thou, My child, o'er hill and dale,
Follow Me ! come, follow Me !

2 Tho' thou hast sinned I pardoned
thee ;
Follow Me ! come, follow Me !
From inbred sin I'll set thee free ;
Follow Me ! come, follow Me !
Oh, look to Me, dismiss thy fears,
And trust Me thro' all coming years !
My hand shall wipe away thy tears,
Follow Me ! come, follow Me !

3 Come, cast upon Me all thy cares !
Follow Me ! come, follow Me !
Thy heavy load Mine arm upbears,
Follow Me ! come, follow Me !
In all thy changeful life I'll be   [sea,
Thy God and Guide o'er land and
Thy bliss through all eternity,
Follow Me ! come, follow Me !

385 O, HOW sweet the glorious
message,
Simple faith may claim ;
Yesterday, to-day, for ever,
Jesus is the same.
Still He loves to save the sinful,
Heal the sick and lame ;
Cheer the mourner, still the tempest,
Glory to His name !

Yesterday, to-day, for ever, Jesus is the same,
All may change, but Jesus never ! glory to His
name.
Glory to His name, glory to His name,
All may change, but Jesus never ! glory to His
name !

2 He who was the Friend of sinners,
Seeks thee, lost one, now ;
Sinner, come, and at His footstool,
Penitently bow.   [thee,
He who said, " I'll not condemn
Go, and sin no more,"
Speaks to thee that word of pardon,
As in days of yore.

3 Him who pardoned erring Peter,
Never need'st thou fear ;
He that came to faithless Thomas,
All thy doubts will clear.
He who let the loved disciple
On His bosom rest,
Bids thee, still, with love as tender,
Lean upon His breast.

4 He who, 'mid the raging billows,
Walk'd upon the sea ;
Still can hush our wildest tempest,
As on Galilee.
He who wept and prayed in anguish
In Gethsemane,
Drinks with us each cup of trembling,
In our agony.

5 As of old He walk'd to Emmaus,
With them to abide ;
So thro' all life's way He walketh
Ever near our side.
Soon again shall we behold Him,
Hasten, Lord, the day !
But 'twill still be "this same Jesus,"
As He went away.

386 AMID the trials which I meet,
Amid the thorns that pierce
my feet,
One thought remains supremely
sweet,
Thou thinkest, Lord, of me !

Thou thinkest, Lord, of me,....
Thou thinkest, Lord, of me,....
What need I fear since Thou art near
And thinkest, Lord, of me !

2 The cares of life come thronging
fast,
Upon my soul their shadow cast ;
Their gloom reminds my heart at
last,
Thou thinkest, Lord, of me !

3 Let shadows come, let shadows go,
Let life be bright or dark with woe,
I am content, for this I know,
Thou thinkest, Lord, of me !

387 ENTHRONED is Jesus now,
       Upon His heav'nly seat ;
The kingly crown is on His brow,
       The saints are at His feet.

There with the glorified, safe by our Saviour's
We shall be satisfied by and by ;   [side,
By . . and by, ... by . . and by . . . .
We shall be satisfied by and by.

2 In shining white they stand,
      That great and countless throng ;
A palmy sceptre in each hand,
      On ev'ry lip a song.

3 They sing the Lamb of God,
      Once slain on earth for them ;
The Lamb, thro' whose atoning blood
      Each wears his diadem.

4 Thy grace, O Holy Ghost,
      Thy blessed help supply,
That we may join that radiant host,
      Triumphant in the sky.

388 SOUND the battle cry !
       See ! the foe is nigh ;
Raise the standard high,
       For the Lord ;
Gird your armour on,
Stand firm, ev'ry one ;
Rest your cause upon
       His holy word.

Rouse, then, soldiers ! rally round the banner !
   Ready, steady, pass the word along,
Onward, forward, shout aloud Hosannah !
   Christ is Captain of the mighty throng.

2 Strong to meet the foe,
      Marching on we go,
While our cause we know
      Must prevail ;
Shield and banner bright,
Gleaming in the light ;
Battling for the right,
      We ne'er can fail.

3 Oh ! Thou God of all,
      Hear us when we call ;
Help us one and all,
      By Thy grace ;
When the battle's done,
And the vict'ry won,
May we wear the crown
      Before Thy face.

389 I'VE reached the land of corn
             and wine,
And all its riches freely mine ;

Here shines undimmed one blissful
             day,
For all my night has passed away.

   Oh, Beulah Land, sweet Beulah Land,
   As on the highest mount I stand,
   I look away across the sea,
   Where mansions are prepared for me,
   And view the shining glory shore,
   My heaven, my home, for evermore.

2 My Saviour comes and walks with
             me,
And sweet communion here have we ;
He gently leads me by His hand,
For this is heaven's borderland.

3 A sweet perfume upon the breeze
Is borne from ever-vernal trees,
And flowers that never-fading grow,
Where streams of life for ever flow.

4 The zephyrs seem to float to me
Sweet sounds of heaven's melody,
As angels with the white-robed
             throng
Join in the sweet redemption song.

390 JESUS, keep me near the Cross,
            There a precious fountain,
Free to all, a healing stream,
            Flows from Calvary's mountain.

   In the Cross, in the Cross
      Be my glory ever,
   Till my raptur'd soul shall find
      Rest beyond the river.

2 Near the Cross, a trembling soul,
      Love and mercy found me ;
There the bright and morning star
      Shed its beams around me.

3 Near the Cross ! oh, Lamb of God,
      Bring its scenes before me ;
Help me walk from day to day,
      With its shadow o'er me.

4 Near the Cross I'll watch and wait,
      Hoping, trusting ever,
Till I reach the golden strand,
      Just beyond the river.

391 HIS grace was sufficient for me !
       When in trembling and fear,
       To His side I drew near,
And to cleanse me from sin,
Made my heart pure within,
His grace was sufficient for me.

   For me,...for me,...
   His grace is sufficient for me ;...
   For me,...for me,...
   His grace is sufficient for me.

2 His grace was sufficient for me!
   And whatever my lot,
   I can hear His "fear not!"
   I am safe in His care,
   Who can guard from each snare,
   His grace is sufficient for me.

3 His grace is sufficient for me!
   All my needs He'll provide,
   And my steps homeward guide;
   And in death I shall sing,
   As I rest 'neath His wing,
   His grace is sufficient for me.

4 His grace is sufficient for me!
   When in mansions of bliss,
   Still my theme shall be this;
   And for aye I shall sing,
   To the praise of my King,
   Whose grace is sufficient for me.

392 WITH His dear and loving care,
   Will the Saviour lead us on
   To the hills and valleys fair,
      Over Jordan?
   Yes, we'll rest our weary feet,
   By the crystal waters sweet,
   When the peaceful shore we greet,
      Over Jordan.

   Over Jordan! over Jordan!
   Yes, we'll rest our weary feet, by the crystal
      waters sweet,
   Over Jordan! over Jordan!
   When the peaceful shore we'll greet, over
      Jordan.

2 Through the rocky wilderness
   Will the Saviour lead us on,
   To the land we shall possess,
      Over Jordan?
   Yes, by night the wondrous ray,
   Cloudy pillar by the day,
   They shall guide us on our way,
      Over Jordan.

3 With His strong and mighty hand,
   Will the Saviour lead us on,
   To that good and pleasant land,
      Over Jordan?
   Yes, where vine and olive grow,
   And the brooks and fountains flow,
   Thirst nor hunger shall we know,
      Over Jordan.

4 In the promised land to be,
   Will the Saviour lead us on,
   Till fair Canaan's shore we see,
      Over Jordan?

Yes, to dwell with Thee at last,
Guide and lead us as Thou hast,
Till the parted wave be past,
   Over Jordan.

393 ONCE it was the blessing,
      Now it is the Lord;
   Once it was the feeling,
      Now it is His Word;
   Once His gifts I wanted,
      Now the Giver own;
   Once I sought for healing,
      Now Himself alone.
         All in all for ever,
            Jesus will I sing;
         Everything in Jesus,
            And Jesus ev'rything.

2 Once 'twas painful trying,
      Now 'tis perfect trust;
   Once a half salvation,
      Now the uttermost;
   Once 'twas ceaseless holding,
      Now He holds me fast;
   Once 'twas constant drifting,
      Now my anchor's cast.

3 Once 'twas busy planning,
      Now 'tis trustful prayer;
   Once 'twas anxious caring,
      Now He has the care;
   Once 'twas what I wanted,
      Now what Jesus says;
   Once 'twas constant asking,
      Now 'tis ceaseless praise.

4 Once it was my working,
      His it hence shall be;
   Once I tried to use Him,
      Now He uses me;
   Once the pow'r I wanted,
      Now the Mighty One;
   Once for self I labour'd,
      Now for Him alone.

5 Once I hoped in Jesus,
      Now I know He's mine;
   Once my lamps were dying,
      Now they brightly shine;
   Once for death I waited,
      Now His coming hail;
   And my hopes are anchor'd
      Safe within the veil.

394 THE King of Love my Shepherd is,
   Whose goodness faileth never;
I nothing lack if I am His,
   And He is mine for ever.

2 Where streams of living water flow,
 My ransom'd soul He leadeth,
And where the verdant pastures grow
 With food celestial feedeth.

3 Perverse and foolish, oft I strayed,
 But yet in love He sought me,
And on His shoulder gently laid,
 And home rejoicing brought me.

4 In death's dark vale I fear no ill,
 With Thee, dear Lord, beside me ;
Thy rod and staff my comfort still
 Thy Cross before to guide me.

5 And so thro' all the length of days
 Thy goodness faileth never ;
Good Shepherd, may I sing Thy praise
 Within Thy house for ever.

395 I AM not skill'd to understand
 What God hath will'd, what God hath plann'd ;
I only know at His right hand
 Stands One who is my Saviour !

2 I take Him at His word indeed :
 " Christ died for sinners," this I read ;
For in my heart I find a need
 Of Him to be my Saviour !

3 That He should leave His place on high,
 And come for sinful man to die,
You count it strange ?—so once did I,
 Before I knew my Saviour !

4 And oh, that He fulfilled may see
 The travail of His soul in me,
And with His work contented be,
 As I with my dear Saviour !

5 Yea, living, dying, let me bring
 My strength, my solace from this spring,
That He who lives to be my King,
 Once died to be my Saviour !

396 I AM dwelling in the mountain
 Where the golden sunlight gleams,
O'er a land whose wondrous beauty
 Far exceeds my fondest dreams ;
Where the air is pure, ethereal,
 Laden with the breath of flow'rs,
That are blooming by the fountain,
 'Neath the never-fading bow'rs.

Is not this the land of Beulah ?
 Blessed, blessed land of light,
Where the flowers bloom for ever,
 And the sun is always bright.

2 I am drinking at the fountain,
 Where I ever would abide ;
For I've tasted life's pure river,
 And my soul is satisfied ;
There's no thirsting for life's pleasures,
 Nor adorning, rich and gay,
For I've found a richer treasure,
 One that fadeth not away.

3 Oh, the Cross has wondrous glory,
 Oft I've proved this to be true ;
When I'm in the way so narrow,
 I can see a pathway through,
And how sweetly Jesus whispers :
 Take the Cross, thou need'st not fear,
For I've tried the way before thee,
 And the glory lingers near.

397 MY times are in Thy hand ;
 My God, I wish them there ;
My life, my friends, my soul I leave
 Entirely to Thy care.

2 My times are in Thy hand,
 Whatever they may be,
Pleasing or painful, dark or bright,
 As best may seem to Thee.

3 My times are in Thy hand ;
 Why should I doubt or fear ?
My Father's hand will never cause
 His child a needless tear.

4 My times are in Thy hand ;
 Jesus, the Crucified !
Those hands my cruel sins had pierced
 Are now my guard and guide.

5 My times are in Thy hand ;
 I'll always trust in Thee ;
And, after death, at Thy right hand
 I shall for ever be.

398 THY way, not mine, O Lord,
 However dark it be ;
Oh, lead me by Thine own right hand,
 Choose Thou the path for me.

2 Smooth let it be or rough,
 It will be still the best ;
Winding or straight, it can but lead
 Right onward to Thy rest.

3 I dare not choose my lot ;
I would not if I might ;
But choose Thou for me, O my God,
So shall I walk aright.

4 Take Thou my cup, and it
With joy or sorrow fill,
As ever best to Thee may seem ;
Choose Thou my good or ill.

5 Choose Thou for me my friends,
My sickness or my health ;
Choose Thou my every care for me,
My poverty or wealth.

6 Not mine, not mine the choice,
In things or great or small ;
Be Thou to me my Guide, my
Strength,
My Wisdom, and my All.

399 I AM trusting Thee, Lord
Jesus,
Trusting only Thee !
Trusting Thee for full salvation,
Great and free.

2 I am trusting Thee for pardon,
At Thy feet I bow,
For Thy grace and tender mercy,
Trusting now.

3 I am trusting Thee for cleansing,
In the crimson flood ;
Trusting Thee to make me holy,
By Thy blood.

4 I am trusting Thee to guide me,
Thou alone shalt lead,
Ev'ry day and hour supplying
All my need.

5 I am trusting Thee for power,
Thine can never fail ; [give me,
Words which Thou Thyself shalt
Must prevail.

6 I am trusting Thee, Lord Jesus,
Never let me fall !
I am trusting Thee for ever,
And for all.

400 SING the wondrous love of
Jesus,
Sing His mercy and His grace ;
In the mansions, bright and blessed,
He'll prepare for us a place.....
When we all...get to heaven
What a day of rejoicing that will be !...
When we all...see Jesus,
We'll sing and shout the victory.....

2 While we walk the pilgrim pathway,
Clouds will overspread the sky ;
But when trav'lling days are over,
Not a shadow, not a sigh.....

3 Let us, then, be true and faithful,
Trusting, serving ev'ry day ;
Just one glimpse of Him in glory
Will the toils of life repay.....

4 Onward to the prize before us !
Soon His beauty we'll behold ;
Soon the pearly gates will open,
We shall tread the streets of gold...

401 DOES Jesus care when my
heart is pained,
Too deeply for mirth or song ;
As the burdens press,
And the cares distress,
And the way grows weary and
long ?
O, yes, He cares ; I know He cares ;
His heart is touched with my grief :
When the days are weary, the long nights
dreary,
I know my Saviour cares.....

2 Does Jesus care when my way is
dark
With a nameless dread and fear ?
As the daylight fades
Into the deep night shades,
Does He care enough to be near ?

3 Does Jesus care when I've tried and
failed,
To resist some temptation strong ;
When in my deep grief
I find no relief,
Tho' my tears flow all the night
long ?

4 Does Jesus care when I've said
" good-bye,"
To the dearest on earth to me,
And my sad heart aches
Till it nearly breaks—
Is this aught to Him ? Does He
see ?

402 I KNOW not what awaits me,
God kindly veils mine eyes ;
And o'er each step of my onward
way
He makes new scenes to rise ;
And ev'ry joy He sends me, comes
A sweet and glad surprise.

Where He may lead I'll follow,
  My trust in Him repose;
And ev'ry hour in perfect peace
  I'll sing, He knows, He knows.

2 One step I see before me,
    'Tis all I need to see,   [shines
  The light of heaven more brightly
    When earth's illusions flee;
  And sweetly through the silence
      came
    His loving, " Follow Me."

3 O blissful lack of wisdom,
    'Tis blessed not to know;
  He holds me with His own right hand
    And will not let me go;
  And lulls my troubled soul to rest
    In Him who loves me so.

4 So on I go not knowing,
    I would not if I might;
  I'd rather walk in the dark with God
    Than go alone in the light;
  I'd rather walk by faith with Him,
    Than go alone by sight.

403   LOVED! then the way will
      not be drear;
  For One we know is ever near,
  Proving it to our hearts so clear
      That we are loved.

2 Loved with an everlasting love
  By Him who left His home above,
  To bring us life, and light, and love,
      Because He loved.

3 Loved when our sky is clouded o'er,
  And days of sorrow press us sore;
  Still will we trust Him evermore,
      For we are loved.

4 Loved, when we leave our native
      soil,
  In heathen lands to live and toil;
  Under His shadow nought can foil—
      Still we are loved.

5 Time, that affects all things below,
  Can never change the love He'll
      show;   [flow,
  The heart of Christ with love will
      And we are loved.

6 Loved in the past of yesterday,
  And all along our future way,
  And in the present of to-day—
      For ever loved.

7 Loved when we sing the glad new
      song
  To Christ, for whom we've waited
      long,   [throng—
  With all the happy, ransomed
      And ever loved.

404   UPON the western plain
      There comes the signal strain,
  'Tis loyalty, loyalty, loyalty to Christ;
    Its music rolls along,
    The hills take up the song,
  Of loyalty, loyalty, yes, loyalty to
      Christ.

" On to victory! on to victory! "
  Cries our great Commander: " On!..."
We'll move at His command, we'll soon possess
      the land,
  Thro' loyalty, loyalty, yes, loyalty to Christ.

2 O hear, ye brave, the sound
    That moves the earth around,
  'Tis loyalty, loyalty, loyalty to Christ;
    Arise to dare and do,
    Ring out the watchword true,
  Of loyalty, loyalty, yes, loyalty to
      Christ.

3 Come, join our loyal throng,
    We'll rout the giant wrong,
  'Tis loyalty, loyalty, loyalty to Christ;
    Where Satan's banners float,
    We'll send the bugle note,
  Of loyalty, loyalty, yes, loyalty to
      Christ.

4 The strength of youth we lay
    At Jesus' feet to-day,
  'Tis loyalty, loyalty, loyalty to Christ;
    His Gospel we'll proclaim,
    Throughout the world's domain,
  Of loyalty, loyalty, yes, loyalty to
      Christ.

405   I AM thinking to-day of that
      beautiful land
    I shall reach when the sun goeth
      down;
  When thro' wonderful grace by my
      Saviour I stand,
    Will there be any stars in my
      crown?

Will there be any stars, any stars in my crown,
When at evening the sun goeth down?
When I wake with the blest in the mansions
    of rest,
Will there be any stars in my crown?

2 In the strength of the Lord let me
labour and pray,
  Let me watch as a winner of souls ;
That bright stars may be mine in
the glorious day,
  When His praise like the sea-
billow rolls.

3 Oh, what joy will it be when His
face I behold,
  Living gems at His feet to lay
down ;
It would sweeten my bliss in the city
of gold,
  Should there be any stars in my
crown.

406 WE would see Jesus—for the
     shadows lengthen
  Across this little landscape of
our life ;
We would see Jesus, our weak faith
to strengthen,
  For the last weariness—the final
strife.

2 We would see Jesus—the great Rock
Foundation,
  Whereon our feet were set with
sovereign grace ;
Not life, not death, with all their
agitation,
  Can thence remove us, if we see
His face.

3 We would see Jesus—other lights
are paling,
  Which for long years we have
rejoiced to see ;
The blessings of our pilgrimage are
failing,
  We would not mourn them, for
we go to Thee.

4 We would see Jesus—this is all we're
needing,
  Strength, joy, and willingness
come with the sight ;
We would see Jesus, dying, risen,
pleading,
  Then welcome day, and farewell
mortal night !

407 SAVIOUR, more than life to
     me,
I am clinging, clinging, close to Thee ;
Let Thy precious blood applied,
Keep me ever, ever near Thy side.

  Ev'ry day,...ev'ry hour,...
  Let me feel Thy cleansing power ;
  May Thy tender love to me
  Bind me closer, closer, Lord, to Thee.

2 Through this changing world below
Lead me gently, gently as I go ;
Trusting Thee I cannot stray,
I can never, never lose my way.

3 Let me love Thee more and more,
Till this fleeting, fleeting life is o'er ;
Till my soul is lost in love,
In a fairer, brighter world above.

408 MY happy soul rejoices,
     The sky is bright above ;
I'll join the heav'nly voices,
  And sing redeeming love.

  For there's pow'r in Jesus' blood,
  Pow'r in Jesus' blood ;
  There's pow'r in Jesus' blood
  To wash me white as snow.

2 I heard the blessed story
  Of Him who died to save ;
The love of Christ swept o'er me,
  My all to Him I gave.

3 His gracious words of pardon
  Were music to my heart ;
He took away my burden,
  And bade my fears depart.

4 I plunged beneath this fountain,
  That cleanseth white as snow ;
It pours from Calv'ry's mountain,
  With blessings in its flow.

5 Oh, crown Him King for ever !
  My Saviour and my Friend ;
By Zion's crystal river
  His praise shall never end.

409 AS the shadows of the night
     round are falling,
  I am thinking of that day by and
by ;
When the trumpet of the Lord shall
be calling,
  As the day breaks o'er the hills.

I'll go singing, I'll go shouting on my journey
home,
  Till the day breaks, till the day breaks,
There'll be singing, there'll be shouting, when
we all get home,
  When the day breaks o'er the hills....

2 When we gather home at last there'll
be singing,
  Such as angels round the throne
never heard ;

For the song of souls redeemed shall
 go ringing,
  As the day breaks o'er the hills.

3 I shall rise to be with Jesus for ever,
  I shall meet the ones who passed
   on before ;
 We shall meet to part no more,
  never, never,
   When the day breaks o'er the hills.

410 IN the harvest field there is
   work to do,
For the grain is ripe, and the
  reapers few ;
And the Master's voice bids the
  workers true
  Heed the call that He gives to-day.

Labour on !...labour on !...
Keep the bright reward in view ;
For the Master has said, He will strength renew;
Labour on till the close of the day !

2 Crowd the garner well with its
  sheaves all bright,
Let the song be glad, and the heart
  be light ;
Fill the precious hours, ere the
  shades of night
  Take the place of the golden day.

3 In the gleaner's path may be rich
  reward,
Tho' the time seems long, and the
  labour hard ;
For the Master's joy, with His chosen
  shared,
 Drives the gloom from the darkest
  day.

4 Lo ! the harvest home in the realms
  above
Shall be gained by each who has
  toil'd and strove,
When the Master's voice, in its
  tones of love,
  Calls away to eternal day.

411 THE sands of time are sinking,
   The dawn of heaven breaks ;
The summer morn I've sighed for,
  The fair sweet morn awakes ;
Dark, dark hath been the midnight,
  But dayspring is at hand,
And glory, glory dwelleth
  In Immanuel's land.

2 O Christ He is the fountain,
  The deep, sweet well of love ;
The streams on earth I've tasted,
  More deep I'll drink above ;
There to an ocean fulness
  His mercy doth expand,
And glory, glory dwelleth
  In Immanuel's land.

3 With mercy and with judgment,
  My web of time He wove,
And aye the dews of sorrow
  Were lustred by His love ;
I'll bless the hand that guided,
  I'll bless the heart that planned,
When throned where glory dwelleth
  In Immanuel's land.

4 The bride eyes not her garment,
  But her dear bridegroom's face ;
I will not gaze at glory,
  But on my King of grace ;
Not at the crown He gifteth,
  But on His pierced hand ;
The Lamb is all the glory
  Of Immanuel's land.

5 I've wrestled on towards heaven,
  'Gainst storm, and wind, and tide ;
Now like a weary traveller
  That leaneth on his guide.
Amid the shades of ev'ning,
  While sinks life's ling'ring sand,
I hail the glory dawning
  In Immanuel's land.

412 ONCE I thought I walk'd with
   Jesus,
  Yet such changeful moods I had ;
Sometimes trusting, sometimes
  doubting,
  Sometimes joyful, sometimes sad.
Oh, the peace my Saviour gives,
Peace I never knew before ;
For my way has brighter grown,
Since I learn'd to trust Him more.

2 For He called me closer to Him,
  Bade my doubting tremors cease ;
And when I had fully trusted,
  Filled my soul with perfect peace.

3 Now I'm trusting ev'ry moment,
  Less than this is not enough ;
And my Saviour bears me gently
  O'er the places once so rough.

4 Blessed Saviour, Thou dost keep me
  By Thy pow'r from day to day,
And my heart is full of gladness,
  For Thou'lt keep me all the way.

413 WHEN peace, like a river,
    attendeth my way,
When sorrows, like sea-billows,
    roll ;
Whatever my lot, Thou hast taught
    me to know,
"It is well, it is well with my
    soul."

It is well...with my soul,...
It is well, it is well with my soul.

2 If Satan should buffet, if trials
    should come,
Let this blest assurance control,
That Christ hath regarded my help-
    less estate,
And hath shed His own blood for
    my soul.

3 My sin—oh, the bliss of this glorious
    thought—
My sin—not in part, but the whole,
Is nail'd to His Cross, and I bear it
    no more ;
Praise the Lord, praise the Lord,
    O my soul !

4 For me, be it Christ, be it Christ
    hence to live !
If Jordan above me shall roll,
No pang shall be mine, for in death
    as in life,
Thou wilt whisper Thy peace to
    my soul.

5 But Lord, 'tis for Thee, for Thy
    coming we wait,
The sky, not the grave, is our goal ;
Oh, trump of the angel ! oh, voice
    of the Lord !
Blessed Hope ! blessed rest of my
    soul !

414 DO you fear the foe will in the
    conflict win ?
Is it dark without you, darker still
    within ?
Clear the darkened windows, open
    wide the door,
Let a little sunshine in.

Let the blessed sunshine in,...
Let the blessed sunshine in ;...
Clear the darkened windows, open wide the
    door,
Let a little sunshine in.

2 Does your faith grow fainter in the
    cause you love ?
Are your prayers unanswered by
    your God above ?

Clear the darkened windows, open
    wide the door,
Let a little sunshine in.

3 Would you go rejoicing on the up-
    ward way,
Knowing naught of darkness, dwell-
    ing in the day ?
Clear the darkened windows, open
    wide the door,
Let a little sunshine in.

415 THE dear loving Saviour hath
    found me,
And shattered the fetters that bound
    me,
Tho' all was confusion around me,
    He came and spake peace to my
    soul ;
The blessed Redeemer that bought
    me,
In tenderness constantly sought me,
The way of salvation He taught me,
    And made my heart perfectly
    whole.

He saves me, He saves me,
His love fills my soul, hallelujah !
Oh, glory, oh, glory,
His Spirit abideth within ;
He saves me, He saves me,
His love fills my soul, hallelujah !
Oh, glory, oh, glory,
His blood cleanseth me from all sin.

2 He sought me so long ere I knew
    Him,
But finally winning me to Him,
I yielded my all to pursue Him,
    And asked to be filled with His
    grace ;
Although a vile sinner before Him,
Through faith I was led to implore
    Him,
And now I rejoice and adore Him,
    Restored to His loving embrace.

3 I never, no never will leave Him,
Grow weary of service, and grieve
    Him,
I'll constantly trust and believe Him,
    Remain in His presence divine ;
Abiding in love ever flowing,
In knowledge and grace ever
    growing,
Confiding implicitly, knowing
    That Jesus the Saviour is mine.

416 LEAD, kindly Light, amid
th' encircling gloom,
    Lead Thou me on ;
The night is dark, and I am far from
home ;
    Lead Thou me on ;
Keep Thou my feet ; I do not ask
to see   [for me.
The distant scene—one step enough

2 I was not ever thus, nor prayed
that Thou
    Shouldst lead me on ;
I loved to choose and see my path ;
but now
    Lead Thou me on ;
I loved the garish day, and spite of
fears,
Pride ruled my will : remember not
past years !

3 So long Thy power hath blessed
me, sure it still
    Will lead me on,
O'er moor and fen, o'er crag and
torrent, till
    The night is gone :
And with the morn those angel-
faces smile,
Which I have loved long since, and
lost awhile.

417 BLESSED assurance, Jesus is
mine,
Oh, what a foretaste of glory divine !
Heir of salvation, purchase of God,
Born of His Spirit, washed in His
blood.
    This is my story, this is my song,
    Praising my Saviour all the day long ;
    This is my story, this is my song,
    Praising my Saviour all the day long.

2 Perfect submission, perfect delight,
Visions of rapture now burst on my
sight ;
Angels descending, bring from above
Echoes of mercy, whispers of love.

3 Perfect submission, all is at rest,
I in my Saviour am happy and blest ;
Watching and waiting, looking above,
Fill'd with His goodness, lost in
His love.

418   LIKE a river glorious
       Is God's perfect peace,
    Over all victorious
       In its bright increase ;

Perfect, yet it floweth
    Fuller every day ;
Perfect, yet it groweth
    Deeper all the way.
    Stayed upon Jehovah,
       Hearts are fully blest ;
    Finding, as He promis'd,
       Perfect peace and rest.

2 Hidden in the hollow
    Of His blessed hand,
Never foe can follow
    Never traitor stand ;
Not a surge of worry,
    Not a shade of care,
Not a blast of hurry
    Touch the spirit there.

3 Ev'ry joy or trial
    Falleth from above,
Traced upon our dial
    By the Son of Love.
We may trust Him fully
    All for us to do,
They who trust Him wholly,
    Find Him wholly true.

419 ELIJAH made a sacrifice
    To offer to Jehovah ;
It had been wet with water thrice,
    Baal's sacrifice was over.
Elijah pray'd : the fire came down
And licked the water all around ;
So doubting ones believed, and found
    Elijah's God was living.
    Elijah's God still lives to-day,
    To take the guilt of sin away ;
    And when I pray my heart's desire,
    Upon my soul He sends the fire.

2 Elijah's God still lives to-day,
    And answers still by fire ;
My friend, just let Him have His way
    He'll grant your heart's desire.
Consume the sacrifice you make,
And bid your slumb'ring soul awake;
The chain of in-bred sin will break ;
    Elijah's God is living.

3 Elijah's God still lives to-day,
    And answers still in power,
As when Elijah pray'd for rain,
    God answered with a shower.
If you would have your soul
refreshed,
With rain that falls from heaven,
You must " pray through " like all
the rest,
    And showers shall be given.

420 MY hope is built on nothing less
Than Jesus' blood and righteousness;
I dare not trust the sweetest frame,
But wholly lean on Jesus' Name.

On Christ, the solid Rock, I stand;
All other ground is sinking sand,
All other ground is sinking sand.

2 When darkness seems to veil His face,
I rest on His unchanging grace;
In ev'ry high and stormy gale,
My anchor holds within the veil.

3 His oath, His covenant and blood,
Support me in the 'whelming flood;
When all around my soul gives way,
He then is all my hope and stay.

421 FACE to face with Christ, my Saviour,
Face to face—what will it be?
When with rapture I behold Him,
Jesus Christ, who died for me.

Face to face shall I behold Him,
Far beyond the starry sky;
Face to face in all His glory,
I shall see Him by and by!

2 Only faintly now I see Him,
With the darkling veil between,
But a blessed day is coming,
When His glory shall be seen.

3 What rejoicing in His presence,
When are banished grief and pain;
When the crooked ways are straightened,
And the dark things shall be plain.

4 Face to face! O! blissful moment!
Face to face—to see and know;
Face to face with my Redeemer,
Jesus Christ, who loves me so.

422 IN the good old way where the saints have gone,
And the King leads on before us,
We are travelling home to the heavenly hills,
With the day-star shining o'er us.

Travelling home to the mansions fair,
Crowns of rejoicing and life to wear;
O what a shout when we all get there,
Safe in the glory land!

2 In the good old way, like the ransomed throng,
Unto Zion now returning,
We are travelling home at the King's command,
And our lamps are trimmed and burning.

3 In the good old way, with a steadfast faith,
In the bonds of love and union;
What a joy is ours! for the King we see,
And with Him we hold communion.

4 Tho' our feet must stand on the cold, cold brink
Of the Jordan's stormy river,
With the King we'll cross to the other side,
And we'll sing His praise for ever.

423 ANYWHERE with Jesus I can safely go,
Anywhere He leads me in this world below,
Anywhere without Him dearest joys would fade,
Anywhere with Jesus I am not afraid.

Anywhere! anywhere!
Fear I cannot know.
Anywhere with Jesus
I can safely go.

2 Anywhere with Jesus I am not alone,
Other friends may fail me, He is still my own;
Though His hand may lead me over drearest ways,
Anywhere with Jesus is a house of praise.

3 Anywhere with Jesus I can go to sleep,
When the darkling shadows round about me creep;
Knowing I shall waken never more to roam,
Anywhere with Jesus will be home, sweet home.

424 THE cross that He gave may be heavy,
But it ne'er outweights His grace;
The storm that I feared may surround me,
But it ne'er excludes His face.

The cross is not greater than His grace,...
The storm cannot hide His blessed face ;...
I am satisfied to know that with Jesus here
  I can conquer ev'ry foe.   [below,

2 The thorns in my path are not
    sharper
  Than composed His crown for me ;
  The cup that I drink not more bitter
  Than He drank in Gethsemane.

3 The light of His love shineth
    brighter,
  As it falls on paths of woe ;
  The toil of my work groweth lighter
  As I stoop to raise the low.

4 His will I have joy in fulfilling,
  As I'm walking in His sight ;
  My all to the blood I am bringing,
  It alone can keep me right.

425 WHEN the storms of life are
    raging,
  Tempests wild on sea and land,
I will seek a place of refuge
  In the shadow of God's hand.

He will hide..me,..He will hide..me,..
Where no harm..can e'er betide me ;
He will hide..me,..safely hide..me
In the sha - - dow of His hand.

2 Though He may send some affliction,
  'Twill but make me long for
    home ;
  For in love and not in anger,
  All His chastenings will come.

3 Enemies may strive to injure,
  Satan all his arts employ ;
  He will turn what seems to harm me
  Into everlasting joy.

4 So, while here the cross I'm bearing,
  Meeting storms and billows wild,
  Jesus for my soul is caring,
  Naught can harm His Father's
    child.

426 'TIS so sweet to trust in Jesus,
    Just to take Him at His
    Word ;
Just to rest upon His promise,
  Just to know, " Thus saith the
    Lord."

Jesus, Jesus, how I trust Him !
  How I've prov'd Him o'er and o'er !
Jesus, Jesus, precious Jesus !
  Oh, for grace to trust Him more.

2 Oh, how sweet to trust in Jesus,
    Just to trust His cleansing blood ;
Just in simple faith to plunge me
  'Neath the healing, cleansing flood.

3 Yes, 'tis sweet to trust in Jesus,
    Just from sin and self to cease ;
Just from Jesus simply taking
  Life and rest, and joy and peace.

4 I'm so glad I learned to trust Thee,
    Precious Jesus, Saviour, Friend ;
And I know that Thou art with me,
  Wilt be with me to the end.

427 TRUSTING in Jesus, my
    Saviour divine,
  I have the witness that still He is
    mine ;
  Great are the blessings He giveth
    to me,
  Oh, I am happy as mortal can be.

I am redeemed,..and I know it full well,..
Saved by His grace,..I with Him shall dwell ;..
I am redeemed,..and the child of His love,..
Heir to a glo - - rious crown above...

2 Once I was far from my Saviour and
    King,
  Now He has taught me His mercy
    to sing ;
  Peace in believing He giveth to me ;
  Oh, I am happy as mortal can be.

3 Trusting in Jesus, oh, what should
    I fear ?
  Nothing can harm me when He is
    so near ;
  Sweet is the promise He giveth to
    me ;
  Oh, I am happy as mortal can be.

4 If while a stranger I journey below,
    Fill'd with His fulness such rapture
    I know,
  What will the bliss of eternity be,
  When in His beauty the King I
    shall see ?

428 JESUS, lover of my soul,
    Let me to Thy bosom fly,
While the nearer waters roll,
  While the tempest still is high ;
Hide me, O my Saviour, hide,
  Till the storm of life is past ;
Safe into the haven guide ;
  Oh, receive my soul at last.

2 Other refuge have I none ;
　Hangs my helpless soul on Thee ;
Leave, ah ! leave me not alone,
　Still support and comfort me.
All my trust on Thee is stay'd,
　All my help from Thee I bring ;
Cover my defenceless head
　With the shadow of Thy wing.

3 Thou, O Christ ! art all I want ;
　More than all in Thee I find ;
Raise the fallen, cheer the faint,
　Heal the sick, and lead the blind.
Just and holy is Thy name,
　I am all unrighteousness ;
Vile and full of sin I am,
　Thou art full of truth and grace.

4 Plenteous grace with Thee is found,
　Grace to cover all my sin ;
Let the healing streams abound,
　Make and keep me pure within ;
Thou of life the fountain art,
　Freely let me take of Thee ;
Spring Thou up within my heart,
　Rise to all eternity.

429 WORK, for the night is
　　　coming !
Work thro' the morning hours ;
Work while the dew is sparkling ;
　Work 'mid springing flowers ;
Work while the day grows brighter,
　Under the glowing sun ;
Work, for the night is coming,
　When man's work is done.

2 Work, for the night is coming !
　Work through the sunny noon ;
Fill the bright hours with labour,
　Rest comes sure and soon.
Give to each flying minute
　Something to keep in store ;
Work, for the night is coming,
　When man works no more.

3 Work, for the night is coming !
　Under the sunset skies ;
While their bright tints are glowing,
　Work, for daylight flies.
Work till the last beam fadeth,
　Fadeth to shine no more ;
Work, while the night is dark'ning,
　When man's work is o'er.

430 JESUS, and shall it ever be,
　　　A mortal man asham'd of Thee ?

Asham'd of Thee, whom angels
　praise !
Whose glories shine thro' endless
　days !

2 Asham'd of Jesus ! sooner far
Let evening blush to own a star ;
He sheds the beams of light divine
O'er this benighted soul of mine.

3 Asham'd of Jesus ! just as soon
Let midnight be asham'd of noon ;
'Twas midnight with my soul, till He,
Bright Morning Star, bade darkness
　flee.

4 Asham'd of Jesus ! that dear Friend
On whom my hopes of heaven
　depend !
No ! when I blush, be this my shame,
That I no more revere His name.

431 SOLDIERS of Jesus ! soldiers
　　　of the Cross !
Follow your Captain, counting all
　but loss ;
If you fight the battle, you shall gain
　renown ;
And if you are faithful you shall
　wear a crown.

March on ! March on ! soldiers of Immanuel ;
　March on ! March on ! singing as we go ;
Glory ! glory to the Lamb of Calvary !
　In His might we conquer ev'ry foe.

2 Soldiers of Jesus ! gird ye to the
　fray ; 　　　　　　　[day !
Stand in your armour, in this evil
Where the battle rages, there may
　ye be found,
Where the need is greatest, that is
　holy ground.

3 Soldiers of Jesus ! lift your standard
　high ! 　　　　　　　[to die,"
Write on your banners, " Jesus came
By the Cross of Jesus we the vict'ry
　win, 　　　　　　　[all sin.
For the blood of Jesus cleanseth from

4 Soldiers of Jesus ! when the battle's
　done,
Foes all are vanquished, and the
　vict'ry won ;
Then with shouts of triumph we
　shall hail the King,
When the vaults of heaven with His
　praises ring.

5 Soldiers of Jesus ! of the Lamb once
    slain,   [to reign ;
    Know ye that Jesus soon will come
    Lift your heads in gladness, victory
      is nigh !
    Send a shout of welcome thro' the
      earth and sky.

Come, Lord Jesus ! come and take Thy people
    home !
    Come, oh come ! we long Thy face to see !
Come, Lord Jesus, claim the kingdom and the
    pow'r ;
    Set the earth from all its bondage free.

432   MORE about Jesus would I
           know,
    More of His grace to others show ;
    More of His saving fulness see,
    More of His love, who died for me.

      More, more about Jesus,
      More, more about Jesus ;
      More of His saving fulness see,
      More of His love who died for me.

2 More about Jesus let me learn,
    More of His holy will discern ;
    Spirit of God, my teacher be,
    Showing the things of Christ to me.

3 More about Jesus, in His Word,
    Holding communion with my Lord ;
    Hearing His voice in ev'ry line,
    Making each faithful saying mine.

4 More about Jesus, on His throne,
    Riches in glory all His own ;
    More of His Kingdom's sure increase,
    More of His coming, Prince of Peace.

433   MY heart is resting, O my God,
           I will give thanks and sing ;
    My heart is at the secret source
    Of ev'ry precious thing.

2 Now the frail vessel Thou hast made,
    No hand but Thine shall fill ;
    For the waters of this world have
      failed,
    And I am thirsty still.

3 I thirst for springs of heav'nly life,
    And here all day they rise ;
    I seek the treasure of Thy love,
    And close at hand it lies.

4 And a new song is in my mouth,
    To long loved music set—
    Glory to Thee for all Thy grace
    I have not tasted yet.

5 " Thou art my portion," saith my
    Ten thousand voices say,   [soul,
    And the music of their glad Amen
    Will never die away.

434   SOMETIME we'll stand before
           the judgment bar,
    The quick, the risen dead ;
    The Lord will then make known the
      record there ;
    Our names will all be read.

I'll be present when the roll is called,
    Pure and spotless thro' the crimson flood ;
I will answer when they call my name ;
    Sav'd thro' Jesus' blood.

2 I'll then receive a bright and starry
    As only God can give ;   [crown,
    And when I've been with Him ten
      thousand years,
    I'll have no less to live.

3 Then we shall meet to never part
      again,
    Our toil will then be o'er ;
    We'll lay our burdens down at Jesus'
    And rest for evermore.   [feet,

435   RESCUE the perishing,
           Care for the dying,
Snatch them in pity from sin and the
    Weep o'er the erring ones,   [grave ;
    Lift up the fallen,
Tell them of Jesus, the mighty to save.

Rescue the perishing, care for the dying ;
Jesus is merciful, Jesus will save.

2 Tho' they are slighting Him,
    Still He is waiting,
Waiting the penitent child to receive ;
    Plead with them earnestly,
    Plead with them gently,
He will forgive if they only believe.

3 Down in the human heart,
    Crush'd by the tempter,   [restore ;
Feelings lie buried that grace can
    Touched by a loving heart,
    Wakened by kindness,
Cords that were broken will vibrate
    once more.

4 Rescue the perishing,
    Duty demands it ;
Strength for Thy labour the Lord will
    Back to the narrow way,   [provide.
    Patiently win them ;   [died.
Tell the poor wand'rer a Saviour has

436 BEHOLD, what love, what
boundless love,
The Father hath bestowed
On sinners lost, that we should be
Now called the sons of God !

Behold, what manner of love !...
What manner of love the Father hath
bestowed upon us,
That we, that we should be call'd,...
Should be call'd the sons of God.

2 No longer far from Him, but now
By " precious blood " made nigh ;
Accepted in the " well-beloved,"
Near to God's heart we lie.

3 What we in glory soon shall be,
" It doth not yet appear ; "
But when our precious Lord we see,
We shall His image bear.

4 With such a blessed hope in view,
We would more holy be ;
More like our risen, glorious Lord,
Whose face we soon shall see.

437 PEACE, perfect peace, in this
dark world of sin ?
The blood of Jesus whispers peace
within.

2 Peace, perfect peace, by thronging
duties pressed ?
To do the will of Jesus, this is rest.

3 Peace, perfect peace, with sorrows
surging round ?
On Jesus' bosom naught but calm
is found.

4 Peace, perfect peace, with loved
ones far away ?
In Jesus' keeping we are safe and
they.

5 Peace, perfect peace, our future all
unknown ?
Jesus we know, and He is on the
throne.

6 Peace, perfect peace, death shadow-
ing us and ours ?
Jesus has vanquished death and all
its powers.

7 It is enough ; earth's struggles soon
shall cease,
And Jesus call us to Heaven's perfect
peace.

438 I'VE seen the face of Jesus—
He smiled in love on me ;
It filled my heart with rapture,
My soul with ecstasy.
The scars of deepest anguish
Were lost in glory bright ;
I've seen the face of Jesus—
It was a wondrous sight !

Oh ! glorious face of beauty,
Oh ! gentle touch of care ;
If here it is so blessed,
What will it be up there ?

2 And since I've seen His beauty,
All else I count. but loss ;
The world, its fame and pleasure,
Is now to me but dross.
His light dispelled my darkness,
His smile was, oh, so sweet !
I've seen the face of Jesus—
I can but kiss His feet.

3 I've heard the voice of Jesus—
He told me of His love,
And called me His own treasure,
His undefiled, His dove.
It came like softest music
Across an ocean calm,
And seemed to play so sweetly
Some wondrous holy psalm.

4 I felt the hand of Jesus—
My brow it throbbed with care ;
He placed it there so softly,
And whispered, " Do not fear."
Like clouds before the sunshine,
My cares have rolled away ;
I'm sitting in His presence—
It is a cloudless day.

5 I know He's coming shortly
To take us all above ;
We'll sing redemption's story,
The story of His love ;
We ll hear His voice and music,
We'll feel His hand of care ;
He'll never rest—He says so—
Until He has us there.

439 MY Jesus, I love Thee, I know
Thou art mine,
For Thee all the pleasures of sin I
resign ;
My gracious Redeemer, my Saviour
art Thou,
If ever I loved Thee, my Jesus, 'tis
now.

2 I love Thee because Thou hast first
   loved me,
And purchased my pardon when
   nailed to the tree ;
I love Thee for wearing the thorns
   on Thy brow,   [now.
If ever I loved Thee, my Jesus, 'tis

3 I will love Thee in life, I will love
   Thee in death,
And praise Thee as long as Thou
   lendest me breath ;
And say, when the death-dew lies
   cold on my brow,   [now.
If ever I loved Thee, my Jesus, 'tis

440 OH, I love to read of Jesus
          and His love,
How He left His Father's mansion
   far above ;
How He came on earth to live,
How He came His life to give ;
Oh, I love to read of Jesus and His
   love !
" It's just like Him " to take my sins away,
To make me glad and free, to keep me day
   by day ;
" It's just like Him " to give His life for me,
That I might go to heaven, and ever with
   Him be.

2 Oh, I love to read of Jesus as He
   went   [intent ;
Ev'rywhere, to do His Father's will
How He gave the blind their sight,
How He gave the wrong'd ones
   right,
How He swift deliv'rance to the
   captive sent !

3 Oh, I love to read of Jesus on the
   tree,
For it shows how great the love that
   died for me ;
And the blood that from His side
Flow'd, when on the Cross He
   died,
Paid my debt, and evermore doth
   make me free.

4 Oh, my dear and precious Saviour,
   at Thy feet,
Here I give myself and all I have
   complete ;
I will serve Thee all my days
With a heart all fill'd with praise,
And I'll thank Thee face to face
   when we shall meet !

441 'TIS the old time religion,
   'Tis the old time religion,
   'Tis the old time religion,
     It's good enough for me.
'Tis the old time religion,
'Tis the old time religion,
'Tis the old time religion,
It's good enough for me.

2 It was good for our mothers,
   It's good enough for me.

3 Makes me love ev'rybody,
   It's good enough for me.

4 It has saved our fathers,
   It's good enough for me.

5 It was good for the Prophet Daniel,
   It's good enough for me.

6 It was good for the Hebrew children,
   It's good enough for me.

7 It was tried in the fiery furnace,
   It's good enough for me.

8 It was good for Paul and Silas,
   It's good enough for me.

9 It will do when I am dying,
   It's good enough for me.

10 It will take us all to heaven,
   It's good enough for me.

442 HAVE you ever heard the
          story
Of the Babe of Bethlehem,
Who was worshipp'd by the angels
   And the wise and holy men ;
How He taught the learned doctors
   In the temple far away ?
Oh, I'm glad, so glad to tell you,
   He is just the same to-day.
He is just....the same to-day,....
He is just....the same to-day,....
Seeking those who are astray,
Saving souls along the way ;
Thank God, He is just the same to-day.

2 Have you ever heard the story,
   How He walked upon the sea,
To His dear disciples tossing
   On the waves of Galilee ;
How the waves in angry motion
   Quickly would His will obey ?
Oh, I'm glad, so glad to tell you,
   He is just the same to-day.

3 Have you ever heard of Jesus
   Praying in Gethsemane,
And the ever-thrilling story
   How He died upon the tree ;

Cruel thorns His forehead piercing,
As His spirit passed away ?
This He did for you, my brother,
And He's just the same to-day.

443 HAVE you on the Lord be-
lieved ?
Still there's more to follow ;
Of His grace have you received ?
Still there's more to follow ;
Oh, the grace the Father shows !
Still there's more to follow !
Freely He His grace bestows,
Still there's more to follow !

More and more, more and more,
Always more to follow !
Oh, His matchless, boundless love !
Still there's more to follow !

2 Have you felt the Saviour near ?
Still there's more to follow ;
Does His blessed presence cheer ?
Still there's more to follow ;
Oh, the love that Jesus shows !
Still there's more to follow !
Freely He His love bestows !
Still there's more to follow !

3 Have you felt the Spirit's power ?
Still there's more to follow ;
Falling like the gentle shower ?
Still there's more to follow ;
Oh, the power the Spirit shows !
Still there's more to follow !
Freely He His power bestows !
Still there's more to follow !

444 THERE are songs of joy that
I love to sing,
When my heart was blithe as a bird
in spring ;
But the song I have learn'd is so
full of cheer,   [darkness drear.
That the dawn shines out in the

O, the new,...new song !...O, the new,... new
song !...
I can sing...it now...with the ran - - som'd
throng ;
Power and dominion to Him that shall reign,...
Glory and praise to the Lamb that was slain.

2 There are strains of home that are
dear as life,
And I list to them oft 'mid the din
of strife ;
But I know of a home that is wondrous fair,   [singing there.
And I sing the psalms they are

3 Can my lips be mute, or my heart
be sad,
When the gracious Master hath made
me glad ?
When He points where the many
mansions be,
And sweetly says, " There is one for
thee ? "

4 I shall catch the gleam of its jasper
wall,
When I come to the gloom of the
even-fall ;
For I know that the shadows, dreary
and dim,
Have a path of light that will lead
to Him.

445 ALL the way my Saviour leads
me :
What have I to ask beside ?
Can I doubt His tender mercy,
Who through life has been my
Guide ?

2 Heav'nly peace, divinest comfort,
Here by faith in Him to dwell !
For I know, whate'er befall me,
Jesus doeth all things well.

3 All the way my Saviour leads me :
Cheers each winding path I tread ;
Gives me grace for ev'ry trial,
Feeds me with the living bread.

4 Tho' my weary steps may falter,
And my soul athirst may be,
Gushing from the rock before me,
Lo ! a spring of joy I see.

5 All the way my Saviour leads me ;
Oh, the fulness of His love !
Perfect rest to me is promis'd,
In my Father's house above.

6 When my spirit, cloth'd immortal,
Wings its flight to realms of day,
This my song through endless ages—
Jesus led me all the way.

446 ON for Jesus ! steady be your
arm and brave ;
Onward, onward ; take the shield
and sword ;
On for Jesus ! standard of your
Captain wave,
Pressing onward, trusting in His
Word.

Marching, marching on,...
We're marching onward still for Jesus ;
Marching, marching on ...
Beneath the banner of the free ;
" On for Jesus ! " this shall be the battle-cry,
Ne'er retreating, ever pressing on ;
On for Jesus ! marching on to victory,
As we shout the glad redemption song.

2 On for Jesus ! tiresome tho' the
    conflict be,
    Tho' the hosts of sin are pressing
      hard ;
    On for Jesus ! striving for the
      victory,
    Endless life will soon be your
      reward.

3 On for Jesus ! till the sound of
    strife is o'er !
    When the great Commander calls
      for thee,
    Thou shalt wear a crown of life for
      evermore,
    And with Jesus reign eternally.

447 I HAVE a Friend, and He
    came to seek me,
    I was afar on the ocean wave ;
    Into the fold of His love He brought
      me ;
    Peace to my soul from that hour
      He gave.

Glory, glory, Jesus is my Saviour,
I will sing and praise Him in the glad, new song ;
Glory, glory, I will give Him glory,
When mine eyes behold Him, in the blood-
    wash'd throng.

2 O how my heart with its joy is
    bounding,   [He ;
    O what a Saviour and Friend is
    Full of compassion and rich in
      blessing,
    O how He loves and cares for me.

3 I have a Friend that will ne'er
    forsake me,   [pow'r ;
    1 shall be kept by His mighty
    Safe in the arms of His love that
      folds me,   [hour.
    Moment by moment and hour by

4 I have a hope that is sure and stead-
    fast—   [I stand ;
    Firm as the rock where by faith
    I have the pledge of a rest eternal,
    Waiting for me in the soul's bright
      land.

448 ABIDING, oh, so wondrous
    sweet !
    I'm resting at the Saviour's feet ;
    I trust in Him—I'm satisfied,
    I'm resting on the Crucified !

Abid - - ing, abid - - ing,
    Oh ! so wondrous sweet !...
I'm rest - - ing, rest - - ing
    At the Saviour's feet....

2 He speaks, and by His word is giv'n
    His peace, a rich fortaste of heav'n !
    Not as the world He peace doth give,
    'Tis thro' this hope my soul shall
      live.

3 I live ; not I ; through Him alone
    By whom the mighty work is done ;
    Dead to myself, alive to Him,
    I count all lost His rest to gain.

4 Now rest, my heart, the work is done,
    I'm saved thro' the Eternal Son !
    Let all pow'rs my soul employ,
    To tell the world my peace and joy.

449 THERE stands a Rock on
    shores of time,
    That rears to heav'n its head
      sublime;
    That Rock is cleft, and they are
      blest
    Who find within this cleft a rest.

Some build their hopes on the ever drifting
    sand,
Some on their fame, or their treasure, or their
    land ;
Mine's on a Rock that for ever will stand,
    Jesus, the " Rock of Ages."

2 That Rock's a cross, its arms out-
    spread,
    Celestial glory bathes its head ;
    To its firm base my all I bring,
    And to the Rock of Ages cling.

3 That Rock's a tower, whose lofty
    height,   [light.
    Illum'd with heav'n's unclouded
    Opes wide its gate beneath the
      dome,   [at home.
    Where saints find rest with Christ

450 WHEN the pearly gates are
    opened
    To a sinner " saved by grace,"
    When thro' everlasting mercy,
    I behold my Saviour's face ;

When I enter in the mansions
Of the city bright and fair,
I shall have a royal welcome,
For I'll be no stranger there.

I shall be...no stranger there,
Jesus will...my place prepare ;
He will meet me,...He will greet me,...
I shall be...no stranger there.

2 Thro' time's ever-changing seasons,
I am pressing toward the goal ;
'Tis my heart's sweet native country,
'Tis the home-land of my soul ;
Many lov'd ones, cloth'd with
beauty,
In those wondrous glories share ;
When I rise, redeem'd, forgiven,
I shall be no stranger there.

3 There my dear Redeemer liveth,
Blessed Lamb upon the throne ;
By the crimson marks upon them,
He will surely claim His own.
So, whenever sad or lonely,
Look beyond the earthly care ;
Weary child of God, remember,
You will be no stranger there.

451 I WANDERED in the shades
of night,
Till Jesus came to me,
And, with the sunlight of His love,
Bade all my darkness flee.

Sunlight, sunlight, in my soul to-day...
Sunlight, sunlight all along the way,...
Since the Saviour found me, took away my sin,...
I have had the sunlight of His love within.

2 Though clouds may gather in the
sky,
And billows round me roll,
However dark the world may be,
I've sunlight in my soul.

3 While walking in the light of God,
I sweet communion find ;
I press with holy vigour on,
And leave the world behind.

4 I cross the wide extended fields,
I journey o'er the plain ;
And in the sunlight of His love,
I reap the golden grain.

5 Soon shall I see Him as He is,
The Light that came to me ;
Behold the brightness of His face,
Throughout eternity.

452 TRAV'LING on the sea of life,
we're homeward bound,
Drifting wrecks and struggling souls
are all around ;
But we do not fear the voyage, for
we know
That the Saviour steers us as we
onward go.

We're homeward bound for glory,....homeward
bound for glory ;...
There we'll meet with lov'd ones gone before,
We're homeward bound for glory,..homeward
bound for glory,...
All the storms of life will soon be o'er.

2 Jesus guides our storm-toss'd barque
across the seas,
He will bring us safely to the port of
peace ;
He's the Pilot ; He is standing at
the helm,
And no angry winds or waves can
overwhelm.

3 Come on board the gospel vessel, do
not stay,
And we'll help you as we journey
on the way ;
Soon to harbour at our Father's
blest abode,
We will worship in the city of our
God.

453 ONE more day's work for
Jesus ;
One less of life for me !
But heaven is nearer,
And Christ is dearer,
Than yesterday to me ;
His love and light
Fill all my soul to-night.

One more day's work for Jesus,
One more day's work for Jesus,
One more day's work for Jesus,
One less of life for me.

2 One more day's work for Jesus ;
How glorious is my King !
'Tis joy, not duty,
To speak His beauty,
My soul mounts on the wing
At the mere thought
How Christ my life has bought.

3 One more day's work for Jesus ;
How sweet the work has been ;
To tell the story,
To show the glory,

When Christ's flock enter in !
How it did shine
In this poor heart of mine.

4 One more day's work for Jesus—
Oh, yes, a weary day ;
But heav'n shines clearer,
And rest comes nearer,
At each step of the way ;
And Christ in all—
Before His face I fall.

5 Oh, blessed work for Jesus !
Oh, rest at Jesus' feet !
There toil seems pleasure,
My wants are treasure,
And pain for Him is sweet ;
Lord, if I may,
I'll serve another day.

454 TO my blessed Lord and
Saviour, as He walks before
me here,   [day ;....
I am getting nearer, nearer ev'ry
And He says I shall be like Him,
when before Him I appear,
And I'm getting nearer, nearer
ev'ry day.

Ev'ry day, praise the Lord, I'm getting nearer,
And the way, praise the Lord, is getting clearer;
From my Lord no more I'll roam, for I see the
lights of home,
And I'm getting nearer, nearer ev'ry day....

2 To the pure and perfect stature of
our great and living Head,
I am getting nearer, nearer ev'ry
day ;....
To the perfect will of Jesus, in the
way that I am led,   [day.
I am getting nearer, nearer ev'ry

3 To the time when I shall gladly lay
my cross and burdens down,
I am getting nearer, nearer, ev'ry
day ;....
To the time when from my Saviour
I'll receive a robe and crown,
I am getting nearer, nearer, ev'ry
day.

4 To that blest eternal city that lies
just across the foam,
I am getting nearer, nearer, ev'ry
day ;....
Often thro' faith's open vision I can
see the spires of home,
And I'm getting nearer, nearer
ev'ry day.

455 BRIGHTLY beams our
Father's mercy
From His lighthouse evermore ;
But to us He gives the keeping
Of the lights along the shore.

Let the lower lights be burning !
Send a gleam across the wave !
Some poor fainting, struggling seaman
You may rescue, you may save !

2 Dark the night of sin has settled,
Loud the angry billows roar ;
Eager eyes are watching, longing,
For the lights along the shore.

3 Trim your feeble lamp, my brother,
Some poor sailor, tempest-tossed,
Trying now to make the harbour,
In the darkness *may be lost*.

456 TELL me the story of Jesus
Write on my heart ev'ry
word,
Tell me the story most precious,
Sweetest that ever was heard ;
Tell how the angels, in chorus,
Sang as they welcomed His birth,
Glory to God in the highest !
Peace and good tidings to earth.

Tell me the story of Jesus,
Write on my heart ev'ry word ;
Tell me the story most precious,
Sweetest that ever was heard.

2 Fasting, alone in the desert,
Tell of the days that He passed,
How for our sins He was tempted,
Yet was triumphant at last ;
Tell of the years of His labour,
Tell of the sorrow He bore,
He was despised and afflicted,
Homeless, rejected, and poor.

3 Tell of the Cross where they nailed
Him,
Writhing in anguish and pain ;
Tell of the grave where they laid
Him,
Tell how He liveth again ;
Love in that story so tender,
Clearer than ever I see ;
Stay, let me weep while you whisper,
Love paid the ransom for me.

457 IT pays to serve Jesus—I
speak from my heart ;
He'll always be with us, if we do our
part ;

There's naught in this wide world
   can pleasure afford,
There's peace and contentment in
   serving the Lord.

I love Him far better than in days of yore,
I'll serve Him more truly than ever before,
I'll do as He bids me whatever the cost,
I'll be a true soldier—I'll die at my post.

2 And oft when I'm tempted to turn
   from the track   [wanders back
  I think of my Saviour—my mind
  To the place where they nailed Him
   on Calvary's tree,   [for thee."
  I heard a voice saying, "I suffered

3 A place I remember where I was
   set free,   [heaven to me;
  'Twas where I found pardon—a
  There Jesus spoke sweetly to my
   weary soul,   [heart whole.
  My sins were forgiven, He made my

4 How rich is the blessing the world
   cannot give,
  I'm satisfied fully for Jesus to live;
  Tho' friends may forsake me and
   trials arise,   [never dies.
  I am trusting in Jesus, His love

5 There is no one like Jesus can cheer
   me to-day,   [fade away;
  His love and His kindness can ne'er
  In winter, in summer, in sunshine
   and rain,
  His love and affection are always
   the same.

6 Will you have this blessing that
   Jesus bestows,
  A free, full salvation from sin's
   bitter throes ?
  O come to the Saviour, to Calvary
   flee,   [for thee.
  The fountain is opened, is flowing

458   TO Jesus ev'ry day I find my
       heart is closer drawn ;
He's fairer than the glory of the gold
   and purple dawn ;
He's all my fancy pictured in its
   fairest dreams and more ;
Each day He grows still sweeter than
   He was the day before.

The half...cannot be fancied...this side...the
   golden shore ;...
O there...He'll be still sweeter than He ever
   was before.

2 His glory broke upon me when I saw
   Him from afar ;
  He's fairer than the lily, brighter
   than the morning star ;
  He fills and satisfies my longing
   spirit o'er and o'er ;
  Each day He grows still sweeter
   than He was the day before.

3 My heart is sometimes heavy, but
   He comes with sweet relief ;
  He folds me to His bosom when I
   droop with blighting grief ;
  I love the Christ who all my burdens
   in His body bore ;
  Each day He grows still sweeter
   than He was the day before.

459   WHEN we walk with the Lord,
      In the light of His word,
What a glory He sheds on our way !
  While we do His good will
  He abides with us still,
And with all who will trust and obey.

Trust and obey ; for there's no other way
To be happy in Jesus, but to trust and obey.

2 Not a shadow can rise,
  Not a cloud in the skies,
But His smile quickly drives it away ;
  Not a doubt nor a fear,
  Not a sigh nor a tear,
Can abide while we trust and obey.

3 Not a burden we bear,
  Not a sorrow we share,
But our toil He doth richly repay ;
  Not a grief nor a loss,
  Not a frown nor a cross,
But is blest if we trust and obey.

4 But we never can prove
  The delights of His love
Until all on the altar we lay ;
  For the favours He shows
  And the joy He bestows,
Are for them who will trust and obey.

5 Then in fellowship sweet
  We will sit at His feet,
Or we'll walk by His side in the way ;
  What He says we will do,
  Where He sends we will go,
Never fear, only trust and obey.

460   ONWARD, Christian soldiers !
      marching as to war,
  Looking unto Jesus, who is gone
   before ;

Christ, the Royal Master, leads
against the foe ;   [go.
Forward into battle see His banners

Onward, Christian soldiers ! marching as to war,
Looking unto Jesus, who is gone before.

2 At the name of Jesus Satan's host
doth flee ;   [victory !
On then, Christian soldiers, on to
Hell's foundations quiver at the
shout of praise ;
Brothers, lift your voices, loud your
anthems raise.

3 Like a mighty army moves the
Church of God ;
Brothers, we are treading where the
saints have trod ;
We are not divided, all one body we,
One in hope and doctrine, one in
charity.

4 Crowns and thrones may perish,
kingdoms rise and wane ;
But the church of Jesus constant
will remain ;
Gates of hell can never 'gainst that
Church prevail ;
We have Christ's own promise, and
that cannot fail.

5 Onward then, ye people, join our
happy throng ;
Blend with ours your voices in the
triumph song :
" Glory, praise, and honour, unto
Christ the King "—
This, through countless ages, men
and angels sing.

461   WHEN a sinner comes, as a
sinner may,
There is joy,....there is joy ;....
When he turns to God in the gospel
way,
There is joy,....there is joy.

There is joy among the angels,
And their harps with music ring ;...
When a sinner comes repenting,
Bending low before the King.

2 When a soul is born in the kingdom
bright,
There is joy,...there is joy ;....
When it walks by faith in the gospel
light,
There is joy,....there is joy.

3 When a pilgrim comes to the river
wide,
There is joy,....there is joy ;....
When he dwells secure on the other
side,
There is joy,....there is joy.

462   THE Lord hath made this
world of ours
Most beautiful and bright ;
The golden sun to rule by day,
The moon and stars by night ;
But souls are wand'ring far from
Him,
In darkened paths astray ;
So make me, Saviour, more and
A light along the way.   [more,

A light along the way, make me, dear Lord,
I pray !
Love's happy rays show forth Thy praise, a
light along the way ;
A light along the way, make me, dear Lord, I
pray ;
Love's happy rays show forth Thy praise, a
light along the way.

2 So many need a helping hand,
A kindly word of cheer,
To tell them of the mighty Friend
Whose grace is always near.
O make me prompt to hear Thy
voice,
And ready to obey,
That I may be, to saddened hearts,
A light along the way.

3 Some lives shine out like beacons
grand,
Some seem but candles small,
But if we truly shine for Him,
The Lord hath need of all.
O may His Spirit fill my soul,
And lead me day by day,
That, though unworthy, I shall be
A light along the way.

463   SOWING in the morning,
sowing seeds of kindness,
Sowing in the noontide, and the
dewy eve ;
Waiting for the harvest, and the
time of reaping,
We shall come rejoicing, bringing
in the sheaves.

Bringing in the sheaves, bringing in the sheaves,
We shall come, rejoicing, bringing in the sheaves.

2 Sowing in the sunshine, sowing in
    the shadows,
    Fearing neither clouds nor winter's
      chilling breeze ;
By and by the harvest, and the
    labour ended,
    We shall come rejoicing, bringing
      in the sheaves.

3 Go then, ever weeping, sowing for
    the Master,
    Tho' the loss sustained our spirit
      often grieves ;
When our weeping's over, He will
    bid us welcome,
    We shall come rejoicing, bringing
      in the sheaves.

464 THO' dark the path my feet
      may tread, it is a joy to know
    There'll be no shadows on the
      other side.
We should not fear the wildest
    storm, but sing as on we go,
    There'll be no shadows on the
      other side.

There'll be no shadows, no...shadows,
  Jesus is the sunshine of that land so fair ;
There'll be no shadows, no...shadows,
  Pain and death can never enter there....

2 Life's brightest day may have its
    clouds, but still our hearts
    should sing,   [side ;
There'll be no shadows on the other
'Twill not be long till cares are o'er,
    and we are with the King,
    There'll be no shadows on the
      other side.

3 We're marching homeward to a land
    where weary feet may rest ;
    There'll be no shadows on the
      other side ;
No pain or sorrow e'er can touch the
    regions of the blest :
    There'll be no shadows on the
      other side.

465 TAKE the name of Jesus
      with you,
    Child of sorrow and of woe ;
It will joy and comfort give you—
    Take it then where'er you go.

Precious name,...oh, how sweet !...
  Hope of earth and joy of heaven ;
Precious name,...oh, how sweet !...
  Hope of earth and joy of heaven.

2 Take the name of Jesus ever,
    As a shield from ev'ry snare ;
If temptations round you gather,
    Breathe that holy name in prayer

3 Oh, the precious name of Jesus !
    How it thrills our souls with joy,
When His loving arms receive us,
    And His songs our tongues employ

4 At the name of Jesus bowing,
    Falling prostrate at His feet ;
King of kings, in heaven we'll
    crown Him,
    When our journey is complete.

466 I SHALL wear a golden crown,
    When I get home ;
I shall lay my burdens down,
    When I get home ;
Clad in robes of glory,
I shall sing the story,
Of the Lord who bought me,
    When I get home.

When I..get..home,..when I..get..home ..
  All sorrow will be over when I get home ;
When I..get..home,..when I..get..home...
  All sorrow will be over, when I get home.

2 All the darkness will be past,
    When I get home ;
I shall see the light at last,
    When I get home ;
Light from heaven streaming,
O'er my pathway beaming,
Ever guides me onward,
    Till I get home.

3 I shall see my Saviour's face,
    When I get home ;
Sing again of saving grace,
    When I get home ;
I shall stand before Him ;
Gladly I'll adore Him,
Ever to be with Him,
    When I get home.

467 THE Lord is my Shepherd, I
      shall not want,
He maketh me down to lie
In pastures green, He leadeth me
    The quiet waters by.

His yoke is easy, His burden is light,
  I've found it so, I've found it so ;
He leadeth me by day and by night
  Where living waters flow.

2 My soul crieth out, "Restore me
  again,
    And give me the strength to take
  The narrow path of righteousness,
    E'en for His own name's sake."

3 Yea, though I should walk in the
  valley of death,
    E'en yet will I fear no ill ;
  For Thou art with me and Thy rod
    And staff they comfort still.

468 WE are building in sorrow,
    and building in joy,
  A temple the world cannot see ;
    But we know it will stand if we
  found it on a rock,
    Thro' the ages of eternity.

We are building day by day as the moments
    glide away,
  Our temple which the world may not see ;...
Ev'ry vict'ry won by grace will be sure to find
    its place
  In our building for eternity....

2 Ev'ry deed forms a part in this
  building of ours,
    That is done in the name of the
  Lord ;
    For the love that we show, and the
  kindness we bestow,   [reward.
    He has promis'd us a bright

3 Then be watchful and wise, let the
  temple we rear
    Be one that no tempest can shock ;
  For the Master has said, and He
  taught us in His Word,
    We must build upon the solid
  rock.

469 HOME to Zion we are bound,
    Happy in the love of Jesus ;
  Peace abiding we have found,
    Happy in the love of Jesus.

Happy, happy,
Singing all the way, happy all the day ;
  Happy, happy,
Happy in the love of Jesus.

2 Trusting, we will forward go,
    Happy in the love of Jesus ;
  Treading changeful paths below,
    Happy in the love of Jesus.

3 Soon we'll reach the homeland fair,
    Happy in the love of Jesus ;
  And shall dwell for ever there,
    Happy in the love of Jesus.

470 YONDER'S the land where the
    lov'd ones are,
  Soon will the mist roll away !
Joy soon to rest in that realm afar,
  Soon will the mist roll away !
There in the loving smile of Christ
    to abide,
  Visions of glory day by day !
Faith fondly whispers while in
    shadows we hide,
  Soon will the mist roll away !

Yonder's the land where the lov'd ones are,
  Soon will the mist roll away !
Joy soon to rest in that realm afar,
  Soon will the mist roll away !

2 Dark looms the path, but the promise
    heed,
  Soon will the mist roll away !
Jesus alone can relieve thy need,
  Soon will the mist roll away !
Clear will the purpose of the Lord
    be to thee,
  Hasten the Master to obey ;
Blissful the vision that beyond we
    shall see,
  Soon will the mist roll away !

3 Bear thou the cross till the crown
    is won,
  Soon will the mist roll away !
Work till the will of the Lord be
    done,
  Soon will the mist roll away !
All will be reconciled to thee by and
    by,
  Faith guideth on to perfect day ;
Soon shall the glory dawn upon
    ev'ry eye,
  Soon will the mist roll away !

471 OUR souls cry out, hallelujah !
    And our faith enraptured
    sings,
  While we throw to the breeze the
    standard,
    Of the mighty King of kings.

On the vict'ry side, on the vict'ry side,
  In the ranks of the Lord are we ;
On the vict'ry side we will boldly stand,
  Till the glory land we see.

2 Our souls cry out, hallelujah !
    For the Lord Himself comes near,
  And the shout of a royal army
    On the battle-field we hear.

3 Our souls cry out, hallelujah !
  For the tempter flies apace
And the chains he has forged are
  breaking,   [grace.
Thro' the pow'r of redeeming

4 Our souls cry out, hallelujah !
  And our hearts beat high with
    praise,   [conquer,
Unto Him, in whose name we'll
  And our song of triumph raise.

472 I BELIEVE in the story never
  old,
    I believe it !   [told,
I believe it in the Saviour long fore-
    I believe it !   [than gold,
I believe He's more precious far
    I believe it !   [name.
I am saved by believing on His

I am saved by believing on His name,....
I am saved, for His Word is just the same,....
'Tis the same " whosoever," for His love
  changeth never,
I am saved by believing on His name.

2 I believe in the tidings of His birth,
    I believe it !   [earth,
I believe in the song of peace on
    I believe it !   [mirth,
I believe 'twas a time of joy and
    I believe it !
I am saved by believing on His name.

3 I believe that the shepherds heard
    I believe it !   [the song,
I believe that they saw the heav'nly
    I believe it !   [throng,
I believe that the glory shone around,
    I believe it !
I am saved by believing on His name.

4 I believe that the wise men saw His
    I believe it !   [star,
I believe that they followed from
    I believe it !   [afar,
I believe that they found the
  Saviour there,
    I believe it !
I am saved by believing on His name.

5 I believe that He came to seek and
    I believe it !   [save,
I believe that eternal life He gave,
    I believe it !   [grave,
I believe I shall live beyond the
    I believe it !
I am saved by believing on His name.

473 SUFFICIENT for me, suffi-
  cient for me,
His grace so abundant and free ;
In sorrow or pain this joy shall
  remain :
His grace is sufficient for me.....

474 THERE is a land of pure
  delight,
  Where saints immortal reign,
Infinite day excludes the night,
  And pleasures banish pain.

We're feeding on the Living Bread,
We're drinking at the Fountain-head ;
And who-so drinketh, Jesus said,
Shall never, never thirst again.
What, never thirst again ?
No, never thirst again !
And who-so drinketh, Jesus said,
Shall never, never thirst again !

2 There everlasting Spring abides,
  And never-with'ring flowers :
Death, like a narrow sea, divides
  This heavenly land from ours.

3 O could we make our doubts remove,
  Those gloomy thoughts that rise,
And see the Canaan that we love
  With unbeclouded eyes.

4 Could we but climb where Moses
  stood,
  And view the landscape o'er,
Not Jordan's stream, nor death's
  cold flood,
Should fright us from the shore.

The following Chorus may be substituted :—
We're marching through Immanuel's ground,
And soon shall hear the trumpet sound,
And then we shall with Jesus reign,
And never, never part again.
What, never part again ?
No, never part again !
And then we shall with Jesus reign,
And never, never part again !

475 THOU Shepherd of Israel, and
  mine,
  The joy and desire of my heart,
For closer communion I pine,
  I long to reside where Thou art.

2 The pasture I languish to find,
  Where all who their Shepherd
    obey,
Are fed on His bosom reclined,
  And screened from the heat of the
    day.

3 Ah, show me that happiest place,
   That place of Thy people's abode,
Where saints in an ecstasy gaze,
   And hang on a crucified God.

4 Thy love for a sinner declare,
   Thy passion and death on the tree,
My spirit to Calvary bear,
   To suffer and triumph with Thee.

5 'Tis there, with the lambs of Thy
         flock,
   There only I covet to rest ;
To lie at the foot of the Rock,
   Or rise to be hid in Thy breast.

6 'Tis there I would always abide,
   And never a moment depart,
Concealed in the cleft of Thy side,
   Eternally hid in Thy heart

476 HOW good is the God we
         adore,
   Our faithful, unchangeable Friend,
Whose love is as great as His power,
   And knows neither measure nor
      end.

2 'Tis Jesus, the First and the Last,
   Whose Spirit shall guide us safe
      home ;
We'll praise Him for all that is past,
   And trust Him for all that's to
      come.

477 A FEW more marchings weary,
   Then we'll gather home !
A few more storm-clouds dreary,
   Then we'll gather home !
A few more days the cross to bear,
And then with Christ a crown to
      wear ;
   A few more marchings weary,
      Then we'll gather home !

         O'er....time's rapid river,
         Soon....we'll rest for ever.
         No more marchings weary
         When we gather home !

2 A few more nights of weeping,
   Then we'll gather home !
A few more watches keeping,
   Then we'll gather home !
A few more vict'ries over sin,
A few more sheaves to gather in ;
   A few more marchings weary,
      Then we'll gather home !

3 A few more sweet links broken,
   Then we'll gather home !
A few more kind words spoken,
   Then we'll gather home !
A few more partings on the strand
And then away to Canaan's land ;
   A few more marchings weary,
      Then we'll gather home !

478 FROM Egypt's cruel bondage
         fled,
   Obedient to our Lord's command,
And by His Word and Spirit led,
   We're on the way to Canaan's
      Land !

   We're on the way, a pilgrim band ;
   We're on the way to Canaan's land ;
   Divinely guided day by day,
   We're on the way, we're on the way.

2 Through wildernesses wide and drear,
   Our Lord will guide our steps
      aright ;
Behold, to prove His presence here,
   The cloud by day, the fire by
      night !

3 His pow'r the smitten rock controls,
   A crystal stream our need supplies;
He feeds our hungry, fainting souls
   With daily manna from the skies !

4 In hostile lands we feel no fear ;
   No foe our onward march can stay ;
In ev'ry conflict He is near,
   Whose presence cheers us on the
      way.

5 Ere long, the river crossed, we'll
         meet   [hand ;
   The ransomed host at His right
And there receive a welcome sweet,
   From our dear Lord, to Canaan's
      Land !

479 THE sunshine I have found
         will fill each day with joy,
   And ev'ry moment sweetly bless ;
The rays that gently fall upon my
         daily path   [eousness.
   Are given by the Sun of Right-

So if the sky is dark, and if the day is dreary,
   The sun is shining somewhere, this I know,
      I know,
And so to keep my heart from ever growing
      weary,
   I'll carry my sunshine with me ev'rywhere
      I go.

E

2 Look up and praise the Lord! the
    flowers need the rain
    That falls upon them day by day,
Just as our thirsty souls would seek
    the cooling springs
    If we were walking in a desert way.

3 But for the child of God there
    always is a ray,
    That struggles thro' the clouds
    above ;
That shines across his path and helps
    his wav'ring faith
    To rest securely in a Father's
    love.

4 It is the light that shines, when
    Jesus speaks to me,
And tells me I am saved by grace ;
The sunshine I have found is free to
    all who seek
    The sunshine of my blessed
    Saviour's face.

480   AM I a soldier of the Cross,....
        A follower of the Lamb ?....
And shall I fear to own His cause,
    Or blush to speak His name ?

> We will stand...the storm,....
> We will anchor by-and-by....

2 Must I be carried to the skies,....
    On flow'ry beds of ease,....
While others fought to win the
    prize,
    And sailed through bloody seas ?

3 Are there no foes for me to face ?....
    Must I not stem the flood ?....
Is this vile world a friend to grace,
    To help me on to God ?

4 Since I must fight if I would reign,....
    Increase my courage, Lord !....
I'll bear the toil, endure the pain,
    Supported by Thy word.

481   JESUS, my all, to heav'n is
        gone,
He whom I fix my hopes upon ;
His track I see, and I'll pursue
The narrow way till Him I view.

2 The way the holy prophets went,
    The road that leads from banish-
    ment ;
The King's highway of holiness
I'll go, for all His paths are peace.

3 This is the way I long have sought,
    And mourn'd because I found it not ;
Till late I heard my Saviour say,
"Come hither, child ; I am the Way."

482   SOLDIERS of Christ, arise—
        And put your armour on ;
Strong in the strength which God
    supplies
    Through His eternal Son !

2 Strong in the Lord of hosts,
    Stand in His mighty pow'r ;
Who in the strength of Jesus trusts
    Is more than conqueror !

3 Stand then in His great might,
    With all His strength endued ;
And take, to arm you for the fight,
    The panoply of God.

4 To keep your armour bright,
    Attend with constant care ;
Still marching in your Captain's
    sight,
    And watching unto pray'r.

5 Jesus hath died for you—
    What can His love withstand ?
Believe, hold fast your shield, and
    who
    Shall pluck you from His hand ?

6 Then, having all things done,
    And ev'ry conflict past—
Accepted each through Christ alone,
    You shall be crowned at last.

483   I WAITED for the Lord my God,
        And patiently did bear ;
At length to me He did incline
    My voice and cry to hear.

2 He took me from a fearful pit,
    And from the miry clay,
And on a rock He set my feet,
    Establishing my way.

3 He put a new song in my mouth,
    Our God to magnify ;
Many shall see it, and shall fear,
    And on the Lord rely.

4 O blessed is the man whose trust
    Upon the Lord relies ;
Respecting not the proud, nor such
    As turn aside to lies.

5 In Thee let all be glad, and joy,
    Who seeking Thee abide ;
Who Thy salvation love, say still,
    The Lord be magnified.

484 CHRISTIAN ! seek not yet repose ;
Hear thy guardian angel say,
Thou art in the midst of foes ;
    Watch and pray.

2 Principalities and powers,
    Must'ring their unseen array,
Wait for thy unguarded hours :
    Watch and pray.

3 Gird thy heavenly armour on ;
    Wear it ever, night and day ;
Ambushed lies the evil one :
    Watch and pray.

4 Hear the victors who o'ercame ;
    Still they mark each warrior's way ;
All with one sweet voice exclaim,
    " Watch and pray."

5 Hear, above all, hear thy Lord,
    Him thou lovest to obey ;
Hide within thy heart His Word—
    " Watch and pray."

6 Watch as if on that alone
    Hung the issue of the day ;
Pray that help may be sent down :
    Watch and pray.

485 THERE is a Name I love to hear,
    I love to sing its worth ;
It sounds like music in mine ear,
    The sweetest Name on earth.

2 It tells me of a Saviour's love,
    Who died to set me free ;
It tells me of His precious blood,
    The sinner's perfect plea.

3 It bids my trembling soul rejoice,
    And dries each rising tear ;
It tells me in a " still, small voice,"
    To trust and never fear.

4 Jesus, the Name I love so well,
    The Name I love to hear,
No saint on earth its worth can tell,
    No heart conceive how dear.

5 This Name shall shed its fragrance
    Along this thorny road,   [still
Shall sweetly smooth the rugged hill
    That leads me up to God.

6 And there, with all the blood-bought throng,
    From sin and sorrow free,
I'll sing the new eternal song
    Of Jesus' love to me.

486 THE Lord's my Shepherd, I'll not want,
He makes me down to lie
In pastures green ; He leadeth me
    The quiet waters by.

2 My soul He doth restore again,
    And me to walk doth make
Within the paths of righteousness,
    Ev'n for His own Name's sake.

3 Yea, though I walk in death's dark vale,
    Yet will I fear none ill ;
For Thou art with me ; and Thy rod
    And staff me comfort still.

4 My table Thou hast furnished
    In presence of my foes ;
My head Thou dost with oil anoint,
    And my cup overflows.

5 Goodness and mercy all my life
    Shall surely follow me,
And in God's house for evermore
    My dwelling-place shall be.

487 TO Calvary, Lord, in spirit now
Our weary souls repair,
To dwell upon Thy dying love,
    And taste its sweetness there.

2 Sweet resting place of every heart,
    That feels the plague of sin,
Yet knows that deep, mysterious joy,
    The peace of God within.

3 There through Thine hour of deepest woe,
    Thy suffering spirit passed ;
Grace there its wondrous victory gained,
    And love endured its last.

4 Dear suffering Lamb, Thy bleeding wounds,
    With cords of love divine,
Have drawn our willing hearts to Thee,
    And linked our life with Thine.

5 Our longing eyes would fain behold
    That bright and blessed brow,
Once wrung with bitterest anguish, wear
    Its crown of glory now.

488 COURAGE, brother! do not
stumble,
Though thy path be dark as night;
There's a star to guide the humble,
Trust in God, and do the right.

2 Let the road be rough and dreary,
And its end far out of sight;
Foot it bravely, strong or weary;
Trust in God, and do the right.

3 Perish policy and cunning!
Perish all that fears the light!
Whether losing, whether winning,
Trust in God, and do the right.

4 Trust no party, sect, or faction;
Trust no leaders in the fight;
But in every word and action,
Trust in God, and do the right.

5 Trust no lovely forms of passion,
Fiends may look like angels bright,
Trust no custom, school, or fashion,
Trust in God, and do the right.

6 Simple rule, and safest guiding,
Inward peace, and inward might;
Star upon our path abiding,
Trust in God, and do the right.

7 Some will hate thee, some will love
thee,
Some will flatter, some will slight;
Cease from man, and look above
thee,
Trust in God, and do the right.

489 JESUS calls us; o'er the
tumult
Of our life's wild, restless sea,
Day by day His sweet voice soundeth
Saying, " Christian, follow me ! "

2 As of old, apostles heard it
By the Galilean lake,
Turned from home, and toil, and
kindred,
Leaving all for His dear sake.

3 Jesus calls us from the worship
Of the vain world's golden store;
From each idol that would keep us,
Saying, " Christian, love Me
more."

4 In our joys and in our sorrows,
Days of toil and hours of ease;
Still He calls, in cares and pleasures,
" Christian, love Me more than
these."

5 Jesus calls us ; by Thy mercies,
Saviour, may we hear Thy call;
Give our hearts to Thy obedience,
Serve and love Thee best of all.

490 IN the cross of Christ I glory
Tow'ring o'er the wrecks of
time;
All the light of sacred story
Gathers round its head sublime.

2 When the woes of life o'ertake me,
Hopes deceive and fears annoy,
Never shall the Cross forsake me,
Lo ! it glows with peace and joy.

3 When the sun of bliss is beaming
Light and love upon my way;
From the Cross the radiance stream-
ing,
Adds new lustre to the day.

4 Bane and blessing, pain and pleasure
By the Cross are sanctified;
Peace is there that knows no
measure,
Joys that through all time abide.

491 GLORIOUS things of thee are
spoken,
Zion, city of our God;
He whose word cannot be broken,
Formed thee for His own abode.

2 On the rock of ages founded,
What can shake thy sure repose
With salvation's walls surrounded,
Thou mayest smile at all thy foes.

3 See ! the streams of living waters,
Springing from eternal love,
Well supply thy sons and daughters,
And all fear of want remove.

4 Saviour, if of Zion's city,
I, through grace, a member am,
Let the world deride or pity,
I will glory in Thy name.

5 Fading is the worldling's pleasure,
All his boasted pomp and show;
Solid joys and lasting treasure,
None but Zion's children know.

492 THROUGH the night of doubt
and sorrow
Onward goes the pilgrim band,
Singing songs of expectation,
Marching to the Promised Land.

2 Clear before us through the darkness
   Gleams and burns the guiding
      light,
   Brother clasps the hand of brother,
   Stepping fearless through the
      night.

3 One the strain that lips of thousands
   Lift as from the heart of one ;
   One the conflict, one the peril,
   One the march in God begun ;

4 One the gladness of rejoicing,
   On the far, eternal shore,
   Where the one Almighty Father
   Reigns in love for evermore.

5 Onward, therefore, pilgrim brothers,
   Onward with the Cross our aid !
   Bear its shame, and fight its battle,
   Till we rest beneath its shade.

6 Soon shall come the great awakening,
   Soon the rending of the tomb ;
   Then the scattering of all shadows,
   And the end of toil and gloom.

493   GO, labour on, spend, and be
            spent,
   Thy joy to do the Father's will ;
   It is the way the Master went,
   Should not the servant tread it
      still ?

2 Go, labour on : 'tis not for nought,
   Thy earthly loss is heavenly gain ;
   Men heed thee, love thee, praise thee
      not,   [men ?
   The Master praises : what are

3 Men die in darkness at your side,
   Without a hope to cheer the tomb ;
   Take up the torch, and wave it wide,
   The torch that lights time's
      thickest gloom.

4 Toil on, and in thy toil rejoice,
   For toil comes rest, for exile home ;
   Soon shall thou hear the Bride-
      groom's voice,   [come ! "
   The midnight peal, " Behold I

494   LO ! round the throne at God's
            right hand
   The saints in countless myriads
      stand ;
   Of ev'ry tongue redeemed to God,
   Arrayed in garments washed in
      blood.

2 Through tribulation great they came,
   They bore the cross, despised the
      shame ;   [rest,
   From all their labours now they
   In God's eternal glory blest.

3 Hunger and thirst they feel no more,
   Nor sin, nor pain, nor death deplore ;
   The tears are wiped from every eye,
   And sorrow yields to endless joy.

4 They see their Saviour face to face,
   And sing the triumphs of His grace ;
   Him day and night they ceaseless
      praise,
   To Him their loud Hosannas raise.

5 O may we tread the sacred road
   That holy saints and martyrs trod ;
   Wage to the end the glorious strife,
   And win, like them, the crown of life.

495   I THIRST, Thou wounded
            Lamb of God,
   To wash me in Thy cleansing blood ;
   To dwell within Thy wounds, then
      pain
   Is sweet, and life or death is gain.

2 Take my poor heart, and let it be
   For ever closed to all but Thee !
   Seal Thou my breast, and let me
      wear
   That pledge of love for ever there.

3 How can it be, Thou heavenly King,
   That Thou shouldst us to glory bring?
   Make slaves the partners of Thy
      throne,
   Decked with a never-fading crown?

4 Hence our hearts melt, our eyes o'er-
      flow,   [know,
   Our words are lost : nor will we
   Nor will we think of aught beside,
   " My Lord, my Love is crucified ! "

496   THOU sweet beloved will of
            God,   [hill,
   My anchor ground, my fortress
   My spirit's silent, fair abode,
   In Thee I hide me, and am still.

2 O will, that willest good alone,
   Lead Thou the way, Thou guidest
      best ;
   A little child, I follow on,   [breast.
   And trusting, lean upon Thy

3 Oh, lightest burden, sweetest yoke!
    It lifts, it bears my happy soul;
  It giveth wings to this poor heart;
    My freedom is Thy grand control.

4 Upon God's will I lay me down,
    As child upon its mother's breast;
  No silken couch, nor softest bed,
    Could ever give me such deep
      rest.

5 Thy wonderful grand will, my God,
    With triumph now I make it
      mine;
  And faith shall cry a joyous " Yes !"
    To every dear command of Thine.

497 BRETHREN in Christ, and
      well beloved,
  To Jesus and His servants dear,
  Enter and show yourselves approved;
  Enter and find that God is here.

2 Welcome from earth : lo, the right
    hand
  Of fellowship to you we give !
  With open hearts and hands we
    stand,
  And you in Jesus' name receive.

3 Say, are your hearts resolved as ours?
  Then let them burn with sacred
    love;   [powers,
  Then let them taste the heav'nly
  Partakers of the joys above.

4 Thou God that answerest by fire,
  The Spirit of burning now impart;
  And let the flames of pure desire
  Rise from the altar of our heart.

5 In part we only know Thee here,
  But wait Thy coming from above :
  And we shall then behold Thee near,
  And we shall all be lost in love.

498 WE sing the praise of Him who
      died,
  Of Him who died upon the Cross;
  The sinner's hope let men deride,
  For this we count the world but
    loss.

2 Inscribed upon the Cross we see,
  In shining letters, " God is love ; "
  He bears our sins upon the tree,
  He brings us mercy from above.

3 The Cross ! it takes our guilt away;
  It holds the fainting spirit up;
  It cheers with hope the gloomy day,
  And sweetens every bitter cup.

4 It makes the coward spirit brave,
  And nerves the feeble arm for
    fight;
  It takes its terror from the grave,
  And gilds the bed of death with
    light.

5 The balm of life, the cure of woe,
  The measure and the pledge of
    love;
  The sinner's refuge here below,
  The angels' theme in heaven above.

499 FROM all that dwell below
      the skies,
  Let the Creator's praise arise ;
  Let the Redeemer's name be sung
  Through every land, by every tongue

2 Eternal are Thy mercies, Lord ;
  Eternal truth attends Thy Word ;
  Thy praise shall sound from shore
    to shore,
  Till suns shall rise and set no more.

500 COME, Holy Spirit, calm our
      minds,
  And fit us to approach our God ;
  Remove each vain, each worldly
    thought,
  And lead us to Thy blest abode.

2 Hast Thou imparted to our souls
  A living spark of heavenly fire ?
  Oh, kindle now the sacred flame,
  And make us burn with pure
    desire !

3 Impress upon our wandering hearts
  The love that Christ to sinners bore.
  Help us to look on Him we pierced,
  And our redeeming God adore.

4 A brighter faith and hope impart,
  And let us now Thy glory see ;
  Oh, soothe and cheer each burdened
    heart,
  And bid our spirits rest in Thee !

501 WHILE shepherds watch'd
      their flocks by night,
  All seated on the ground ;
  The angel of the Lord came down,
  And glory shone around.

2 " Fear not ! " said he—for mighty
    dread
    Had seized their troubled mind—
" Glad tidings of great joy I bring
    To you and all mankind.

3 " To you in David's town this day,
    Is born of David's line
The Saviour, who is Christ the Lord,
    And this shall be the sign :

4 " The heavenly babe you there shall
    find
    To human view displayed,
All meanly wrapped in swathing
    bands,
    And in a manger laid."

5 Thus spake the seraph—and forth-
    with
    Appeared a shining throng
Of angels praising God, who thus
    Addressed their joyful song :

6 " All glory be to God on high !
    And to the earth be peace ;
Good-will henceforth from heaven
    to men
    Begin, and never cease ! "

502   OPPRESSED by noonday's
    scorching heat,
    To yonder Cross I flee,
Beneath its shelter take my seat—
    No shade like this to me !

2 Beneath that Cross clear waters
    burst,
    A fountain sparkling free,
And there I quench my desert
    thirst—
    No spring like this to me !

3 For burdened ones, a resting-place
    Beneath that Cross I see ;
Here I cast off my weariness—
    No rest like this for me !

4 A stranger here, I pitch my tent
    Beneath this spreading tree ;
Here shall my pilgrim life be spent—
    No home like this for me !

503   LORD, I have made Thy Word
    my choice,
    My lasting heritage ;
There shall my noblest powers
    rejoice,
    My warmest thoughts engage.

2 I'll read the histories of Thy love,
    And keep Thy laws in sight,
While through Thy promises I rove
    With ever fresh delight.

3 'Tis a broad land of wealth unknown,
    Where springs of life arise,
Seeds of immortal bliss are sown,
    And hidden glory lies.

4 The best relief that mourners have,
    It makes our sorrows blest ;
Our fairest hope beyond the grave,
    And our eternal rest.

504   HAPPY the souls to Jesus
    joined,
    And saved by grace alone ;
Walking in all His ways, they find
    Their heaven on earth begun.

2 The Church triumphant in Thy love,
    Their mighty joys we know ;
They sing the Lamb in hymns above,
    And we in hymns below.

3 Thee in Thy glorious realm they
    praise,
    And bow before Thy throne ;
We in the kingdom of Thy grace—
    The kingdoms are but one.

4 The holy to the holiest leads ;
    From thence our spirits rise ;
And he that in Thy statues treads
    Shall meet Thee in the skies.

505   FATHER of mercies ! in Thy
    Word
    What endless glory shines !
For ever be Thy name adored
    For these celestial lines.

2 Here may the wretched sons of want
    Exhaustless riches find ;
Riches above what earth can grant,
    And lasting as the mind.

3 Here the Redeemer's welcome voice
    Spreads heav'nly peace around ;
And life and everlasting joys
    Attend the blissful sound.

4 Oh, may these heavenly pages be
    My ever dear delight,
And still new beauties may I see,
    And still increasing light.

5 Divine Instructor, gracious Lord !
    Be Thou for ever near ;
Teach me to love Thy sacred Word,
    And view my Saviour there.

506 GOD is our refuge and our
strength,
  In straits a present aid ;
Therefore, although the earth re-
move,
  We will not be afraid.

2 Though hills amidst the seas be cast;
  Though waters roaring make,
And troubled be ; yea, though the
hills
  By swelling seas do shake.

3 A river is, whose streams do glad
  The city of our God ;
The holy place, wherein the Lord
  Most high hath His abode.

4 God in the midst of her doth dwell,
  Nothing shall her remove ;
The Lord to her an helper will,
  And that right early prove.

5 Be still, and know that I am God ;
  Among the heathen I
Will be exalted ; I on earth
Will be exalted high.

507 OH, sing a new song to the
Lord,
  For wonders He hath done ;
His right hand and His holy arm
  Him victory hath won.

2 The Lord God His salvation
  Hath caused to be known ;
His justice in the heathen's sight
  He openly hath shown.

3 He mindful of His grace and truth
  To Israel's house hath been ;
And the salvation of our God
  All ends of th' earth have seen.

4 Let all the earth unto the Lord
  Send forth a joyful noise ;
Lift up your voice aloud to Him,
  Sing praises and rejoice.

5 With harp, with harp, and voice of
psalms,
  Unto Jehovah sing ;
With trumpets, cornets, gladly sound
  Before the Lord the King.

508 WHEN all Thy mercies, O my
God,
  My rising soul surveys,
Transported with the view, I'm lost
  In wonder, love, and praise.

2 Unnumbered comforts on my soul
  Thy tender care bestowed,
Before my infant heart conceived
  From whom these comforts flowed.

3 When worn with sickness oft hast
Thou
  With health renewed my face ;
And when in sins and sorrows sunk,
  Revived my soul with grace.

4 Ten thousand thousand precious
gifts
  My daily thanks employ ;
Nor is the least a cheerful heart
  That tastes those gifts with joy.

5 Through every period of my life
  Thy goodness I'll pursue ;
And after death, in distant worlds,
  he glorious theme renew.

6 Thr ugh all eternity to Thee
  A joyful song I'll raise ;
But oh, eternity's too short
  To utter all Thy praise.

509 HOW bright these glorious
spirits shine !
Whence all their white array ?
How came they to the blissful seats
Of everlasting day ?

2 Lo, these are they from sufferings
great
Who came to realms of light,
And in the blood of Christ have
washed
Those robes which shine so bright.

3 Now, with triumphal palms they
stand
Before the throne on high,
And serve the God they love,
  The glories of the sky.   [amidst

4 Hunger and thirst are felt no more,
Nor suns with scorching ray ;
God is their sun, whose cheering
  Diffuse eternal day.   [beams

5 'Mong pastures green He'll lead His
flock,
Where living streams appear ;
And God the Lord from every eye
Shall wipe off every tear.

6 To Him who sits upon the throne,
The God whom we adore,
And to the Lamb that once was
  Be glory evermore !   [slain,

510 GOD moves in a mysterious
way
His wonders to perform ;
He plants His footsteps in the sea,
And rides upon the storm.

2 Deep in unfathomable mines
Of never-failing skill,
He treasures up His bright designs
And works His sovereign will.

3 Ye fearful saints, fresh courage take !
The clouds ye so much dread
Are big with mercy ; and shall break
In blessing on your head.

4 Judge not the Lord by feeble sense,
But trust Him for His grace ;
Behind a frowning providence
He hides a smiling face.

5 His purposes will ripen fast,
Unfolding every hour ;
The bud may have a bitter taste,
But sweet will be the flower.

6 Blind unbelief is sure to err,
And scan His work in vain ;
God is His own interpreter,
And He will make it plain.

511 JESUS, the very thought of
Thee,
With sweetness fills my breast ;
But sweeter far Thy face to see,
And in Thy presence rest.

2 Nor voice can sing, nor heart can
frame,
Nor can the memory find
A sweeter sound than Thy blest
O Saviour of mankind.   [name,

3 O Hope of ev'ry contrite heart,
O Joy of all the meek,
To those who fall, how kind Thou
art !
How good to those who seek !

4 But what to those who find ? Ah,
this,
Nor tongue nor pen can show ;
The love of Jesus, what it is
None but His loved ones know.

5 Jesus, our only joy be Thou,
As Thou our prize wilt be ;
Jesus, be Thou our glory now,
And through eternity.

512 I LOVE to tell the story,
How Christ the King of Glory,
Left heav'n above to come and
rescue me ;
For sinners He received them,
His blood was shed to save them—
So Jesus died for sinners just like me.

Yes, yes, yes, O yes !
Jesus died to set poor sinners free ;
You say, " How do I know it ? "
John three sixteen will show it ;
That big word " whosoever " just means me.

2 So now I'll try to please Him,
My life I'll give to serve Him ;
His true and faithful servant I will
be ;
And when called home to glory,
I'll sing the good old story,
That Jesus died for sinners just like
me.

3 Then, brother, won't you love
Him ?
And, sister, won't you trust Him ?
I know He died for you as well as
me ;
We need our sins forgiven
That we may go to heaven,
To live with Christ, who died for
you and me.

513 IN my soul oft rises, bringing
pain and woe,
The alarming question, " Am I saved
or no ? "
Then the Word brings comfort, it
doth fully show,
Tho' my faith may waver, Christ,
the Rock, stands fast.

The Rock stand fast, the Rock stands fast !
Tho' my faith may waver, Christ, the Rock,
stands fast !
The Rock stands fast, the Rock stands fast !
Glory be to God ! Christ, the Rock, stands fast !

2 When, before me marshalled, all my
sins arise,   [of paradise,
Swords of flame that bar the gates
Tho' oppressed with doubtings, still
my soul replies :
" Tho' my faith may waver, Christ,
the Rock, stands fast ! "

3 While life's storm is raging, heaping
up hope's wrecks,
While delights allure and sore
temptations vex,

I will cry, tho' fears and doubts my
    soul perplex :
" Tho' my faith may waver, Christ,
    the Rock, stands fast ! "

514 IF our Lord should come
        to-night,
With the bright angelic host,
Would He find us in His vineyard,
    Ev'ry servant at his post ?
Thro' the precious, cleansing blood
    Are our garments clean and white ?
Are we dwelling in the light,
    Should our Lord appear to-night ?

Are we watching, are we waiting
  In the raiment pure and white ?
Should we joy at His appearing
  If our Lord should come to-night ?...

2 If our Lord should come to-night,
    Come as King and Judge of all,
Are there any here assembled
    Who would tremble at His call ?
Is there one, oh, is there one
    Far from Jesus and the light,
Unrepentant, lost, undone,
    If the Judge should come to-
        night ?

3 Christ as King and Judge will come,
    'Tis recorded in His book ;
He will bid us stand before Him,
    Not a soul will He o'erlook !
Are we ready, ev'ry one ?
    Are we in the raiment white,
If the Judge of all mankind
    Should appear this very night ?

THE SECOND COMING

515 'TIS almost time for the Lord
        to come,
I hear the people say ;
The stars of heav'n are growing dim,
    It must be the breaking of the day.

O it must be the breaking of the day,
O it must be the breaking of the day,
The night is almost gone, the day is coming on ;
  O it must be the breaking of the day.

2 The signs foretold in the sun and
        moon,
    In earth, and sea, and sky,
Aloud proclaim to all mankind,
    The coming of the Master draweth
        nigh.

3 It must be time for the waiting
        Church
    To cast her pride away,
With girded loins and burning
        lamps,
    To look for the breaking of the
        day.

4 Go quickly out in the streets and
        lanes,
    And in the broad highway,
And call the maim'd, the halt, and
        blind,
    To be ready for the breaking of
        the day.

516 WHEN the Bridegroom cometh
        by and by,....
When the Bridegroom cometh by
    and by,....

Will your lamps be burning bright,
Will your robes be pure and white,
When the Bridegroom cometh by
    and by ?

Oh be ready ! Oh be ready !
Ready when the Bridegroom comes ;...
  Oh be ready ! Oh be ready !
Ready when the Bridegroom comes.

2 When the Bridegroom cometh by
        and by,....
When the Bridegroom cometh by
        and by,....
    Oh be ready for that day,
    With your sins all washed away,
When the Bridegroom cometh by
        and by.

3 When the Bridegroom cometh by
        and by,....
When the Bridegroom cometh by
        and by,....
    Will your wearied heart rejoice
    At the sound of Jesus' voice,
When the Bridegroom cometh by
        and by ?

4 When the Bridegroom cometh by
        and by,....
When the Bridegroom cometh by
        and by,....
    Will the sorrows of the past
    All be changed to joy at last,
When the Bridegroom cometh by
        and by ?

5 When the Bridegroom cometh by
   and by,....
When the Bridegroom cometh by
   and by,....
   When the Lord shall call His own,
   Can you stand before the throne,
When the Bridegroom cometh by
   and by ?

6 When the Bridegroom cometh by
   and by,....
When the Bridegroom cometh by
   and by,....
   Will you join the ransomed host,
   Or be found among the lost,
When the Bridegroom cometh by
   and by ?

517   WHEN Jesus comes to reward
   His servants,
   Whether it be noon or night,
Faithful to Him He will find us
   watching,
   With our lamps all trimmed and
   bright ?

Oh, can we say we are ready, brother—
   Ready for the soul's bright home ?
Say, will He find you and me still watching,
   Waiting, waiting, when the Lord shall come ?

2 If at the dawn of the early morning,
   He shall call us one by one,
When to the Lord we restore our
   talents,
   Will He answer thee, "Well done ?"

3 Have we been true to the trust He
   left us ?
   Do we seek to do our best ?
If in our hearts there is naught con-
   demns us,
   We shall have a glorious rest.

4 Blessed are those whom the Lord
   finds watching,
   In His glory they shall share ;
If He should come at the dawn or
   midnight,
   Will He find us watching there ?

518   WILL our lamps be filled and
   ready,
   When the Bridegroom comes ?
And our lights be clear and steady,
   When the Bridegroom comes ?
In the night,....that solemn night,....
Will our lamps be burning bright,
   When the Bridegroom comes ?

Oh be ready ! Oh be ready !
Oh be ready when the Bridegroom comes !
Oh be ready ! Oh be ready !
Oh be ready when the Bridegroom comes !

2 Shall we hear a welcome sounding
   When the Bridegroom comes ?
And a shout of joy resounding,
   When the Bridegroom comes ?
In the night,....that solemn night,....
Will our lamps be burning bright,
   When the Bridegroom comes ?

3 Don't delay our preparation
   Till the Bridegroom comes ;
Lest there be a separation,
   When the Bridegroom comes.
In the night,....that solemn night,....
Will our lamps be burning bright,
   When the Bridegroom comes ?

4 It may be a time of sorrow,
   When the Bridegroom comes,
If our oil we hope to borrow
   When the Bridegroom comes ;
In the night,....that solemn night,....
Will our lamps be burning bright,
   When the Bridegroom comes ?

5 Oh, there'll be a glorious meeting,
   When the Bridegroom comes ;
And a hallelujah greeting,
   When the Bridegroom comes.
In that night,....that solemn night,....
With our lamps all burning bright,
   When the Bridegroom comes.

519   THE Lord is coming by and
   by,
   Be ready when He comes ;
He comes from His fair home on
   high,
   Be ready when He comes ;
He is the Lord our righteousness,
And comes His chosen ones to bless,
And at His Father's throne confess ;
   Be ready when He comes.

Will you be ready when the Bridegroom comes?....
Will you be ready when the Bridegroom comes?....
   Will your lamp be trim'd and bright,
   Be it morning, noon, or night ?
Will you be ready when the Bridegroom comes ?

2 He soon will come to earth again,
   Be ready when He comes ;
Begin His universal reign,
   Be ready when He comes ;

With hallelujahs heav'n will ring,
When Jesus does redemption bring ;
O trim your lamps to meet your King !
Be ready when He comes.

3 Behold ! He comes to one and all,
Be ready when He comes ;
He quickly comes with trumpet call,
Be ready when He comes ;
To judgment called at His command,
Drawn thither by His mighty hand,
Before His throne we all must stand ;
Be ready when He comes.

520 IT may be at morn, when the day is awaking,
When sunlight thro' darkness and shadow is breaking,
That Jesus will come in the fulness of glory,
To receive from the world " His own."

O Lord Jesus, how long ?
How long ere we shout the glad song ?...
Christ returneth ! Hallelujah !
Hallelujah ! Amen !
Hallelujah ! Amen !

2 It may be at midday, it may be at twilight,
It may be, perchance, that the blackness of midnight
Will burst into light in the blaze of His glory,
When Jesus receives " His own."

3 While hosts cry Hosanna from heav'n descending,
With glorified saints, and the angels attending,
With grace on His brow, like a halo of glory,
Will Jesus receive " His own."

4 Oh, joy ! oh, delight ! should we go without dying,
No sickness, no sadness, no dread, and no crying ;
Caught up thro' the clouds with our Lord into glory,
When Jesus receives " His own."

521
REJOICE, ye saints, the time draws near [appear,
When Christ will in the clouds
And for His people call.

Trim your lamps and be ready,
Trim your lamps and be ready,
Trim your lamps and be ready for the midnight cry.
For the midnight cry, for the midnight cry,
Trim your lamps and be ready for the midnight cry.

2 The trumpet sounds, the thunders roll ;
The heavens passing as a scroll,
The earth will burn with fire.

3 Poor sinners then on earth will cry,
While lightnings flash from out the sky,
" O mountains, on us fall ! "

4 Come, brethren all, and let us try
To warn poor sinners, and to cry,
" Behold, the Bridegroom comes."

522 JESUS is coming ! sing the glad word !
Coming for those He redeem'd by His blood,
Coming to reign as the glorified Lord !
Jesus is coming again !

Jesus is coming, is coming again !
Jesus is coming again ;...
Shout the glad tidings o'er mountain and plain !
Jesus is coming again !

2 Jesus is coming ! the dead shall arise,
Lov'd ones shall meet in a joyful surprise, [skies,
Caught up together to Him in the
Jesus is coming again !

3 Jesus is coming ! His saints to release ;
Coming to give to the warring earth peace ; [shall cease ;
Sinning, and sighing, and sorrow
Jesus is coming again !

4 Jesus is coming ! the promise is true :
Who are the chosen, the faithful, the few, [review ?
Waiting and watching, prepared for
Jesus is coming again !

523 I'M waiting for Thee, Lord,
Thy beauty to see, Lord,
I'm waiting for Thee, for Thy coming again ;
Thou art gone over there, Lord,
A place to prepare, Lord,
Thy home I shall share at Thy coming again.

2 'Mid danger and fear, Lord,
    I'm oft weary here, Lord,
The day must be near of Thy coming
        again ;
    'Tis all sunshine there, Lord,
    No sighing nor care, Lord,
But glory so fair at Thy coming again.

3 Whilst Thou art away, Lord,
    I stumble and stray, Lord ;
Oh, hasten the day of Thy coming
        again !
    This is not my rest, Lord ;
    A pilgrim confest, Lord,
I wait to·be blest at Thy coming again.

4 Our loved ones before, Lord,
    Their troubles are o'er, Lord,
I'll meet them once more at Thy
        coming again :
    The blood was the sign, Lord,
    That marked them as Thine, Lord,
And brightly they'll shine at Thy
        coming again.

5 E'en now let my ways, Lord,
    Be bright with Thy praise, Lord,
For brief are the days ere Thy coming
        again.
    I'm waiting for Thee, Lord,
    Thy beauty to see, Lord,   [again.
No triumph for me like Thy coming

524 OH, for the peace which floweth
        like a river,
    Making life's desert places bloom
        and smile !
Oh, for the faith to grasp heav'n's
    bright " for ever,"
    Amid the shadows of earth's
        " little while ! "

2 A little while for patient vigil
        keeping,
    To face the storm, to battle with
        the strong ;
A little while to sow the seed with
        weeping,
    Then bind the sheaves and sing
        the harvest song !

3 A little while to keep the oil from
        failing,
    A little while faith's flickering
        lamp to trim ;
And then the Bridegroom's coming
        footsteps hailing,
    To haste to meet Him with the
        bridal hymn !

4 And He who is Himself the Gift and
        Giver ;   [smile—
    The future glory and the present
With the bright promise of the glad
    " for ever."
    Will light the shadows of the
    " little while ! "

525 " TILL He come ! "   Oh, let
        the words
Linger on the trembling chords ;
Let the " little while " between
In their golden light be seen ;
Let us think how heaven and home
Lie beyond that " Till He come ! "

2 When the weary ones we love
Enter on their rest above—
Seems the earth so poor and vast ?
All our life-joy overcast ?
Hush ! be ev'ry murmur dumb ;
It is only " Till He come ! "

3 Clouds and conflicts round us press ;
Would we have one sorrow less ?
All the sharpness of the Cross,
All that tells the world is loss—
Death, and darkness, and the tomb :
Only whisper, " Till He come ! "

4 See, the feast of love is spread,
Drink the wine and break the bread :
Sweet memorials—till the Lord
Call us round His heavenly board ;
Some from earth, from glory some,
Severed only " Till He come."

526 THOU art coming, O my
        Saviour !
    Thou art coming, O my King !
Ev'ry tongue Thy name confessing,
    Well may we rejoice and sing !
Thou art coming ! rays of glory
    Thro' the veil Thy death has rent,
Gladden now our pilgrim pathway,
    Glory from Thy presence sent.

Thou art coming ! Thou art coming !
    We shall meet Thee on Thy way !
Thou art coming ! we shall see Thee,
    And be like Thee on that day !
Thou art coming ! Thou art coming !
    Jesus, our beloved Lord.
Oh, the joy to see Thee reigning,
    Worshipped, glorified, adored.

2 Thou art coming, not a shadow,
    Not a mist, and not a tear,
Not a sin, and not a sorrow,
    On that sunrise, grand and clear ;

Thou art coming! Jesus, Saviour,
Nothing else seems worth a
thought;
Oh, how marvellous the glory,
And the bliss Thy pain hath
bought.

3 Thou art coming! we are waiting
With a " hope " that cannot fail;
Asking not the day or hour,
Anchor'd safe within the veil;
Thou art coming! at Thy table
We are witnesses for this,
As we meet Thee in communion,
Earnest of our coming bliss.

527   HAVE ye heard the song from
the golden land?
Have ye heard the glad new song?
Let us bind our sheaves with a
willing hand,
For the time will not be long.

The Lord of the harvest will soon appear;
His smile, His voice we shall see and hear!
The Lord of the harvest will soon appear,
And gather the reapers home!

2 They are looking down from the
golden land—
Our belov'd are looking down;
They have done their work, they
have borne their cross,
And receiv'd their promis'd crown.

3 Oh! the song rolls on from the golden
land,
And our hearts are strong to-day;
For it nerves our souls with its music
sweet,
As we toil in the noontide ray.

4 Oh! the song rolls on from the
golden land,
From its vales of joy and flow'rs;
And we feel and know by a living
faith
That its tones will soon be ours.

528   WHEN the trumpet of the
Lord shall sound,
And time shall be no more,
And the morning breaks, eternal,
bright and fair,
When the saved of earth shall gather
Over on the other shore,
And the roll is called up yonder,
I'll be there.

When the roll...is called up yon - - der,
When the roll...is called up yon - - der,
When the roll...is called up yon - - der,
When the roll is called up yonder, I'll be there.

2 On that bright and cloudless
morning,
When the dead in Christ shall rise,
And the glory of His resurrection
share;
When His chosen ones will gather
To their home beyond the skies,
And the roll is called up yonder,
I'll be there.

3 Let us labour for the Master
From the dawn till setting sun,
Let us talk of all His wondrous
love and care;
Then, when all of life is over,
And our work on earth is done,
And the roll is called up yonder,
I'll be there.

529   THERE'S an hour which no
man knoweth,
Nor the angels round the throne,
When the Lord shall come in glory
from the sky;   [Him,
All the saints shall rise to meet
For He calleth for His own,
They shall hear the trumpet sound-
ing by and by.

Are you ready?...ready?...looking for the King?
Ready, while you labour, watch, and pray?...
Are you ready? ready? looking for the King?
Ready for the happy Crowning Day?

2 What a blessed transformation
In the twinkling of an eye,
When the mortal shall immortal life
put on!   [Him,
Those who love Him shall be like
When He cometh from on high,
At the noontide, at the midnight,
or at dawn.

3 Though our sins have been as
scarlet,
Let us seek the streams that flow
From the Cross that rose on Cal-
vary's rugged height;
He is able still to keep us,
And present us white as snow,
When He comes again as clouds of
dazzling light.

530 WHEN the King comes back
from the far-off land,
And the trumpet sounds to meet
Him ;
Oh ! the joy that thrills thro' the
raptur'd band   [Him.
Of the saints as they rise to greet

O hasten, Lord, that happy day,
   The Kingdom of Thy glory ;
For our spirits yearn for Thy blest return,
   As we muse on the Gospel story.

2 When the morning breaks on the
hills of time,
And the shadows all are fleeing,
When the Bride awakes to the
marriage chime,
And her faith is lost in seeing.

3 When the fight is o'er, and the
victory won,
And the vanquish'd foe is flying ;
When the Captain calls with His
own " Well done ! "
To the crown of the life undying.

4 Oh ! to share the grace of the holy
place
Where the angel hosts adore Him ;
Where our eyes shall gaze on the
Bridegroom's face,
As we stand all fair before Him !

5 Speed, speed that hour when Thy
blood-bought pow'r
Shall reveal Thy full salvation ;
And the world resound to her utmost
bound
With the song of the new creation.

All blessing, glory, honour be,
  And praise that ceaseth never,
To Him that sits upon the throne,
  And to the Lamb for ever !

531 HAPPY home-coming of our
King,
We'll meet our loved ones gone
before ;   [bring
And sweet the greeting they will
To us upon the golden shore.

Happy home-coming, blessed home-coming,
Glorious home-coming of our Saviour-King
What a glad meeting on that great morning
At the home-coming of our Saviour-King !

2 Blessed home-coming of our King ;
We'll join the everlasting psalm
Of joy that angel voices sing :
" The song of Moses and the
Lamb."

3 Glorious home-coming of our King ;
With Jesus we will live for aye
Where songs of love and gladness
ring
In tune thro' heav'n's eternal day.

532 AS once to earth the Saviour
came,
Sometime He'll come again ;
The sky with heavenly light aflame,
Sometime He'll come again.

Sometime,...sometime,
  Christ shall come to reign ;
Prepare my soul to meet Him,
  Sometime He'll come again.

2 Tell ev'rywhere, with great delight,
Sometime He'll come again ;
Upon the clouds of glory bright,
Sometime He'll come again.

3 O'er all the earth the tidings ring,
Sometime He'll come again ;
Not as a babe, but as a king,
Sometime He'll come again.

4 When dawns that blessed morning
fair,
Sometime He'll come again ;
His saints will meet Him in the air,
Sometime He'll come again.

5 Oh, let us live and do our best,
Sometime He'll come again ;
Then He will take us home to rest,
Sometime He'll come again.

533 HAIL to the Lord's Anointed,
Great David's greater Son ;
Hail in the time appointed,
His reign on earth begun !
He comes to break oppression,
To set the captive free ;
To take away transgression,
And rule in equity.

2 He shall come down like showers
Upon the fruitful earth ;
And love, joy, hope, like flowers,
Spring in His path to birth.
Before Him on the mountains
Shall Peace, the herald, go ;
And righteousness in fountains
From hill to valley flow.

3 Kings shall fall down before Him,
An1 gold and incense bring ;
All nations shall adore Him,
His praise all people sing.

For He shall have dominion
  O'er river, sea, and shore,
Far as the eagle's pinion
  Or dove's light wing can soar.

534   HARK ! hark ! hear the glad
             tidings ;
Soon, soon Jesus will come,
Robed, robed in honour and glory,
To gather His ransomed ones home.
    Yes, yes, oh yes,
    To gather His ransomed ones home.

2 Joy ! joy ! sound it more loudly ;
  Sing, sing glory to God ;
Soon, soon Jesus is coming,
  Publish the tidings abroad :
    Yes, yes, oh yes,
    Publish the tidings abroad.

3 Bright, bright seraphs attending ;
  Shouts, shouts filling the air ;
Down, down, swiftly from heaven
  Jesus our Lord will appear :
    Yes, yes, oh yes,
    Jesus our Lord will appear.

4 Still, still rest on the promise ;
  Cling, cling fast to His word ;
Wait, wait—if He should tarry,
  We'll patiently wait for the Lord :
    Yes, yes, oh yes,
    Patiently wait for the Lord.

535   WHY stand ye idly gazing
    T'wards   heaven's   blessed
      height ?   [again ;
This same Jesus is coming back

The shining angels told it,
  Arrayed in spotless white ;
  This same Jesus is coming back
    again.

This same Jesus, this same Jesus !
  Oh, tell the joyful tidings to all the sons of
    men !
Oh, let us work and pray, rejoicing ev'ry day :
  This same Jesus is coming back again.

2 Receiving His good Spirit,
  We'll know His presence near ;
  This same Jesus is coming back
    again ;
He fills us with His blessing,
  He gives us love and cheer ;
  This same Jesus is coming back
    again.

3 Our lowly talents doubling,
  More faithful may we be ;
  This same Jesus is coming back
    again ;
And spread abroad His Gospel
  With happy hearts and free ;
  This same Jesus is coming back
    again.

4 In ev'ry time of trial
  We'll trust His changeless love ;
  This same Jesus is coming back
    again ;
The mighty King of Glory
  Still reigns for us above :
  This same Jesus is coming back
    again.

THE HOLY SPIRIT

536   OH, spread the tidings round,
    Wherever man is found,
Wherever human hearts and human
  woes abound ;
Let ev'ry Christian tongue proclaim
  the joyful sound :
    The Comforter has come !

The Comforter has come, the Comforter has
    come !
The Holy Ghost from heaven, the Father's
    promise giv'n ;
Oh, spread the tidings round wherever man is
    found—
    The Comforter has come !

2 The long, long night is past,
  The morning breaks at last ;
And hush'd the dreadful wail and
  fury of the blast.

As o'er the golden hills the day
  advances fast !
    The Comforter has come !

3 Lo, the great King of kings,
With healing in His wings
To ev'ry captive soul a full deliv'r-
  ance brings ;
And thro' the vacant cells the song
  of triumph rings :
    The Comforter has come !

4 O boundless love divine !
How shall this tongue of mine
To wond'ring mortals tell the match-
  less grace divine— · [image shine !
That I, a child of hell, should in His
    The Comforter has come !

5 Sing till the echoes fly
  Above the vaunted sky,
  And all the saints above to all below
    reply,
  In strains of endless love, the song
    that ne'er will die :
      The Comforter has come !

537 OPEN my eyes that I may see
    Glimpses of truth Thou hast
    for me ;   [key
Place in my hands the wonderful
That shall unclasp and set me free.
Silently now I wait for Thee,
Ready, my God, Thy will to see ;
Open my eyes, illumine me,
    Spirit divine !

2 Open my ears that I may hear
Voices of truth Thou sendest clear ;
And while the wave notes fall on
  my ear,
Ev'rything false will disappear.
Silently now I wait for Thee,
Ready, my God, Thy will to see ;
Open my ears, illumine me,
    Spirit divine !

3 Open my mouth and let me bear
Gladly the warm truth ev'rywhere ;
Open my heart and let me prepare
Love with Thy children thus to
  share.
Silently now I wait for Thee.
Ready, my God, Thy will to see ;
Open my heart, illumine me,
    Spirit divine !

538 THE Holy Ghost has come—
    We feel His presence here !
Our hearts would now no longer
  roam,
    But bow in filial fear.

2 This tenderness of love,
    The hush of solemn power—
'Tis heaven descending from above
    To fill this favour'd hour !

3 Earth's darkness all has fled,
  Heav'n's light serenely shines ;
And ev'ry heart divinely led,
    To holy thought inclines.

4 No more let sin deceive,
    Nor earthly cares betray ;
Oh, let us never, never grieve
    The Comforter away !

539 OUR blest Redeemer, ere He
    breath'd
    His tender, last farewell,
A Guide, a Comforter bequeath'd
    With us to dwell.

2 He came sweet influence to impart,
    A gracious, willing Guest,
Where He can find one humble
  heart
    Wherein to rest.

3 And His that gentle voice we hear,
    Soft as the breath of even,
That checks each thought, that
  calms each fear,
    And speaks of heaven.

4 And ev'ry virtue we possess,
    And ev'ry conquest won,
And ev'ry thought of holiness
    Are His alone.

5 Spirit of purity and grace,
    Our weakness pitying see ;
O make our hearts Thy dwelling-
  place,
    And worthier Thee.

6 O praise the Father, praise the Son ;
    Blest Spirit, praise to Thee ;
All praise to God, the Three in One,
    The One in Three.

540 COME, gracious Spirit, heav'nly
    Dove,
With light and comfort from above ;
Be Thou our Guardian, Thou our
  Guide,
O'er ev'ry thought and step preside.

2 The light of truth to us display,
That we may know and choose Thy
  way ;
Plant holy fear in ev'ry heart,
That we from God may ne'er depart.

3 Conduct us safe conduct us far
From ev'ry sin and hurtful snare ;
Lead us to Christ, the Living Way,
Nor let us from His pastures stray.

4 Lead us to holiness, the road
That we must take to dwell with
  God ;
Lead us to God, our final rest,
To be with Him for ever blessed !

541 HOLY Spirit, faithful Guide,
 Ever near the Christian's side,
Gently lead us by the hand,
Pilgrims in a desert land :
Weary souls for e'er rejoice
While they hear that sweetest voice,
Whisper softly, " Wand'rer, come,
Follow Me, I'll guide thee home."

2 Ever present, truest Friend,
 Ever near Thine aid to lend ;
Leave us not to doubt and fear,
Groping on in darkness here ;
When the storms are raging sore,
Hearts grow faint and hopes give o'er,
Whisper softly, " Wand'rer, come,
Follow Me, I'll guide thee home."

3 When our days of toil shall cease,
 May our hearts be filled with peace ;
Drawing near in praise and pray'r,
Knowing that our names are there ;
Pleading naught but Jesus' blood,
He'll be with us in the flood,
Whisper softly, " Wand'rer, come,
Follow Me, I'll guide thee home."

542 COME, Holy Ghost, our hearts
    inspire,
 Let us Thine influence prove ;
Source of the old prophetic fire,
 Fountain of light and love.

2 Come, Holy Ghost, for, moved by
   Thee,
 The prophets wrote and spoke ;
Unlock the truth, Thyself the Key,
 Unseal the sacred book.

3 Expand Thy wings, celestial Dove,
 Brood o'er our nature's night ;
On our disordered spirits move,
 And let there now be light.

4 God, thro' Himself, we then shall
   know,
 If Thou within us shine ; [below,
And sound, with all Thy saints
 The depths of love divine.

543 JESUS, Thine all-victorious
   love
 Shed in my heart abroad ;
Then shall my feet no longer rove,
 Rooted and fixed in God.

2 Oh, that in me the sacred fire
 Might now begin to glow,
Burn up the dross of base desire,
 And make the mountains flow.

3 Thou who at Pentecost didst fall,
 And all my sins consume,
Come, Holy Ghost, for Thee I call,
 Spirit of burning, come !

4 Refining fire, go through my heart,
 Illuminate my soul ;
Scatter Thy life through every part,
 And sanctify the whole.

5 My steadfast soul from falling free
 Shall then no longer move ;
While Christ is all the world to me,
 And all my heart is love.

544 SPIRIT Divine, attend our
   prayers,
 And make our hearts Thy home ;
Descend with all Thy gracious
   powers,
 Oh, come, great Spirit, come !

2 Come as the light—to us reveal
 Our need of Thee below ;
And lead us in those paths of life
 Where all the righteous go.

3 Come as the fire—and purge our
   hearts
 With sacrificial flame ;
Let our whole self an offering be
 To our Redeemer's name.

4 Come as the dew—and sweetly bless
 This consecrated hour ;
May barrenness rejoice to own
 Thy fertilising power.

5 Come as the Dove—and spread Thy
   wings,
 The wings of peaceful love ;
And let Thy Church on earth
   become
 Blest as the Church above.

6 Come as the wind—with rushing
   sound
 And Pentecostal grace ;
That all of women born may see
 The glory of Thy face.

545 GRACIOUS Spirit, Love
   divine,
 Let Thy light within me shine ;
All my sin and fear remove,
 Fill me with Thy heavenly love.

2 Speak Thy matchless grace to me,
 From my sin, oh, set me free ;
Lead me to the Lamb of God,
 Wash me in His precious blood.

3 Faith, and hope, and charity,
   Comforter, descend from Thee :
   Thou th' anointing Spirit art ;
   These Thy gifts to me impart.

4 Life and peace to me impart,
   Seal salvation on my heart ;
   Breathe Thyself into my breast,
   Earnest of immortal rest.

546   GRACIOUS Spirit, dwell with
         me :
   I myself would gracious be ;
   And with words that help and heal,
   Would Thy life in mine reveal ;
   And, with actions bold and meek,
   Would for Christ my Saviour speak.

2 Tender Spirit, dwell with me :
   I myself would tender be ;
   Shut my heart up like a flower
   At temptation's darksome hour ;
   Open it when shines the sun,
   And His love by fragrance own.

3 Mighty Spirit, dwell with me :
   I myself would mighty be,
   Mighty so as to prevail
   Where unaided man must fail ;
   Ever by a mighty hope
   Pressing on and bearing up.

4 Holy Spirit, dwell with me :
   I myself would holy be ;
   Separate from sin, I would
   Choose and cherish all things good ;
   And whatever I can be,
   Give to Him who gave me Thee.

547   JOYS are flowing like a river
         Since the Comforter has
         come ;
   He abides with us for ever, [home.
   Makes the trusting heart His

   Blessed quietness, holy quietness,
     What assurance in my soul !
   On the stormy sea, He speaks peace to me,
     How the billows cease to roll.

2 Bringing life and health and glad-
     ness, ·
   All around this heavenly Guest ;
   Banished unbelief and sadness,
   Changed our weariness to rest.

3 Like the rain that falls from heaven,
   Like the sunlight from the sky,
   So the Holy Ghost is given,
   Coming on us from on high.

4 See a fruitful field is growing,
   Blessed fruits of righteousness,
   And the streams of life are flowing
   In the lonely wilderness.

5 What a wonderful salvation,
   Where we always see His face ;
   What a perfect habitation,
   What a quiet resting place !

548   HERE from the world we turn,
         Jesus to seek ;
   Here may His loving voice
     Graciously speak !
   Jesus, our dearest Friend,
   While at Thy feet we bend,
   Oh, let Thy smile descend !
     'Tis Thee we seek.

2 Come, Holy Comforter,
     Presence divine,
   Now in our longing hearts
     Graciously shine !
   Oh, for Thy mighty pow'r !
   Oh, for a blessed show'r,
   Filling this hallowed hour
     With joy divine !

3 Saviour, Thy work revive !
     Here may we see
   Those who are dead in sin
     Quick'ned by Thee !
   Come to our hearts to-night,
   Make ev'ry burden light,
   Cheer Thou our waiting sight ;
     We long for Thee.

549   THEY were in an upper
         chamber,
   They were all with one accord,
   When the Holy Ghost descended,
   As was promised by our Lord.

   O Lord, send the pow'r just now ;
   O Lord, send the pow'r just now ;
   O Lord, send the pow'r just now,
     And baptize ev'ry one.

2 Yes, this pow'r from heav'n de-
     scended
   With the sound of rushing wind ;
   Tongues of fire came down upon
     them,
   As the Lord said He would send.

3 Yes, this " old-time " pow'r was
     given
   To our fathers who were true ;
   This is promised to believers,
   And we all may have it too.

550 JESUS for me, Jesus for me,
All the time ev'rywhere, Jesus
for me.

551 THY Holy Spirit, Lord, alone,
Can turn our hearts from sin;
His power alone can sanctify
And keep us pure within.

O Spirit of Faith and Love,
Come in our midst, we pray,
And purify each waiting heart;
Baptise us with pow'r to-day.

2 Thy Holy Spirit, Lord, alone
Can deeper love inspire;
His power alone within our souls
Can light the sacred fire.

3 Thy Holy Spirit, Lord, can bring
The gifts we seek in pray'r;
His voice can words of comfort speak
And still each wave of care.

4 Thy Holy Spirit, Lord, can give
The grace we need this hour;
And while we wait, O Spirit, come
In sanctifying power.

O Spirit of Love, descend,
Come in our midst, we pray
And like a rushing mighty wind,
Sweep over our souls to-day.

552 THOU art enough for me,
Thou art enough for me;
Oh, precious living, loving Lord,
Yes, Thou art enough for me!

PRAYER AND CONSECRATION

553 ALAS! and did my Saviour
bleed!
And did my Sovereign die?
Would He devote that sacred head
For such a worm as I?

Help me, dear Saviour, Thee to own,
And ever faithful be;
And when Thou sittest on Thy throne,
O Lord, remember me.

2 Was it for crimes that I had done
He groaned upon the tree?
Amazing pity! grace unknown!
And love beyond degree!

3 Well might the sun in darkness hide,
And shut his glories in,
When Christ, the mighty Maker,
died
For man, the creature's sin.

4 Thus might I hide my blushing face,
While His dear cross appears,
Dissolve my heart in thankfulness,
And melt mine eyes to tears.

5 But drops of grief can ne'er repay
The debt of love I owe;
Here, Lord, I give myself away;
'Tis all that I can do.

554 SEARCH me, O God! my
actions try,
And let my life appear,
As seen by Thine all-searching eye—
To mine my ways make clear.

2 Search all my sense, and know my
heart,
Who only canst make known,
And let the deep, the hidden part
To me be fully shown.

3 Throw light into the darkened cells,
Where passion reigns within;
Quicken my conscience till it feels
The loathsomeness of sin.

4 Search all my thoughts, the secret
springs,
The motives that control;
The chambers where polluted things
Hold empire o'er the soul.

5 Search, till Thy fiery glance has
cast
Its holy light through all,
And I by grace am brought at last
Before Thy face to fall.

6 Thus prostrate I shall learn of Thee,
What now I feebly prove,
That God alone in Christ can be
Unutterable love!

555 FROM ev'ry stormy wind that
blows,
From ev'ry swelling tide of woes,
There is a calm, a sure retreat,
'Tis found beneath the Mercy-seat.

2 There is a place where Jesus sheds
The oil of gladness on our heads;
A place that all beside more sweet,
It is the blood-stain'd Mercy-seat.

3 There is a scene where spirits blend,
Where friend holds fellowship with
friend;
Tho' sund'red far, by faith we meet,
Around one common Mercy-seat.

556 LONG my wilful heart said
"no"
To Jesus' tender pleading;
Now I long His love to know,
My stubborn will is yielding.
Yes, dear Lord, yes, dear Lord,
Here I give my all to Thee;
I believe, I believe the blood avails for me.

2 Bringing all I am and have
In humble consecration,
Trusting in the blood, I claim
This uttermost salvation.

3 Giving o'er my doubts and fears
And all my useless trying,
Trusting not my pray'rs or tears,
But on Thy Word relying.

4 Yes, dear Lord, in life or death
With Thee all good possessing,
Not by feeling but by faith
I take the promised blessing.

557 I HAVE heard my Saviour
calling,
I have heard my Saviour calling,
I have heard my Saviour calling,
"Take thy cross and follow, follow
Me."
Where He leads me I will follow,
Where He leads me I will follow,
Where He leads me I will follow,
I'll go with Him, with Him all the way.

2 Tho' He leads me through the
valley.   [way.
I'll go with Him, with Him all the

3 Tho' He leads me thro' the garden,
I'll go with Him, with Him all the
way.

4 Tho' He leads me to the conflict,
I'll go with Him, with Him all the
way.

5 Tho' He leads through fiery trials,
I'll go with Him, with Him all the
way.

558 JESUS, I my cross have taken,
All to leave and follow Thee;
Destitute, despised, forsaken,
Thou from hence my all shalt be.

I will follow Thee, my Saviour,
Thou didst shed Thy blood for me,
And though all the world forsake Thee,
By Thy grace I'll follow Thee.

2 Perish ev'ry fond ambition,
All I've sought, and hoped, and
known;
Yet how rich is my condition!
God and heaven are still mine own.

3 Let the world despise and leave me:
They have left my Saviour too—
Human hearts and looks deceive
me—
Thou art not, like them, untrue.

4 And whilst Thou shalt smile upon me
God of wisdom, love and might,
Foes may hate, and friends disown
me:
Show Thy face and all is bright.

5 Man may trouble and distress me,
'Twill but drive me to Thy breast;
Life with trials hard may press me,
Heaven will bring me sweeter rest.

6 Oh! 'tis not in grief to harm me,
While Thy love is left to me;
Oh! 'twere not in joy to charm me,
Were that joy unmixed with Thee.

559 WHAT a Friend we have in
Jesus,
All our sins and griefs to bear;
What a privilege to carry
Ev'rything to God in pray'r.
Oh, what peace we often forfeit,
Oh, what needless pain we bear—
All because we do not carry
Ev'rything to God in pray'r.

2 Have we trials and temptations?
Is there trouble anywhere?
We should never be discouraged,
Take it to the Lord in pray'r.
Can we find a friend so faithful,
Who will all our sorrows share?
Jesus knows our ev'ry weakness,
Take it to the Lord in pray'r.

3 Are we weak and heavy laden,
Cumbered with a load of care?
Precious Saviour, still our refuge—
Take it to the Lord in pray'r.
Do thy friends despise, forsake thee?
Take it to the Lord in pray'r;
In His arms He'll take and shield
thee,
Thou wilt find a solace there.

560 SWEET hour of pray'r, sweet
　　　hour of pray'r,
That calls me from a world of care,
And bids me, at my Father's throne,
Make all my wants and wishes known
In seasons of distress and grief
My soul has often found relief,
And oft escaped the tempter's snare,
By thy return, sweet hour of pray'r.

2 Sweet hour of pray'r, sweet hour of
　　　pray'r,
The joy I feel, the bliss I share
Of those whose anxious spirits burn
With strong desires for thy return !
With such I hasten to the place
Where God, my Saviour, shows His
　　　face,
And gladly take my station there,
And wait for thee, sweet hour of
　　　pray'r.

3 Sweet hour of pray'r, sweet hour of
　　　pray'r,
Thy wings shall my petition bear
To Him whose truth and faithfulness
Engage the waiting soul to bless ;
And since He bids me seek His face,
Believe His Word, and trust His
　　　grace,
I'll cast on Him my ev'ry care,
And wait for thee, sweet hour of
　　　pray'r.

561 I AM Thine, O Lord, I have
　　　heard Thy voice,
And it told Thy love to me ;
But I long to rise in the arms of
　　　faith,
And be closer drawn to Thee.

Draw me near - - er,...nearer blessed Lord,
To the Cross where Thou hast died ;
Draw me nearer, nearer, nearer, blessed Lord,
To Thy precious, bleeding side.

2 Consecrate me now to Thy service,
　　　Lord,
By the pow'r of grace divine ;
Let my soul look up with a steadfast
　　　hope,
And my will be lost in Thine.

3 Oh, the pure delight of a single hour
That before Thy throne I spend,
When I kneel in prayer, and with
　　　Thee, my God,
I commune as friend with friend.

4 There are depths of love that
　　　cannot know
Till I cross the narrow sea ;
There are heights of joy that I ma
　　　not reach
Till I rest in peace with Thee.

562 WHAT tho' the clouds ar
　　　hovering o'er me,
And I seem to walk alone,
Longing, 'mid my cares and crosses
For the joys that now are flown !
If I've Jesus, " Jesus only,"
Then my sky will have a gem ;
He's the Sun of brightest splendour
And the Star of Bethlehem.

2 What though all my earthly journe
Bringeth naught but weary hours
And in grasping for life's roses,
Thorns I find instead of flowers !
If I've Jesus, " Jesus only,"
I possess a cluster rare ;
He's the " Lily of the Valley,"
And the " Rose of Sharon " fair.

3 What though all my heart is yearn
For the loved of long ago—　[in
Bitter lessons sadly learning
From the shadowy page of woe !
If I've Jesus, " Jesus only,"
He'll be with me to the end ;
And, unseen, by mortal vision,
Angel bands will o'er me bend.

4 When I soar to realms of glory,
And an entrance I await,
If I whisper, " Jesus only ! "
Wide will ope the pearly gate ;
When I join the heavenly chorus,
And the angel hosts I see,
Precious Jesus, " Jesus only,"
Will my theme of rapture be.

563 COME ye yourselves apart and
　　　rest awhile,　　　[throng
Weary I know it, of the press and
Wipe from your brow the sweat and
　　　dust of toil,　　　　[be strong
And in My quiet strength again

2 Come ye aside from all the world
　　　holds dear,　　　[never known
For converse which the world ha
Alone with Me and with My Fathe
　　　here,　　　　　　　[alone
With Me and with My Father no

3 Come, tell Me all that you have said
    and done,
  Your victories and failures, hopes
    and fears ;   [and won ;
I know how hardly souls are wooed
  My choicest wreaths are always
    wet with tears.

4 Come ye and rest ! the journey is
    too great,
  And ye will faint beside the way
    and sink ;
The bread of life is here for you to
    eat,   [to drink.
  And here for you the wine of love

5 Then, fresh from converse with your
    Lord, return
  And work till daylight softens into
    even ;   [ye learn
The brief hours are not lost in which
  More of your Master and His rest
    in heaven.

564   GO bury thy sorrow,
    The world hath its share ;
  Go bury it deeply,
    Go hide it with care ;
  Go think of it calmly,
    When curtain'd by night ;
  Go tell it to Jesus,
    And all will be right.

2 Go tell it to Jesus,
    He knoweth thy grief ;
  Go tell it to Jesus,
    He'll send thee relief ;
  Go gather the sunshine
    He sheds on the way ;
  He'll lighten thy burden,
    Go, weary one, pray.

3 Hearts growing a-weary
    With heavier woe,
  Now droop 'mid the darkness—
    Go comfort them, go !
  Go bury thy sorrow,
    Let others be blest ;
  Go give them the sunshine ;
    Tell Jesus the rest.

565   HARK, my soul ! it is the
    Lord !
'Tis thy Saviour, hear His Word ;
Jesus speaks, and speaks to thee,
  " Say, poor sinner, lov'st thou
    Me ? "

2 " I deliv'red thee when bound,
  And, when bleeding, healed thy
    wound ;
  Sought thee wand'ring, set thee right
  Turned thy darkness into light.

3 " Can a woman's tender care
  Cease towards the child she bare ?
  Yes, she may forgetful be,
  Yet will I remember thee.

4 " Mine is an unchanging love,
  Higher than the heights above,
  Deeper than the depths beneath,
  Free and faithful, strong as death.

5 " Thou shalt see My glory soon,
  When the work of grace is done ;
  Partner of My throne shalt be :
  Say, poor sinner, lov'st thou Me ? "

6 Lord, it is my chief complaint
  That my love is weak and faint ;
  Yet I love Thee and adore ;
  O for grace to love Thee more !

566   SWEET the moments, rich in
    blessing,
  Which before the Cross I spend ;
Life and health, and peace possess-
    ing,
  From the sinner's dying Friend !

2 Here I rest, for ever viewing,
  Mercy poured in streams of blood ;
  Precious drops, my soul bedewing,
  Plead, and claim my peace with
    God.

3 Truly blessed is this station,
  Low before His Cross to lie,
  While I see divine compassion
  Beaming in His languid eye.

4 Here it is I find my heaven,
  While upon the Lamb I gaze ;
  Love I much?—I've much forgiven :
  I'm a miracle of grace.

5 Love and grief my heart abiding,
  With my tears His feet I'll bathe ;
  Constant still in faith abiding—
  Life deriving from His death.

567   SPEAK to my soul, Lord
    Jesus,
  Speak now in tend'rest tone ;
Whisper in loving kindness :
  " Thou art not left alone."

Open my heart to hear Thee,
  Quickly to hear Thy voice ;
Fill Thou my soul with praises,
  Let me in Thee rejoice.

Speak Thou in softest whispers,
  Whispers of love to me ;
" Thou shalt be always conq'ror,
  Thou shalt be always free."
Speak Thou to me each day, Lord,
  Always in tend'rest tone ;
Let me now hear Thy whisper,
  " Thou art not left alone."

2 Speak to Thy children ever,
  Lead in the holy way ;
Fill them with joy and gladness,
  Teach them to watch and pray.
May they in consecration
  Yield their whole lives to Thee ;
Hasten Thy coming kingdom,
  Till our dear Lord we see.

3 Speak now as in the old time
  Thou didst reveal Thy will ;
Let me know all my duty,
  Let me Thy law fulfil.
Lead me to glorify Thee,
  Help me to show Thy praise,
Gladly to do Thy bidding,
  Honour Thee all my days.

568 I NEED Thee ev'ry hour,
    Most gracious Lord ;
  No tender voice like Thine
    Can peace afford.

I need Thee, oh, I need Thee,
  Ev'ry hour I need Thee ;
Oh, bless me now, my Saviour,
  I come to Thee.

2 I need Thee ev'ry hour,
    Stay Thou near by ;
  Temptations lose their pow'r
    When Thou art nigh.

3 I need Thee ev'ry hour,
    In joy or pain ;
  Come quickly and abide,
    Or life is vain.

4 I need Thee ev'ry hour,
    Teach me Thy will ;
  And Thy rich promises
    In me fulfil.

5 I need Thee ev'ry hour,
    Most Holy One ;
  Oh, make me Thine indeed,
    Thou blessed Son !

569 NEARER, my God, to Thee,
    Nearer to Thee ;
  E'en though it be a cross
    That raiseth me ;
  Still all my song shall be,
  Nearer, my God, to Thee,
    Nearer to Thee.

2 Though like a wanderer,
    The sun gone down,
  Darkness be over me,
    My rest a stone ;
  Yet in my dreams I'd be
  Nearer, my God, to Thee,
    Nearer to Thee.

3 There let the way appear,
    Steps unto heav'n ;
  All that Thou sendest me,
    In mercy giv'n ;
  Angels to beckon me
  Nearer, my God, to Thee,
    Nearer to Thee.

4 Then with my waking thoughts,
    Bright with Thy praise,
  Out of my stony griefs
    Bethel I'll raise ;
  So by my woes to be
  Nearer, my God, to Thee,
    Nearer to Thee.

5 Or if on joyful wing,
    Cleaving the sky,.
  Sun, moon, and stars forgot,
    Upward I fly ;
  Still all my song shall be,
  Nearer, my God, to Thee,
    Nearer to Thee.

570 THY life was given for Me !
    Thy blood, O Lord, was shed
  That I might ransomed be,
    And quickened from the dead.
  Thy life, Thy life was given for me ;
  What have I given for Thee ?

2 Long years were spent for me
    In weariness and woe,
  That through eternity
    Thy glory I might know.
  Long years, long years were spent for
  Have I spent one for Thee ?   [me :

3 Thy Father's home of light,
    Thy rainbow circled throne,
  Were left for earthly night—
    For wand'rings sad and lone.
  Yea, all, yea, all was left for me :
  Have I left aught for Thee ?

4 Thou, Lord, hast borne for me
   More than my tongue can tell
Of bitterest agony,
   To rescue me from hell.
Thou sufferedst all for me, for me :
   What have I borne for Thee ?

5 And Thou has brought to me,
   Down from Thy home above,
Salvation full and free,
   Thy pardon and Thy love.
Great   gifts,   great   gifts   Thou
      broughtest me :
   What have I brought to Thee ?

6 Oh, let my life be given,
   My years for Thee be spent ;
World-fetters all be riven,
   And joy with suffering blent ;
To Thee, to Thee my all I bring,
   My Saviour and my King !

571 ONCE I was dead *in* sin, and
         hope within me died,
But now I'm dead *to* sin, with Jesus
   crucified.

   *And can it be that " He loved me,
      And gave Himself for me ? "*

2 O height I cannot reach ! O depth
   I cannot sound !
O love, O boundless love, in my
   Redeemer found !

3 O cold, ungrateful heart, that can
   from Jesus turn,
When living fires of love should on
   His altar burn !

4 I live—and yet not I, but Christ
   that lives in me ;
Who from the law of sin and death
   hath made me free.

572 PRAY'R is the key,
         With the bending knee,
To open the morn's first hours ;
   See the incense rise
   To the starry skies,
Like perfume from the flow'rs.

2 Not a soul so sad,
   Not a heart so glad,
When cometh the shades of night,
   But the daybreak song
   Will the joy prolong,
And some darkness turn to light.

3 Take the golden key
   In your hand and see,
As the night tide drifts away,
   How its blessed hold
   Is a crown of gold,
Through the weary hours of day.

4 When the shadows fall,
   And the vesper call
Is sobbing its low refrain,
   'Tis a garland sweet
   To the toil-worn feet,
And an antidote for pain.

5 Soon the year's dark door
   Shall be shut no more ;
Life's tears shall be wiped away,
   As the pearl gates swing,
   And the gold harps ring,
And the sun unsheathes for aye.

573 WHEN I survey the wondrous
         Cross
   On which the Prince of Glory
      died,
My richest gain I count but loss,
   And pour contempt on all my
      pride.

2 Forbid it, Lord, that I should boast,
   Save in the death of Christ, my
      God ;
All the vain things that charm me
      most,
   I sacrifice them to His blood.

3 See, from His head, His hands, His
      feet,
   Sorrow and love flow mingled
      down ;
Did e'er such love and sorrow meet,
   Or thorns compose so rich a crown?

4 Were the whole realm of nature
      mine,
   That were an offering far too
      small ;
Love so amazing, so divine,
   Demands my soul, my life, my all.

574 WOULD you live for Jesus, and
         be always pure and good ?
Would you walk with Him within
   the narrow road ?
Would you have Him bear your
   burden, carry all your load ?
Let Him have His way with Thee.

His power can make you what you ought to be !
His blood can cleanse your heart and make
    you free ;
His love can fill your soul, and you will see
'Twas best for Him to have His way with thee.

2 Would you have Him make you
    free, and follow at His call ?
Would you know the peace that
    comes by giving all ?
Would you have Him save you, so
    that you need never fall ?
Let Him have His way with thee.

3 Would you in His kingdom find a
    place of constant rest ?
Would you prove Him true each
    providential test ?
Would you in His service labour
    always at your best ?
Let Him have His way with thee.

575 ALL, all to Jesus, I consecrate
    anew ;
He is my portion for ever.
Only His glory henceforth will I
    pursue ;
He is my portion for ever.

Take, take the world, with all its gilded toys,
Take, take the world, I covet not its joys.
Mine is a wealth no moth nor rust destroys :
    Jesus my portion for ever.

2 All, all to Jesus, my trusting heart
    can say ;
He is my portion for ever.
Led by His mercy, I'm walking ev'ry
    day ;
He is my portion for ever.

3 Tho' He may try me, this blessed
    truth I know :
He is my portion for ever.
He will not leave me, His promise
    tells me so :
He is my portion for ever.

4 All, all to Jesus, I cheerfully resign ;
He is my portion for ever.
I have the witness that He, my
    Lord, is mine :
He is my portion for ever.

The following Chorus may be substituted :—
Make Jesus Christ the centre of your life,
He'll reign supreme where only sin was rife ;
He'll speak the word, and end the deadly
    strife ;
    Make Him the centre for ever.

576 MY spirit, soul, and body,
    Jesus, I give to Thee,
A consecrated off'ring,
    Thine evermore to be.

My all is on the altar,
    Lord, I am all Thine own ;
Oh, may my faith ne'er falter,
    Lord, keep me Thine alone.

2 O Jesus, mighty Saviour,
    I trust in Thy great name ;
I look for Thy salvation,
    Thy promise now I claim.

3 Now, Lord, I yield my members,
    From sin's dominion free,
For warfare and for triumph,
    As weapons unto Thee.

4 I'm Thine, O blessed Jesus,
    Washed in Thy precious blood,
Sealed by Thy Holy Spirit,
    A sacrifice to God.

577 PRAY, always pray ; the Holy
    Spirit pleads
Within thee all thy daily, hourly
    needs.

2 Pray, always pray ; beneath sin's
    heaviest load,
Prayer sees the blood from Jesus'
    side that flowed.

3 Pray, always pray ; though weary,
    faint, and lone ;
Prayer nestles by the Father's
    sheltering throne.

4 Pray, always pray ; amid the world's
    turmoil,
Prayer keeps the heart at rest, and
    nerves for toil.

5 Pray, always pray ; if joys thy
    pathway throng,
Prayer strikes the harp, and sings
    the angels' song.

6 Pray, always pray ; if loved ones
    pass the veil,
Prayer drinks with them of springs
    that cannot fail.

7 All earthly things with earth shall
    fade away ;
Prayer grasps eternity ; pray, always
    pray.

578 SAVIOUR! Thy dying love
    Thou gavest me,
Nor should I aught withhold,
  My Lord, from Thee ;
In love my soul would bow,
My heart fulfil its vow,
Some off'ring bring Thee now,
  Something for Thee.

2 At the blest Mercy-seat,
    Pleading for me,
My feeble faith looks up,
  Jesus, to Thee ;
Help me the cross to bear,
Thy wondrous love declare,
Some song to raise, or prayer,
  Something for Thee.

3 Give me a faithful heart—
    Likeness to Thee—
That each departing day
  Henceforth may see
Some work of love begun,
Some deed of kindness done,
Some wanderer sought and won,
  Something for Thee.

4 All that I am and have—
    Thy gifts so free—
In joy, in grief, through life,
  O Lord, for Thee !
And when Thy face I see,
My ransomed soul shall be,
Through all eternity,
  Something for Thee.

579 COME, ye disconsolate ! wher-
  e'er ye languish,
Come to the Mercy-seat, fervently
  kneel ;
Here bring your wounded hearts,
  here tell your anguish,
Earth has no sorrow that heav'n
  cannot heal.

2 Joy of the desolate ! light of the
  straying,   [pure !
Hope of the penitent, fadeless and
Here speaks the Comforter, tenderly
  saying,   [cannot cure.
Earth has no sorrow that heav'n

3 Here see the bread of life ; see
  waters flowing
Forth from the throne of God,
  pure from above ;
Come to the feast of love ; come
  ever knowing,   [can remove.
Earth has no sorrow but heav'n

580 MY faith looks up to Thee,
    Thou Lamb of Calvary,
  Saviour divine ;
Now hear me while I pray,
Take all my guilt away ;
Oh, let me from this day
  Be wholly Thine !

2 May Thy rich grace impart
Strength to my fainting heart,
  My zeal inspire !
As Thou hast died for me,
Oh, may my love to Thee,
Pure, warm, and changeless be
  A living fire !

3 While life's dark maze I tread,
And griefs around me spread,
  Be Thou my Guide ;
Bid darkness turn to day,
Wipe sorrow's tears away,
Nor let me ever stray
  From Thee aside.

4 When ends life's transient dream,
When death's cold, sullen stream
  Shall o'er me roll ;
Blest Saviour, then, in love,
Fear and distrust remove ;
Oh, bear me safe above,
  A ransomed soul !

581 ALL to Jesus I surrender,
    All to Him I freely give ;
I will ever love and trust Him,
  In His presence daily live.

    I surrender all....
    I surrender all....
  All to Thee, my blessed **Saviour,**
    I surrender all.

2 All to Jesus I surrender,
  Humbly at His feet I bow ;
Worldly pleasures all forsaken,
  Take me, Jesus, take me now.

3 All to Jesus I surrender,
  Make me, Saviour, wholly Thine ;
Let me feel the Holy Spirit,
  Truly know that Thou art mine.

4 All to Jesus I surrender,
  Lord, I give myself to Thee ;
Fill me with Thy love and power,
  Let Thy blessing fall on me.

5 All to Jesus I surrender,
  Now I feel the sacred flame ;
O the joy of full salvation !
  Glory, glory to His name !

582 'TIS the blessed hour of prayer,
When our hearts lowly bend,
And we gather to Jesus, our Saviour
and Friend ;
If we come to Him in faith, His
protection to share ;
What a balm for the weary ! O how
sweet to be there !

> Blessed hour of prayer,
> Blessed hour of prayer ;
> What a balm for the weary !
> O how sweet to be there.

2 'Tis the blessed hour of prayer, when
the Saviour draws near,
With a tender compassion His
children to hear ;
When He tells us we may cast at
His feet ev'ry care ;
What a balm for the weary ! O how
sweet to be there !

3 'Tis the blessed hour of prayer, when
the tempted and tried
To the Saviour who loves them their
sorrow confide ;
With a sympathising heart He
removes ev'ry care ;
What a balm for the weary ! O how
sweet to be there.

4 At the blessed hour of prayer,
trusting Him we believe
That the blessings we're needing
we'll surely receive,
In the fulness of this trust we shall
lose ev'ry care ;
What a balm for the weary ! O how
sweet to be there.

583   TEACH us to pray !
O Father, we look up to Thee,
And this our one request shall be,
Teach us to pray, teach us to pray.

2   Teach us to pray !
A form of words will not suffice ;
The heart must bring its sacrifice ;
Teach us to pray, teach us to pray.

3   Teach us to pray !
To whom shall we, Thy children,
turn ?
Teach us the lesson we should learn ;
Teach us to pray, teach us to pray.

4   Teach us to pray !
To Thee alone our hearts look up ;
Prayer is our only door of hope ;
Teach us to pray, teach us to pray.

584 NEARER, still nearer, close
to Thy heart,
Draw me, my Saviour, so precious
Thou art ;   [breast,
Fold me, O fold me close to Thy
Shelter me safe in that " Haven of
Rest,"   [Rest."
Shelter me safe in that " Haven of

2 Nearer, still nearer, nothing I
bring,   [King ;
Naught as an off'ring to Jesus, my
Only my sinful, now contrite heart,
Grant me the cleansing Thy blood
doth impart.

3 Nearer, still nearer, Lord, to be
Thine,
Sin, with its follies, I gladly resign ;
All of its pleasures, pomp and its
pride,   [crucified.
Give me but Jesus, my Lord

4 Nearer, still nearer, while life shall
last,   [past ;
Till all its struggles and trials are
Then thro' eternity, ever I'll be
Nearer, my Saviour, still nearer to
Thee.

585 SOFTLY now the light of day
Fades upon our sight away ;
Free from care, from labour free,
Lord, we would commune with Thee.

2 Thou whose all-pervading eye
Naught escapes, without, within ;
Pardon each infirmity,
Open fault and secret sin.

3 Soon for us the light of day
Shall for ever pass away ;
Then from sin and sorrow free,
Take us, Lord, to dwell with Thee.

586 I AM praying, blessed Saviour,
To be more and more like
Thee ;
I am praying that Thy Spirit
Like a dove may rest on me.

> Thou who knowest all my weakness,
> Thou who knowest all my care,
> While I plead each precious promise,
> Hear, oh, hear and answer pray'r.

2 I am praying, blessed Saviour,
For a faith so clear and bright,
That its eye will see Thy glory
Through the deepest, darkest
night.

3 I am praying to be humbled
   By the pow'r of grace divine,
To be clothed upon with meekness,
   And to have no will but Thine.

4 I am praying, blessed Saviour,
   And my constant pray'r shall be,
For a perfect consecration,
   That shall make me more like Thee

587 TAKE my life, and let it be
   Consecrated, Lord, to Thee ;
Take my moments and my days,
Let them flow in ceaseless praise.

2 Take my hands, and let them move
At the impulse of Thy love ;
Take my feet, and let them be
Swift and beautiful for Thee.

3 Take my voice, and let me sing
Always, only, for my King ;
Take my lips, and let them be
Filled with messages from Thee.

4 Take my silver and my gold,
Not a mite would I withhold ;
Take my intellect, and use
Ev'ry power as Thou shalt choose.

5 Take my will and make it Thine,
It shall be no longer mine ;
Take my heart, it *is* Thine own ;
It shall be Thy royal throne.

6 Take my love ; my Lord, I pour
At Thy feet its treasure store ;
Take myself, and I will be
Ever, *only*, ALL for Thee !

588 LORD Jesus Christ, we seek
   Thy face ;
   Within the vail we bow the knee,
Oh, let Thy glory fill the place,
   And bless us while we wait on
   Thee.

2 We thank Thee for the precious
   blood
   That purged our sins and brought
   us nigh,
All cleansed and sanctified to God,
   Thy holy Name to magnify.

3 Shut in with Thee, far, far above
   The restless world that wars below;
We seek to learn and prove Thy
   love,   [know.
Thy wisdom and Thy grace to

4 Thy brow that once with thorns
   was bound,
   Thy hands, Thy side we fain
   would see ;
Draw near, Lord Jesus, glory
   crowned,
   And bless us while we wait on
   Thee.

589 THO' the foes of right oppress,
   Keep on praying ;
Christ the Lord, is near to bless,
   All prevailing.
Let not fear your heart appal,
Naught of evil can befall,
Stronger is your God than all,
   Keep on praying.

Keep on praying, keep on praying,
Thro' the Saviour's blessed name, all prevailing.

2 Christian, has your faith grown
   weak ?
   Keep on praying ;
Do the tears roll down your cheek ?
   Keep on praying.
Soon you never more will sigh,
Tears no more shall dim your eye ;
Pray to Him who's always nigh,
   Never failing.

3 Pilgrim, have you weary grown ?
   Keep on praying ;
God is yet upon His throne,
   Keep on praying.
He will hear your faithful cry,
He to help is ever nigh,
You shall conquer by and by,
   Keep on praying.

4 Praises shall with prayers ascend,
   Keep on praying ;
Pray and praise till life shall end,
   Keep on praying.
Till you reach the golden gate,
Where the ransom'd souls await,
Claiming there your triumph great
   Keep on praying.

590 MORE holiness give me,
   More strivings within ;
More patience in suff'ring,
   More sorrow for sin ;
More faith in my Saviour,
   More sense of His care ;
More joy in His service,
   More purpose in prayer.

2 More gratitude give me,
 More trust in the Lord ;
More pride in His glory,
 More hope in His Word ;
More tears for His sorrows,
 More pain at His grief ;
More meekness in trial,
 More praise for relief.

3 More purity give me,
 More strength to o'ercome ;
More freedom from earth stains,
 More longings for home ;
More fit for the kingdom,
 More use would I be ;
More blessed and holy,
 More, Saviour, like Thee.

591 I'M over in Canaan where
 riches abound,
Living on the vict'ry side ;
Each day going on to possess higher
 ground,
Living on the vict'ry side.

 Sing glo - ry, hallelujah !...
 I'm living on the vict'ry side ;
 Since Christ my soul hath sanctified,
 I'm living on the vict'ry side.

2 No longer by fears am I fettered
 and bound,
Living on the vict'ry side.
Sweet freedom in service for Christ
 I have found,
Living on the vict'ry side.

3 I walk in the sunshine of God's holy
 light,
Living on the vict'ry side ;
The will of my Lord is my joy and
 delight,
Living on the vict'ry side.

4 The Lord whom I trust is my
 strength and my song,
Living on the vict'ry side ;
No foes can alarm since to Him I
 belong,
Living on the vict'ry side.

592 ARE you weary, are you
 heavy-hearted ?
Tell it to Jesus, tell it to Jesus.
Are you grieving over joys departed?
Tell it to Jesus alone.

 Tell it to Jesus, tell it to Jesus.
 He is a Friend that's well known
 You have no other such a friend or brother,
 Tell it to Jesus alone.

2 Do the tears flow down your cheeks
 unbidden ?
Tell it to Jesus, tell it to Jesus.
Have you sins that to man's eyes
 are hidden ?
Tell it to Jesus alone.

3 Do you fear the gath'ring clouds of
 sorrow ?
Tell it to Jesus, tell it to Jesus.
Are you anxious what shall be
 to-morrow ?
Tell it to Jesus alone.

4 Are you troubled with the thought
 of dying ?
Tell it to Jesus, tell it to Jesus.
For Christ's coming kingdom are
 you sighing ?
Tell it to Jesus alone.

593 EVER Thine, Thine alone,
 Henceforth, Saviour, I will
 be ;
This my joy, my life's ambition,
Day by day to grow like Thee.

594 PRAYER is the soul's sincere
 desire,
Uttered or unexpressed,
The motion of a hidden fire
That trembles in the breast.

2 Prayer is the burden of a sigh,
 The falling of a tear,
The upward glancing of an eye,
 When none but God is near.

3 Prayer is the simplest form of
 speech
 That infant lips can try ;
Prayer, the sublimest strains that
 reach
 The Majesty on high.

4 Prayer is the Christian's vital breath,
 The Christian's native air ;
His watchword at the gates of
 death,
He enters heaven with prayer.

5 Prayer is the contrite sinner's voice,
 Returning from his ways ;
While angels in their songs rejoice,
 And cry, " Behold, he prays ! "

6 O Thou by whom we come to God,
 The Life, the Truth, the Way !
The path of prayer Thyself hast trod,
 Lord, teach us how to pray !

595 MORE love to Thee, O Christ!
  More love to Thee;
Hear Thou the pray'r I make
  On bended knee.
This is my earnest plea—
More love, O Christ, to Thee!
  More love to Thee!

2 Once earthly joy I crav'd,
  Sought peace and rest;
Now Thee alone I seek,
  Give what is best.
This all my pray'r shall be—
More love, O Christ, to Thee!
  More love to Thee!

3 Let sorrow do its work,
  Come grief or pain;
Sweet are Thy messengers,
  Sweet their refrain,
When they can sing with me—
More love, O Christ, to Thee!
  More love to Thee!

4 Then shall my latest breath
  Whisper Thy praise;
This be the parting cry
  My heart shall raise;
This still its prayer shall be—
More love, O Christ, to Thee!
  More love to Thee!

596 O TEACH me more of Thy
  blest ways,
Thou Holy Lamb of God!
And fix and root me in Thy grace,
  As one redeemed by blood.

2 Oh, tell me often of Thy love,
  Of all Thy grief and pain,
And let my heart with joy confess
  That thence comes all my gain.

3 For this, oh, may I freely count
  Whate'er I have but loss,
The dearest object of my love,
  Compared with Thee, but dross.

4 Engrave this deeply on my heart,
  With an eternal pen,
That I may, in some small degree,
  Return Thy love again.

597 APPROACH, my soul, the
  mercy-seat,
Where Jesus answers prayer;
There humbly fall before His feet,
  For none can perish there.

2 Thy promise is my only plea,
  With this I venture nigh;
Thou callest burdened souls to Thee,
  And such, O Lord, am I!

3 Bowed down beneath a load of sin,
  By Satan sorely prest;
By wars without, and fears within—
  I come to Thee for rest.

4 Be Thou my shield and hiding-place;
  That, sheltered near Thy side,
I may my fierce accuser face,
  And tell him Thou hast died.

5 Oh, wondrous love—to bleed and
  die,
To bear the Cross and shame,
That guilty sinners such as I
  Might plead Thy gracious name.

598 I'VE found the "Pearl of
  greatest price,"
My heart doth sing for joy:
And sing I must, for Christ I have—
  Oh, what a Christ have I!

2 My Christ He is the "Lord of lords,"
  The Sovereign "King of kings,"
The risen "Sun of Righteousness,
  With healing in His wings."

3 My Christ He is "the Tree of Life,"
  That in God's Eden grows,
The living "clear as crystal"
  stream
Whence life for ever flows.

4 Christ is my Meat, Christ is my
  Drink,
My Medicine and my Health;
My Portion, mine Inheritance,
  Yea, all my Boundless Wealth.

599 OH, for a heart to praise my
  God,
A heart from sin set free;
A heart that always feels the blood
  So freely shed for me;

2 A heart resigned, submissive, meek,
  My great Redeemer's throne,
Where only Christ is heard to speak,
  Where Jesus reigns alone;

3 A humble, holy, contrite heart,
  Believing, true, and clean,
Which neither life, nor death can
  part
From Him that dwells within.

4 A heart in every thought renewed,
    And full of love divine,
Perfect, and right, and pure, and
        good,
    A copy, Lord, of Thine!

5 Thy nature, gracious Lord, impart;
    Come quickly from above;
Write Thy new name upon my
        heart—
    Thy new, best name of love.

600 WHAT various hindrances we
        meet
    In coming to the Mercy Seat!
Yet who, that knows the worth of
        prayer,
    But wishes to be often there?

2 Prayer makes the darkened clouds
        withdraw,
Prayer climbs the ladder Jacob saw;
Gives exercise to faith and love,
    Brings ev'ry blessing from above.

3 Restraining prayer, we cease to
        fight,
Prayer makes the Christian's armour
        bright;
And Satan trembles when he sees
The weakest saint upon his knees.

4 While Moses stood with arms spread
        wide,
Success was found on Israel's side:
But when through weariness they
        failed,
That moment Amalek prevailed.

5 Have you no words? ah! think
        again,   [plain,
Words flow apace when you com-
And fill your fellow-creatures' ear
With the sad tale of all your care.

6 Were half the breath thus vainly
        spent,
To heaven in supplication sent,
Your cheerful song would oftener
    be,   [me!"
" Hear what the Lord has done for

601 JESUS, Thou joy of loving
        hearts,
    Thou fount of life, Thou light of
        men!   [imparts
From the best bliss that earth
    We turn unfilled to Thee again.

2 Thy truth unchang'd hath ever
        stood,
    Thou savest those that on Thee
        call;   [good,
    To them that seek Thee Thou art
    To them that find Thee, All in all!

3 We taste Thee, O Thou living
        bread,   [still;
    And long to feast upon Thee
We drink of Thee, the fountain-
        head,   [to fill.
    And thirst our souls from Thee

4 Our restless spirits yearn for Thee,
    Where'er our changeful lot is
        cast,   [see,
    Glad when Thy gracious smile we
    Blest when our faith can hold
        Thee fast.

5 O Jesus, ever with us stay!
    Make all our moments calm and
        bright;
Chase the dark night of sin away;
    Shed o'er the world Thy holy
        light.

602 LORD, speak to me, that I
        may speak
    In living echoes of Thy tone;
As Thou hast sought, so let me seek
    Thy erring children lost and lone.

2 Oh, lead me, Lord, that I may lead
    The wandering and the wavering
        feet;
Oh, feed me, Lord, that I may feed
    Thy hungering ones with manna
        sweet.

3 Oh, teach me, Lord, that I may
        teach   [impart,
    The precious things Thou dost
And wing my words, that they
        may reach   [heart.
    The hidden depths of many a

4 Oh, give Thine own sweet rest to
        me,   [power
    That I may speak with soothing
A word in season, as from Thee,
    To weary ones in needful hour.

5 Oh, fill me with Thy fulness, Lord,
    Until my very heart o'erflow
In kindling thought, and glowing
        word,   [show.
    Thy love to tell, Thy praise to

6 Oh, use me, Lord, use even me,
　Just as Thou wilt, and how, and
　　where :
Until Thy blessed face I see,
Thy rest, Thy joy, Thy glory share.

603 WHO shall roll the stone
　　away ?
Who shall break the seal ?
Who can drive the clouds away,
Wounded hearts to heal ?

　Only God can lift the weight
　　That keeps fast the glory gate !
　Even now, Lord, while we pray,
　Thou can'st roll the stones away !

2 Who can lead the weary soul
　To the Saviour's Cross ?
Who can make us joyfully
　Count all else but loss ?

3 Who can banish unbelief,
　As in prayer we bow ?
Who can ope the silent lips ?
　God can—here and now !

4 Who can cleanse our sins away,
　By His precious blood ?
Only one can these things do—
　Christ the Son of God.

5 Who will come to Jesus now ?
　Now, this very hour ?
He will save you willingly,
　Keep you by His pow'r !

604 IS your name written there,
　　On the page white and fair ?
In the book of His kingdom,
Is your name written there ?

TESTIMONY AND ASSURANCE

605 NAUGHT have I gotten but
　　what I received ;
Grace hath bestowed it since I have
　believed,
Boasting excluded, pride I abase ;
I'm only a sinner saved by grace !

　Only a sinner saved by grace !
　Only a sinner saved by grace !
　This is my story—to God be the Glory—
　I'm only a sinner saved by grace.

2 Once I was foolish, and sin ruled
　my heart, 　　[depart ;
Causing my footsteps from God to
Jesus hath found me, happy my
　case—
I now am a sinner saved by grace !

3 Tears unavailing, no merit had I :
Mercy had saved me, or else I must
　die ;
Sin had alarm'd me, fearing God's
　face ; 　　[grace !
But now I'm a sinner saved by

4 Suffer a sinner whose heart over-
　flows, 　　[knows ;
Loving his Saviour, to tell what he
Once more to tell it, would I em-
　brace—
I'm only a sinner saved by grace !

606 I LOVE to tell the story
　　Of unseen things above,
Of Jesus and His glory,
Of Jesus and His love !

I love to tell the story !
　Because I know it's true !
It satisfies my longings
　As nothing else would do.

　I love to tell the story !
　'Twill be my theme in glory
　To tell the Old, Old Story
　　Of Jesus and His love.

2 I love to tell the story !
　More wonderful it seems
Than all the golden fancies
　Of all our golden dreams ;
I love to tell the story !
　It did so much for me !
And that is just the reason
　I tell it now to thee.

3 I love to tell the story !
　'Tis pleasant to repeat
What seems, each time I tell it,
　More wonderfully sweet.
I love to tell the story !
　For some have never heard
The message of salvation
　From God's own Holy Word.

4 I love to tell the story !
　For those who know it best
Seem hungering and thirsting
　To hear it, like the rest.
And when in scenes of glory,
　I sing the NEW, NEW SONG,
'Twill be—the OLD, OLD STORY
　That I have loved so long.

F

607 I WAS a sinner, but now I'm
free,   [me ;
   His wondrous grace has rescued
Once I was blind, but now I see,
   A brand from the burning, He
   rescued me.

He rescued me His own to be,
  A brand from the burning, He set me free ;
Oh, how I'll praise Him thro' eternity,
  A brand from the burning, He rescued me.

2 Once I was wayward, afar would
stray,   [me ;
   His wondrous grace has rescued
Now I am on the "King's highway,"
   A brand from the burning, He set
   me free.

3 Once evil led me, but now God
reigns,   [me ;
   His wondrous grace has rescued
Broken for e'er are sin's dark
chains,   [me free.
   A brand from the burning, He set

608 O BROTHER, have you told
how the Lord forgave ?
   Let us hear you tell it over once
   again ;
Thy coming to the Cross, where He
   died to save,   [again.
   Let us hear you tell it over once
Are you walking now in His blessed
   light ?
   Are you cleansed from ev'ry
   guilty stain ?
Is He your joy by day and your
   song by night ?   [again.
   Let us hear you tell it over once

Let us hear...you tell it o - ver,...
Tell it o - - ver once again....
Tell the sweet and blessed story,
It will help you on to glory,
Let us hear you tell it over once again.

2 When toiling up the way was the
   Saviour there ?   [again ;
   Let us hear you tell it over once
Did Jesus bear you up in His tender
   care ?   [again.
   Let us hear you tell it over once
Never have you found such a Friend
   as He,
   Who can help you 'midst the toil
   and pain ;
O all the world should hear what
   He's done for thee !   [again.
   Let us hear you tell it over once

3 Was ever on your tongue such a
   blessed theme ?   [again ;
   Let us hear you tell it over once
'Tis ever sweeter far than the
   sweetest dream ;   [again.
   Let us hear you tell it over once
There are aching hearts in the
   world's great throng,
   Who have sought for rest, and
   all in vain ;
Hold Jesus up to them by your
   word and song ;   [again.
   Let us hear you tell it over once

4 The battles you have fought, and
   the vict'ries won,   [again ;
   Let us hear you tell it over once
'Twill help them on the way who
   have just begun,   [again.
   Let us hear you tell it over once
We are striving now with the hosts
   of sin,   [shall reign ;
   Soon with Christ our Saviour we
Ye ransomed of the Lord, try a soul
   to win ;   [again.
   Let us hear you tell it over once

609 NOW just a word for Jesus,
   Your dearest Friend so true ;
Come cheer our hearts and tell us
   What He has done for you.

Now just a word for Jesus—
  'Twill help us on our way ;
One little word for Jesus,
  O speak, or sing, or pray.

2 Now just a word for Jesus,
   You feel your sins forgiv'n,
And by His grace are striving
   To reach a home in heav'n.

3 Now just a word for Jesus,
   A cross it cannot be
To say I love my Saviour,
   Who gave His life for me.

4 Now just a word for Jesus,
   Let not the time be lost ;
The heart's neglected duty
   Brings sorrow to its cost.

5 Now just a word for Jesus,
   And if your faith be dim,
Arise in all your weakness,
   And leave the rest to Him.

610 I HAVE a Shepherd, One I
love so well ;
How He has blessed me tongue can
never tell ;

On the Cross He suffered, shed His
blood and died,
That I might ever in His love confide.

Following Jesus, ever day by day,
Nothing can harm me when He leads the way ;
Darkness or sunshine, whate'er befall,
Jesus, the Shepherd, is my All in all.

2 Pastures abundant doth His hand
provide,
Still waters flowing ever at my side ;
Goodness and mercy follow on my
track,   [I lack.
With such a Shepherd nothing can

3 When I would wander from the path
astray,   [the way ;
Then He will draw me back into
In the darkest valley I need fear no
ill,   [me still.
For He, my Shepherd, will be with

4 When labour's ended and the
journey done,
Then He will lead me safely to my
home ;
There I shall dwell in rapture sure
and sweet,
With all the loved ones gathered
round His feet.

611 I'M not ashamed to own my
Lord,
Or to defend His cause ;
Maintain the honour of His Word,
The glory of His Cross.

At the Cross, at the Cross, where I first saw
the light,
And the burden of my heart roll'd away,...
It was there by faith I received my sight,
And now I am happy all the day.

2 Jesus, my Lord ! I know His name—
His name is all my trust,
Nor will He put my soul to shame,
Nor let my hope be lost.

3 Firm as His throne His promise
stands,
And He can well secure
What I've committed to His hands,
Till the decisive hour.

4 Then will He own my worthless
name
Before His Father's face ;
And, in the new Jerusalem,
Appoint my soul a place.

612 I WAS wrecked on a rocky
and desolate shore, [sea ;
Sinking slowly beneath the wild
When all of my struggles and efforts
were o'er,   [me.
Christ threw out the life-line to

He threw out the life-line to me,...
He threw out the life-line to me,...
From Calvary's tree, far over the sea,
Christ threw out the life-line to me.

2 The billows were dashing, the waves
rolling high,   [see ;
No help from the land could I
When hope had all vanished, and
danger was nigh,   [me.
Christ threw out the life-line to

3 When all was confusion 'midst dark
billows' roll,   [see,
No light thro' the gloom could I
By trusting Him fully He rescued
my soul,   [me.
Christ threw out the life-line to

4 And now as I wander I sing as I go,
His mercy is boundless and free,
And tell the glad story, that others
may know,   [me.
Christ threw out the life-line to

5 Your sins like the billows around you
may rise,
And dangers your frail barque
pursue ;
There's One who will heed you, and
hear your faint cries,
He'll throw out the life-line to you.

613 MY path was always rough
and drear,
My soul was always sad ;
But now my path is smooth and
bright,
My soul for ever glad.

It was Je - - sus, my Saviour, who wrought
this change in me ;
It was Je - - sus, my Saviour, blest Lamb
of Calvary,
I came to Him just as I was, from sin He
set me free ;
It was Je - - sus, my Saviour, who wrought
this change in me.

2 My soul was stained with many sins,
I lived in fear and dread ;
But now my soul is free from stain,
And all my fears have fled.

3 O wand'ring one in paths of sin,
  The Saviour calls to thee ;
He longs to give you peace and rest,
  From sin to set you free.

614 I WAS once far away from
      the Saviour,
  And as vile as a sinner could be ;
And I wondered if Christ the
      Redeemer
  Could save a poor sinner like me.

2 I wander'd on in the darkness,
  Not a ray of light could I see ;
And the thought fill'd my heart
  with sadness,   [me.
  There's no hope for a sinner like

3 And then, in that dark lonely hour,
  A voice sweetly whisper'd to me,
Saying, "Christ the Redeemer has
  pow'r
  To save a poor sinner like thee."

4 I listened, and lo ! 'twas the
      Saviour   [me ;
  That was speaking so kindly to
I cried, " I'm the chief of sinners,
  Thou canst save a poor sinner like
  me ! "

5 I then fully trusted in Jesus ;
  And oh, what a joy came to me !
My heart was filled with His praises,
  For saving a sinner like me.

6 No longer in darkness I'm walking,
  For the light is now shining on
  me ;
And now unto others I'm telling
  How He saved a poor sinner like
  me.

7 And when life's journey is over,
  And I the dear Saviour shall see,
I'll praise Him for ever and ever,
  For saving a sinner like me.

615 I'M happy in Jesus, my
      Saviour, my King,
  And all the day long of His goodness
  I sing ;
To Him in my weakness I lovingly
  cling,
  For He is so precious to me.

  For He is so precious to me,...
  For He is so precious to me,...
  'Tis heaven below my Redeemer to know.
  For He is so precious to me....

2 He stood at the door amid sunshine
      and rain,
So patiently waiting an entrance to
  gain ;
What shame that so long He en-
  treated in vain,
  For He is so precious to me.

3 I stand on the mountain of sunshine
      at last,
No cloud in the heavens a shadow
  to cast ;
His smile is upon me, the valley is
  past,
  For He is so precious to me.

4 I praise Him because He appointed
      a place,
Where, some day, thro' faith in His
  marvellous grace,
My eyes shall behold Him, shall look
  on His face,
  For He is so precious to me.

616 O WHAT a change ! from the
      darkness of night,
Into the blaze of the clear shining
  light ;
Out of my weakness to power and
  might,   [change !
  O what a change ! O what a

  O what a change in my heart there has been,
  O what a change since the Saviour came in,
  O what a change, to be free from all sin,
  O what a change ! O what a change !

2 O what a change ! From my hunger
      for bread,
Into a place where God's children
  are fed ;
Into the blessing of life from the
  dead,   [change !
  O what a change ! O what a

3 O what a change ! From my burden
      of care,
Into His love He invites me to share;
Into His joy from the sorrow I bear,
  O what a change ! O what a
  change !

4 O what a change ! In the flash of
      an eye,
When we shall meet with our Lord
  by and by ;
Into a realm where we never shall
  die,   [change !
  O what a change ! O what a

617 I KNOW not why God's
      wondrous grace
  To me He hath made known,
Nor why, unworthy of such love,
  He bought me for His own—

> But " I know whom I have believed,
> And am persuaded that He is able
> To keep that which I've committed
> Unto Him against that day."

2 I know not how this saving faith
  To me He did impart,
Nor how believing in His Word
  Wrought peace within my heart—

3 I know not how the Spirit moves—
  Convincing men of sin—
Revealing Jesus through the Word,
  Creating faith in Him—

4 I know not what of good or ill
  May be reserved for me,
Of weary ways or golden days
  Before His face I see—

5 I know not when my Lord may
    come,
  At night or noonday fair—
Nor if I'll walk the vale with Him,
  Or " meet Him in the air."

618 TO the feet of my Saviour in
      trembling and fear,
  A penitent sinner I came ;
He saw, and in mercy He bade me
    draw near ;
  All glory and praise to His name.

> He touched me and thus made me whole,..
> Bringing comfort and rest to my soul ;...
> O glad happy day, all my sins rolled away !·
> For He touched me and thus made me whole....

2 I knew not the tender compassion
    and love
  That Jesus, my Saviour, had
    shown ;
Tho' burdened with grief, His dear
    hand brought relief ;
  He healed me and called me His
    own.

3 " My grace is sufficient," I heard
    His dear voice,   [soul ;
  " O come and find rest for your
From sin you to save My life freely
  I gave ;   [whole."
I died that you might be made

4 O Jesus, dear Jesus, Thy name I
    adore,
  For saving and keeping my soul ;
Thy praises I'll sing, my Redeemer
    and King,
  Thy dear loving hand made me
    whole.

5 O come, my dear brother, He's
    waiting for you,
  Your sin-burdened heart to con-
    sole ;
Your weary head rest on His dear,
    loving breast ;
  He suffered and died for your
    soul.

619 I FLED from Egypt's bondage,
    I heard that help was near ;
I cast my care on Jesus,
  And He dispersed my fear ;
I pass'd between the billows,
  Walled up on ev'ry hand,
I trusted to my Captain,
  And sought the promised land.

> I am over, yes, over ;
>   On Canaan's shore I stand ;
> I am over, yes, over,
>   In the promised land.

2 I sang a song of triumph,
  I shouted o'er and o'er,
And then pursued my journey
  For Canaan's happy shore ;
I came to Sinai's mountain,
  I trod the desert sand,
I drank at Horeb's fountain,
  Seeking the promised land.

3 The spies brought back their
    message,
  Some wept, some said, " We can ;"
The land was all 'twas promised,
  But who would lead the van ?
At last, my heart despairing
  Of ent'ring with this band,
I cried aloud to Jesus
  To show the promised land.

4 Then, after weary marches,
  And many a longing sigh,
I found the river crossing,
  And saw the land was nigh.
The Lord look'd down in mercy,
  By faith I touched His hand,
I followed close beside Him,
  And found the promised land.

5 And now my song of gladness,
   I'm singing day by day,
For fellowship with Jesus
   Makes calm and bright my way.
I fear not for the morrow,
   For His almighty hand
I know shall lead and keep me
   In this the promised land.

620   THERE'S a song in my heart
     that my lips cannot sing,
'Tis praise in the highest to Jesus
   my King ;
Its music each moment is thrilling
   my soul,
For I was a sinner, but Christ made
   me whole.

A sinner made whole ! a sinner made whole !
The Saviour hath bought me and ransomed
   my soul !
My heart it is singing, the anthem is ringing,
For I was a sinner, but Christ made me whole.

2 I shall stand one day faultless and
   pure by His throne,
Transformed from my image, con-
   formed to His own ;
Then I shall find words for the song
   in my soul,
For I was a sinner, but Christ made
   me whole.

3 All the music of heaven, so perfect
   and sweet,
Will blend with my song, and will
   make it complete ;
Thro' ages unending the echoes will
   roll,
For I was a sinner, but Christ made
   me whole.

621   TELL what the Lord has done
     for you,
Speak just a word, speak just a
   word ;   [true,
Stand for the right, be brave and
Speak just a word for Jesus.

Speak just a word, speak just a word,
   Gladly His love proclaim :
Tell what the Lord has done for you,
   Speak just a word for Jesus.

2 Early begin to bear the cross,
Speak just a word, speak just a
   word ;
They who deny Him suffer loss,
Speak just a word for Jesus.

3 Tell if the Lord has cleansed your
   sin,
Speak just a word, speak just a
   word ;
It may to Him some others win,
Speak just a word for Jesus.

4 Fear not the world, nor heed its
   frown,
Speak just a word, speak just a
   word ;
They who endure shall wear the
   crown,
Speak just a word for Jesus.

622   OH, happy day, that fixed my
     choice,
On Thee, my Saviour and my
   God !
Well may this glowing heart re-
   joice,
And tell its raptures all abroad.

Happy day, happy day,
When Jesus washed my sins away !
   He taught me how to watch and pray,
   And live rejoicing ev'ry day.
Happy day, happy day,
When Jesus washed my sins away.

2 'Tis done, the great transaction's
   done !
I am my Lord's and He is mine ;
He drew me, and I followed on,
   Charmed to confess the voice
   divine.

3 Now rest, my long-divided heart,
   Fixed on this blissful centre, rest ;
Nor ever from thy Lord depart,
   With Him of every good possessed.

4 High heaven that heard the solemn
   vow,
That vow renewed shall daily
   hear,
Till in life's latest hour I bow,
   And bless in death a bond so dear.

623   HE brought me out of the
     miry clay,
He set my feet on the Rock to stay ;
He puts a song in my soul to-day,
   A song of praise, Hallelujah !

624   I CAME to Jesus, weary, worn,
     and sad,
He took my sins away,
He took my sins away ;

His wondrous love has made my heart so glad,
He took my sins away.

He took my sins away, He took my sins away
And keeps my footsteps day by day ;
I'm so glad He saved my guilty soul
And took my sins away.

2 The load of sin was more than I could bear,
He took it all away,
He took it all away ;
And now on Him I roll my ev'ry care,
He took my sins away.

3 No condemnation have I in my heart,
He took my sins away,
And keeps me day by day ;
His perfect peace He did to me impart,
He took my sins away.

4 If you will come to Jesus Christ to-day,
He'll take your sins away,
He'll take your sins away ;
And keep you happy in the narrow way,
He'll take your sins away.

MISSIONARY

625 I HEAR ten thousand voices singing
Their praises to the Lord on high ;
Far distant shores and hills are ringing
With anthems of their nation's joy:
" Praise ye the Lord ! for He has given
To lands in darkness hid His light;
As morning rays light up the heaven,
His Word has chased away our night."

2 On China's shores I heard His praises
From lips that once kissed idol stones ;
Soon as His banner He upraises,
The Spirit moves the breathless bones ;
" Speed, speed Thy Word o'er land and ocean ;
The Lord in triumph has gone forth ;
The nations hear with strange emotion ;
From East to West, from South to North."

3 The song has sounded o'er the waters
And India's plains re-echo joy ;
Beneath the moon sit India's daughters,
Soft singing as the wheel they ply—
" Thanks to Thee, Lord, for hopes of glory,
For peace on earth to us revealed ;
Our cherished idols fall before Thee,
Thy Spirit has our pardon sealed."

626 FROM Greenland's icy mountains,
From India's coral strand,
Where Afric's sunny fountains
Roll down their golden sand ;
From many an ancient river,
From many a palmy plain,
They call us to deliver
Their land from error's chain.

2 What though the spicy breezes
Blow soft o'er Ceylon's isle,
Though ev'ry prospect pleases,
And only man is vile ;
In vain with lavish kindness
The gifts of God are strewn,
The heathen in his blindness
Bows down to wood and stone.

3 Can we, whose souls are lighted
With wisdom from on high,
Can we to men benighted
The lamp of life deny ?
Salvation ! O Salvation !
The joyful sound proclaim,
Till each remotest nation
Has learnt Messiah's name.

4 Waft, waft, ye winds, His story,
And you, ye waters, roll,
Till, like a sea of glory,
It spreads from pole to pole ;
Till o'er our ransomed nature,
The Lamb for sinners slain,
Redeemer, King, Creator,
In bliss returns to reign.

627 OVER the mountains so bleak and so cold,
Far from the beautiful city of gold,

Lost ones are straying, because you
and I
Never have told them a Saviour
stood nigh.

Oh, won't somebody tell them,
  Tell them of Calvary's tree ;
Tell them the story of Jesus,
  What a great Saviour is He !

2 Lost ones are groping in sin's awful
night,
Falling and dying away from the
right ;
Many the message of Christ never
heard,
Lost ones for whom no one ever has
cared.

3 Speed with the message, oh, speed
in His name,
Hasten the story of Christ to proclaim !
Hasten to bring back the fallen and
lost ;
Speed with the message, whatever
the cost.

628   THERE'S a call comes ringing
        o'er the restless wave,
  Send the light !...Send the light !...
There are souls to rescue, there are
  souls to save,
  Send the light !...Send the light !...

Send the light...the blessed Gospel light,
Let it shine...from shore to shore !...
Send the light !...and let its radiant beams
Light the world...for evermore.

2 We have heard the Macedonian call
  to-day,
  Send the light !...Send the light !...
And a golden off'ring at the Cross we
  lay,
  Send the light !...Send the light !...

3 Let us pray that grace may ev'ry-
  where abound,
  Send the light !...Send the light !...
And the Christ-like spirit ev'ry-
  where be found,
  Send the light !...Send the light !...

4 Let us not grow weary in the work
  of love,
  Send the light !...Send the light !...
Let us gather jewels for a crown
  above.
  Send the light !...Send the light !...

629   BLOW ye the trumpet, blow
        The gladly solemn sound ;
Let all the nations know
  To earth's remotest bound
The year of jubilee is come,
Return, ye ransom'd sinners, home.

2 Jesus, our great High Priest,
    Has full atonement made,
  Ye weary spirits, rest,
    Ye mourning souls, be glad ;
  The year of jubilee is come,
  Return, ye ransom'd sinners, home.

3 Exalt the Lamb of God,
    The sin-atoning Lamb,
  Redemption by His blood
    Through all the world proclaim ;
  The year of jubilee is come,
  Return, ye ransom'd sinners, home.

630   COMING, coming, yes, they are,
        Coming, coming from afar,
From the wild and scorching desert,
Afric's sons of colour deep ;
Jesus' love has drawn and won them,
At His Cross they bow and weep.

2   Coming, coming, yes, they are,
    Coming, coming, from afar ;
  From the fields and crowded cities,
  China gathers to His feet ;
  In His love Shem's gentle children
  Now have found a safe retreat.

3   Coming, coming, yes, they are,
    Coming, coming, from afar ;
  From the Indus and the Ganges,
  Steady flows the living stream,
  To love's ocean, to His bosom,
  Calvary their wond'ring theme.

4   Coming, coming, yes, they are,
    Coming, coming from afar ;
  From the steppes of Russia dreary,
    From Slavonia's scattered lands,
  They are yielding soul and spirit
  Into Jesus' loving hands.

5   Coming, coming, yes, they are,
    Coming, coming from afar ;
  From the frozen realms of midnight,
  Over many a weary mile,
  To exchange their souls' long winter
  For the summer of His smile.

6   Coming, coming, yes, they are,
    Coming, coming from afar.

All to meet in plains of glory,
All to sing His praises sweet;
What a chorus, what a meeting,
With the family complete!

631 HOW many sheep are straying,
        Lost from the Saviour's fold!
Upon the lonely mountain
    They shiver with the cold;
Within the tangled thickets,
    Where poison vines do creep,
And over rocky ledges
    Wander the poor, lost sheep.

Oh, come, let us go and find them;
  In the paths of death they roam,
At the close of the day, 'twill be sweet to say,
  " I have brought some lost one home."

2 Oh, who will go to find them?
    Who, for the Saviour's sake
Will search with tireless patience
    Through brier and through brake?
Unheeding thirst or hunger,
    Who still, from day to day,
Will seek, as for a treasure,
    The sheep that go astray?

3 Say, will *you* seek to find them?
    From pleasant bowers of ease,
Will you go forth determined
    To find the " least of these? "
For still the Saviour calls them,
    And looks across the wold;
And still He holds wide open
    The door into His fold.

4 How sweet 'twould be at evening,
    If you and I could say,
" Good Shepherd, we've been seek-
        ing
    The sheep that went astray!
Heart-sore and faint with hunger,
    We heard them making moan,
And lo! we come at nightfall,
    And bear them safely home."

632 SOMEONE shall go at the
        Master's word
    Over the seas to the lands afar,
Telling to those who have never
        heard
    What His wonderful mercies are.
    Shall it be you—Shall it be I
Who shall haste to tell what we
        know so well?
        Shall you? Shall I?

2 Someone will gather the sheaves for
        Him,
    Someone shall bind them with
        joyful hand;
Someone shall toil through the
        shadows dim,
    For the morn in the heavenly land.
    Shall it be you—Shall it be I
Who shall bind the corn for the
        golden morn?
        Shall you? Shall I?

3 Someone shall travel with eager feet
    Over the mountain and through
        the wild,
Bringing the news of redemption
        sweet
    To each wandering sinful child.
    Shall it be you—Shall it be I
Who shall sound the tale over hill
        and dale?
        Shall you? Shall I?

4 Someone shall carry His banner high,
    Waving it out where the foe holds
        sway;
Some in His service shall live and die,
    And with Jesus shall win the day!
    Shall it be you—Shall it be I
Who His name shall bear, and His
        triumph share?
        Shall you? Shall I?

633 SPEED away! speed away on
        your mission of light,
To the lands that are lying in dark-
        ness and night;
'Tis the Master's command: go ye
        forth in His name,   [claim.
The wonderful Gospel of Jesus pro-
Take your lives in your hand, to the
        work while 'tis day,
Speed away! speed away! speed
        away!

2 Speed away! speed away with the
        life-giving Word,
To the nations that know not the
        voice of the Lord;
Take the wings of the morning and
        fly o'er the wave,
In the strength of your Master the
        lost ones to save.
He is calling once more—not a
        moment's delay!
Speed away! speed away! speed
        away!

3 Speed away! speed away with the
message of rest
To the souls by the tempter in
bondage opprest;
For the Saviour has purchased their
ransom from sin,
And the banquet is ready: oh,
gather them in!
To the rescue make haste, there's
no time for delay:
Speed away! speed away! speed
away!

634 FAR, far away in heathen
darkness dwelling,
Millions of souls for ever may be
lost;
Who, who will go, Salvation's story
telling—
Looking to Jesus, counting not
the cost?

" All power is given unto Me!
All power is given unto Me!
Go ye into all the world and preach the Gospel;
and lo I am with you alway."

2 See, o'er the world, wide open doors
inviting; [in!
Soldiers of Christ, arise and enter
Christians, awake! your forces all
uniting,
Send forth the Gospel, break the
chain of sin!

3 "Why will ye die?" the voice of
God is calling: [His Name;
"Why will ye die?" re-echo in
Jesus hath died to save from death
appalling:
Life and salvation therefore go
proclaim.

4 God speed the day when those of
every nation,
"Glory to God" triumphantly
shall sing:
Ransomed, redeemed, rejoicing in
salvation,
Shout "Hallelujah, for the Lord
is King!"

635 IT may not be on the moun-
tain's height,
Or over the stormy sea;
It may not be at the battle's front
My Lord will have need of me;

But if by a still small voice He calls
To paths that I do not know,
I'll answer, "dear Lord, with my
hand in Thine,
I'll go where You want me to go."

I'll go where You want me to go, dear Lord,
Over mountain, or plain, or sea,
I'll say what You want me to say, dear Lord,
I'll be what You want me to be.

2 Perhaps to-day there are loving
words [speak;
Which Jesus would have me
There may be now in the path of sin
Some wand'rer whom I should
seek, [Guide,
O Saviour, if Thou wilt be my
Tho' dark and rugged the way,
My voice shall echo the message
sweet,
I'll say what You want me to say.

3 There's surely somewhere a lowly
place,
In earth's harvest field so wide,
Where I may labour thro' life's
short day
For Jesus the crucified;
So, trusting my all to Thy tender
care,
And knowing Thou lovest me,
I'll do Thy will with a heart sincere,
I'll be what You want me to be.

636 WE'VE a story to tell to the
nations,
That shall turn their hearts to
the right;
A story of truth and sweetness,
A story of peace and light.

For the darkness shall turn to dawning,
And the dawning to noonday bright,
And Christ's great kingdom shall come on
earth,
The Kingdom of Love and Light.

2 We've a song to be sung to the
nations.
That shall lift their heart to the
Lord;
A song that shall conquer evil
And shatter the spear and sword:

3 We've a message to give to the
nations,
That the Lord who reigneth above
Hath sent us His Son to save us,
And show us that God is love.

4 We've a Saviour to show to the
    nations,
  Who the path of sorrow hath trod,
That all of the world's great peoples
  Might come to the truth of God.

637 HEAR the wail across the sea,
        Comes from millions unto
        thee,
Weary ones who might be free,
  Did they but know of Calvary.

> Wailing, wailing o'er the sea ;
>   Wailing, wailing unto thee ;
> Wailing, wailing to be free :
>   Go, tell them all of Calvary !

2 Wailing of the prophet cursed,
  Of fanatics, wildest, worst,
Help us, Lord, their chains to burst,
  And set them free by Calvary.

3 Wailings reach this favoured shore,
  Wailings ceasing nevermore ;
Men are dying evermore—
  Go, tell them all of Calvary.

638 FAR and near the fields are
        teeming
  With the waves of ripen'd grain ;
Far and near their gold is gleaming,
  O'er the sunny slope and plain.

> Lord of harvest, send forth reapers !
>   Hear us, Lord, to Thee we cry ;
> Send them now the sheaves to gather,
>   Ere the harvest time pass by.

2 Send them forth with morn's first
    beaming,
  Send them in the noontide's glare ;
When the sun's last rays are gleam-
    ing,
  Bid them gather ev'rywhere.

3 O Thou, whom thy Lord is sending,
  Gather now the sheaves of gold,
Heav'nward then at ev'ning wending
  Thou shalt come with joy untold.

639 OH, where are the reapers that
        garner in
  The sheaves of the good from the
    fields of sin ?
With sickles of truth must the work
    be done,   [home."
And no one may rest till the "harvest

> Where are the reapers ? O who will come
> And share in the glory of the " harvest home ?"
> Oh, who will help us to garner in
> The sheaves of good from the fields of sin ?

2 Go out in the byeways and search
    them all,
  The wheat may be there, tho' the
    weeds are tall ;
Then search in the highway, and
    pass none by,   [high.
But gather from all for the home on

3 The fields are all rip'ning, and far
    and wide,
  The world is awaiting the harvest
    tide ;   [great,
But reapers are few, and the work is
  And much will be lost should the
    harvest wait.

4 So come with your sickles, ye sons
    of men,   [grain ;
  And gather together the golden
Toil on till the Lord of the harvest
    come,
Then share in the joy of the "harvest
    home."

640 THE whole wide world for
        Jesus—
  This shall our watchword be,
Upon the highest mountain,
  Down by the widest sea ;
The whole wide world for Jesus !
  To Him all men shall bow,
In city or in prairie—
  The world for Jesus now !

> The whole wide world, the whole wide world—
> Proclaim the Gospel tidings thro' the whole
>   wide world ;
> Lift up the Cross for Jesus, His banner be
>   unfurl'd
> Till ev'ry tongue confess Him thro' the whole
>   wide world !

2 The whole wide world for Jesus
  Inspires us with the thought
That ev'ry son of Adam
  Should by His blood be bought ;
The whole wide world for Jesus !
  O faint not by the way !
The Cross shall surely conquer
  In this our glorious day.

3 The whole wide world for Jesus—
  The marching order sound ;
Go ye and preach the Gospel
  Wherever man is found.
The whole wide world for Jesus !
  Our banner is unfurl'd ;
We battle now for Jesus,
  And faith demands the world !

4 The whole wide world for Jesus—
In the Father's house above
Are many wondrous mansions—
Mansions of light and love ;
The whole wide world for Jesus !
Ride forth, O conqu'ring King,
Thro' all the mighty nations
The world to glory bring !

641 OUR Saviour's voice is soft
and sweet
When, bending from above,
He bids us gather round His feet,
And calls us by His love.

2 But while our thankful hearts
rejoice
That thus He bids us come,
" Jesus," we cry with pleading voice,
" Bring heathen wand'rers home."

3 They never heard the Saviour's name
They have not learn'd His way ;
They do not know His grace who
came
To take their sins away.

4 Dear Saviour, let the joyful sound
In distant lands be heard ;
And oh ! wherever sin is found,
Send forth Thy pardoning Word.

5 And if our lips may breathe a prayer,
Though raised in trembling fear,
Oh ! let Thy grace our hearts
prepare
And choose some herald here.

642 TELL it out among the heathen
that the Lord is King !
Tell it out !...Tell it out !...
Tell it out among the nations, bid
them shout and sing !
Tell it out !...Tell it out !...
Tell it out with adoration that He
shall increase,
That the mighty King of Glory is
the King of Peace :
Tell it out with jubilation, tho' the
waves may roar,
That He sitteth on the water floods,
our King for evermore !

Tell it out among the heathen that the
Lord is King !
Tell it out !...Tell it out !...
Tell it out among the nations, bid them
shout and sing !
Tell it out !...Tell it out !

2 Tell it out among the heathen that
the Saviour reigns !
Tell it out !...Tell it out !...
Tell it out among the nations, bid
them burst their chains !
Tell it out !...Tell it out !...
Tell it out among the weeping ones
that Jesus lives ;
Tell it out among the weary ones
what rest He gives ;
Tell it out among the sinners that
He came to save ;
Tell it out among the dying that He
triumphed o'er the grave.

3 Tell it out among the heathen, Jesus
reigns above !
Tell it out !...Tell it out !...
Tell it out among the nations that
He reigns in love !
Tell it out !...Tell it out !...
Tell it out among the highways and
the lanes at home ;
Let it ring across the mountains
and the ocean foam !
Like the sound of many waters let
our glad shout be,
Till it echo and re-echo from the
islands of the sea !

643 HARVEST fields are waiting,
White the waving grain ;
Christ the Master calleth,
Soon the day will wane.
Hasten at His bidding,
Join the reaper band ;
Help them at their labour,
Work with willing hand.

Har - - vest fields are wait - - ing,
La - - bour while you may ;...
Time...is swiftly fly - - ing,
Come and work to-day.

2 Harvest fields are waiting,
Do not linger long ;
Borne upon the breezes
Comes the reaper's song.
Patiently, O toiler,
Pluck the golden grain,
Ere the shades of evening
Fall o'er hill and plain.

3 Harvest fields are waiting,
Who will come to-day,
Join the band of reapers,
Bear the sheaves away ?

Soon the day of toiling,
Will be ever past ;
May the Master's greeting
Be " Well done " at last !

644 LET the song go round the
earth—
Jesus Christ is Lord !
Sound His praises, tell His worth,
Be His name adored ;
Ev'ry clime and ev'ry tongue
Join the grand, the glorious song !

2 Let the song go round the earth !
From the Eastern sea,
Where the daylight has its birth,
Glad, and bright, and free ;
China's millions join the strains,
Waft them on to India's plains.

3 Let the song go round the earth !
Lands where Islam's sway
Darkly broods o'er home and hearth,
Cast their bonds away !
Let His praise from Afric's shore
Rise and swell her wide lands o'er !

4 Let the song go round the earth !
Where the summer smiles ;
Let the notes of holy mirth
Break from distant isles !
Inland forests dark and dim,
Snow-bound coasts give back the
hymn.

5 Let the song go round the earth !
Jesus Christ is King !
With the story of His worth
Let the whole world ring !
Him creation all adore
Evermore and evermore !

645 LO ! the golden fields are
smiling,
Wherefore idle shouldst thou be ?
Great the harvest, few the workers,
And the Lord hath need of thee.
Go and work, the time is waning,
Let thy earnest heart reply
To the call so oft repeated,
" Blessed Master, here am I."

Hark ! the song, the song of busy workers,
In the fields so fair to see ;
Go and fill thy place among them,
For the Lord hath need of thee.

2 Take the balm of consolation
That so oft has cheered thy heart ;

Let some weary brother toiler,
In thy comfort share a part,
Go and lift the heavy burden
He has struggled long to bear ;
Go, and kneeling down beside him,
Blend thy faith with his in
prayer.

3 Go and gather souls for Jesus,
Precious souls thy love may win ;
Lead them to the door of mercy ;
Tell them how to enter in.
Go and gather souls for Jesus ;
Work while strength and breath
remain ;
What are years of constant labour
To the joy thou yet shall gain ?

4 Go, then, work ! the Master calleth ;
Go, no longer idle be ;
Waste no more thy precious mo-
ments,
For the Lord hath need of thee.
Once He gave His life thy ransom,
That thy soul with Him might
live ;
Now the service He demandeth
Can thy heart refuse to give ?

646 JESUS shall reign where'er
the sun
Does his successive journeys run ;
His kingdom spread from shore to
shore,
Till moons shall wax and wane no
more.

2 To Him shall endless prayer be
made,
And endless praises crown His head ;
His name like sweet perfume shall
rise
With ev'ry morning sacrifice.

3 People and realms of ev'ry tongue
Dwell on His love with sweetest song;
And infant voices shall proclaim
Their early blessings on His name.

4 Blessings abound where'er He reigns,
The pris'ner leaps to loose his chains ;
The weary find eternal rest,
And all the sons of want are blest.

5 Let ev'ry creature rise and bring
Peculiar honours to our King ;
Angels descend with songs again ;
And earth repeat the loud Amen !

647 HE expecteth, He expecteth!
Down the stream of time,
Still the words come softly ringing,
Like a chime.

2 Oft-times faint, now waxing louder,
As the hour draws near,
When the King in all His glory
Shall appear.

3 He is waiting with long patience
For His crowning day,
For that kingdom which shall never
Pass away.

4 And till ev'ry tribe and nation
Bow before His throne
He expecteth loyal service
From His own.

5 He expecteth—but He heareth
Still the bitter cry
From earth's millions, "Come and help us,
For we die."

6 He expecteth—does He see us
Busy here and there,
Heedless of those pleading accents
Of despair?

7 Shall we—dare we disappoint Him?
Brethren, let us rise!
He who died for us is watching
From the skies;

8 Watching till His royal banner
Floateth far and wide,
Till He seeth of His travail
Satisfied!

648 " HE was not willing that any
should perish;"
Jesus enthroned in the glory above,   [sorrows,
Saw our poor fallen world, pities our
Poured out His life for us, wonderful love!
Perishing, perishing! thronging our pathway,
Hearts break with burdens too heavy to bear,
Jesus would save, but there's no one to tell them,   [despair.
No one to lift them from sin and

2 " He was not willing that any
should perish;"
Cloth'd in our flesh with its sorrow and pain;

Came He to seek the lost, comfort the mourner,
Heal the heart broken by sorrow and shame.
Perishing, perishing! Harvest is passing,
Reapers are few, and the night draweth near;
Jesus is calling thee, haste to the reaping,
Thou shalt have souls, precious souls for thy hire.

3 Plenty for preasure, but little for Jesus;
Time for the world with its troubles and toys;
No time for Jesus' work, feeding the hungry,
Lifting lost souls to eternity's joys.
Perishing, perishing! Hark, how they call us;
Bring us our Saviour, oh, tell us of Him;
We are so weary, so heavily laden,
And with long weeping our eyes have grown dim.

4 " He was not willing that any
should perish;"
Am I His follower, and can I live
Longer at ease with a soul going downward,
Lost for the lack of the help I might give?
Perishing, perishing! Thou wast not willing;
Master, forgive, and inspire us anew;   [ever
Banish our worldliness, help us to
Live with eternity's values in view.

649 O'ER those gloomy hills of darkness,
Look, my soul, be still, and gaze;
All the promises do travail
With a glorious day of grace;
Blessed jubilee! blessed jubilee!
Let thy glorious morning dawn.

2 Let the Indian, let the Negro,
Let the rude barbarian see
That divine and glorious conquest
Once obtained on Calvary;
Let the Gospel, let the Gospel
Loud resound from pole to pole

3 Kingdoms wide that sit in darkness,
  Let them have the glorious light;
And from eastern coast to western
  May the morning chase the night;
And redemption, and redemption,
  Freely purchased, win the day.

4 Fly abroad, eternal Gospel,
  Win and conquer, never cease;
May Thy lasting, wide dominions
  Multiply and still increase;
May Thy sceptre, may Thy sceptre,
  Sway th' enlightened world around.

650 O JESUS, **Thou** Shepherd divine;
  Keep us in the safe, narrow way;
And out of the cold lead into Thy fold
  Some poor wand'ring soul, we pray.

651 LORD, Thou hast gone two
         thousand years,
  Yet they have never heard
Tidings of Thy redeeming love,
  Or seen Thy holy Word.   [lain,
Sleeping and still Thy Church has
  Heedless of the high command—
" Go forth to ev'ry tribe and tongue,
  To ev'ry distant land."

  Send them, O Lord, to speak of Thee,
    Tell - - ing of Thy love and grace;
  Send them, O Lord, to tell of Thee,
    To ev'ry tribe and race.

2 Once o'er this bright and favour'd
         land
  Lay there the pall of night;
Gloom of a savage heathendom,
  With foul and bloody rite.
Brave ones arose and came to us,
  Bringing o'er the tidings sweet,
Then cruel men bent low to Thee,
  And worshipped at Thy feet.

3 So would we do for other lands
  Lying in deepest death,

Sinking to meet their awful doom
  With ev'ry passing breath.
Hear, Jesus, hear our fervent pray'r,
  Wake Thy sleeping Church to
         know
Her hour of privilege and power,
  And bid her rise and go.

652 THOU whose almighty word
         Chaos and darkness heard,
         And took their flight,
  Hear us, we humbly pray,
  And where the Gospel day
  Sheds not its glorious ray,
         Let there be light!

2 Thou who didst come to bring
  On Thy redeeming wing
         Healing and sight;
  Health to the sick in mind,
  Sight to the inly blind,
  O now to all mankind
         Let there be light!

3 Spirit of truth and love,
  Life-giving, holy Dove,
         Speed forth Thy flight;
  Move on the water's face,
  Spreading the beams of grace,
  And in earth's darkest place
         Let there be light!

4 Blessed and holy Three,
  Glorious Trinity,
         Wisdom, Love, Might;
  Boundless as ocean's tide,
  Rolling in fullest pride,
  Through the earth far and wide,
         Let there be light!

653 JESUS is the Way—the only
         Way,
  Lovingly He calleth, thus the
    Scriptures say,   [day—
  Whosoever will let Him come to-
  The blessed Jesus is the only Way.

CHILDREN

654 JESUS wants me for a sunbeam
         To shine for Him each day;
  In ev'ry way try to please Him,
    At home, at school, at play.

    A sunbeam, a sunbeam,
    Jesus wants me for a sunbeam,
    A sunbeam, a sunbeam,
    I'll be a sunbeam for Him.

2 Jesus wants me to be loving,
  And kind to all I see;
Showing how pleasant and happy
  His little one can be.

3 I will ask Jesus to help me
  To keep my heart from sin;
Ever reflecting His goodness,
  And always shine for Him.

4 I'll be a sunbeam for Jesus,
I can, if I but try,
Serving Him moment by moment,
Then live with Him on high.

655 IN a world where sorrow
Ever will be known,
Where are found the needy,
And the sad and lone ;
How much joy and comfort
You can all bestow,
If you scatter sunshine
Ev'rywhere you go.

Scat - - ter sunshine all along your way,...
Cheer, and bless, and brighten
Ev'ry passing day.

2 Slightest actions often
Meet the sorest needs,
For the world wants daily
Little kindly deeds ;
Oh, what care and sorrow
You may help remove,
With your songs and courage,
Sympathy and love.

3 When the days are gloomy,
Sing some happy song,
Meet the world's repining
With a courage strong ;
Go with faith undaunted
Through the ills of life,
Scatter smiles and sunshine
O'er its toil and strife.

656 I LOVE to hear the story
Which angel voices tell,
How once the King of Glory
Came down on earth to dwell ;
I am both weak and sinful,
But this I surely know,
The Lord came down to save me,
Because He loved me so.

2 I'm glad my blessed Saviour
Was once a child like me,
To show how pure and holy
His little ones might be ;
And if I try to follow
His footsteps here below,
He never will forget me,
Because He loved me so.

3 To sing His love and mercy,
My sweetest songs I'll raise,
And, though I cannot see Him,
I know He hears my praise ;

For He has kindly promised
That I shall surely go
To sing among the angels,
Because He loved me so.

657 THERE'S a Friend for little
children
Above the bright blue sky,
A Friend that never changes,
Whose love will never die ;
Unlike our friends by nature,
Who change with changing years,
This Friend is always worthy
The precious name He bears.

2 There's a rest for little children
Above the bright blue sky,
Who love the blessed Saviour,
And to His Father cry ;
A rest from ev'ry trouble,
From sin and danger free ;
There ev'ry little pilgrim
Shall rest eternally.

3 There's a home for little children
Above the bright blue sky,
Where Jesus reigns in glory,
A home of peace and joy ;
No home on earth is like it,
Nor can with it compare ;
For ev'ryone is happy,
Nor can be happier there.

4 There's a crown for little children
Above the bright blue sky,
And all who look to Jesus
Shall wear it by and by ;
A crown of brightest glory,
Which He shall sure bestow
On all who love the Saviour,
And walk with Him below.

5 There's a song for little children
Above the bright blue sky,
And a harp of sweetest music
For their hymn of victory ;
And all above is pleasure,
And found in Christ alone ;
O come, dear little children,
That all may be your own !

658 THE world looks very beautiful
And full of joy to me ;
The sun shines out in glory
On ev'rything I see ;
I know I shall be happy
While in the world I stay,

For I will follow Jesus
  All the way.
  For I will follow Jesus
  All the way.

2 I'm but a youthful pilgrim,
  My journey's just begun;
They say I'll meet with sorrow
  Before my journey's done;
The world is full of trouble,
  And trials, too, they say;
But I will follow Jesus
  All the way.

3 Then, like a little pilgrim,
  Whatever I may meet,
I'll take it—joy or sorrow—
  And lay at Jesus' feet;
He'll comfort me in trouble,
  He'll wipe my tears away;
With joy I'll follow Jesus
  All the way.

4 Then trials cannot vex me,
  And pain I need not fear,
For when I'm close by Jesus,
  Grief cannot come too near;
Not even death can harm me,
  When death I meet one day;
To heav'n I'll follow Jesus
  All the way.

659 WHEN He cometh, when He
    cometh
  To make up His jewels,
All His jewels, precious jewels,
  His loved and His own.
  Like the stars of the morning,
  His bright crown adorning,
  They shall shine in their beauty,
  Bright gems for His crown.

2 He will gather, He will gather
  Bright gems for His kingdom,
All the pure ones, all the bright ones,
  His loved and His own.

3 Little children, little children
  Who love their Redeemer,
Are the jewels, precious jewels,
  His loved and His own.

660 JESUS bids us shine
    With a clear, pure light,
Like a little candle
  Burning in the night;
In this world is darkness
  So we must shine,
You in your small corner,
  And I in mine.

2 Jesus bids us shine,
  First of all for Him;
Well He sees and knows it
  If our light is dim;
He looks down from heaven
  To see us shine,
You in your small corner,
  And I in mine.

3 Jesus bids us shine,
  Then, for all around,
Many kinds of darkness
  In this world abound;
Sin and want and sorrow,
  So we must shine,
You in your small corner,
  And I in mine.

661 GOD make my life a little light,
    Within the world to glow;
A little flame that burneth bright
  Wherever I may go.

2 God make my life a little flower,
  That giveth joy to all;
Content to bloom in native bower,
  Although the place be small.

3 God make my life a little song,
  That comforteth the sad;
That helpeth others to be strong,
  And makes the singer glad.

4 God make my life a little staff,
  Whereon the weak may rest;
That so what health and strength I
    have
  May serve my neighbours best.

5 God make my life a little hymn
  Of tenderness and praise,
Of faith that never waxeth dim,
  In all His wondrous ways.

662 JESUS found me wand'ring,
    Far from Him astray,
Tenderly He led me
  To the shining way;
Words of peace He whispered,
  Bade my fears depart;
Oh! 'twas sweet to hear Him
  Whisp'ring in my heart!

Whisp'ring, whisp'ring, oh, what joy is mine!
Whisp'ring, whisp'ring, words of love divine.
No strain of earthly music such rapture can
  impart:
I'm glad I ever heard Him whisp'ring in my
  heart.

2 I can hear Him whisper,
  When my soul is tried,
" Fear not, I am with thee;
  I am at thy side."
When the foe assails me
  Jesus takes my part;
I rejoice to hear Him
  Whisp'ring in my heart.

3 Would you hear the Saviour's
  Gentle voice within?
Now, while He is calling,
  Leave the path of sin.
Peace that passeth knowledge
  Freely He'll impart;
You to-day may hear Him
  Whisp'ring in your heart.

663 SAFE in the arms of Jesus,
  Safe on His gentle breast,
There by His love o'ershaded,
  Sweetly my soul shall rest.
Hark! 'tis the voice of angels,
  Borne in a song to me,
Over the fields of glory,
  Over the jasper sea.

> Safe in the arms of Jesus,
> Safe on His gentle breast,
> There by His love o'ershaded,
> Sweetly my soul shall rest.

2 Safe in the arms of Jesus,
  Safe from corroding care,
Safe from the world's temptations,
  Sin cannot harm me there.
Free from the blight of sorrow,
  Free from my doubts and fears;
Only a few more trials,
  Only a few more tears!

3 Jesus, my heart's dear refuge,
  Jesus has died for me;
Firm on the Rock of Ages
  Ever my trust shall be.
Here will I wait with patience,
  Wait till the night is o'er;
Wait till I see the morning
  Break on the golden shore.

664 SHALL we gather at the river,
  Where bright angel feet have
    trod,
With its crystal tide for ever
  Flowing from the throne of God?

> Yes, we'll gather at the river,
> The beautiful, the beautiful river,
> Gather with the saints at the river
> That flows from the throne of God.

2 On the margin of the river,
  Washing up its silver spray,
We will walk and worship ever,
  All the happy golden day.

3 Ere we reach the shining river,
  Lay we ev'ry burden down;
Grace our spirits will deliver,
  And provide a robe and crown.

4 At the smiling of the river,
  Mirror of the Saviour's face,
Saints whom death will never sever,
  Lift their songs of saving grace.

5 Soon we'll reach the shining river,
  Soon our pilgrimage will cease;
Soon our happy hearts will quiver
  With the melody of peace.

665 SHINING for Jesus ev'rywhere
  I go;
Shining for Jesus in this world of
  woe;   [grow;
Shining for Jesus, more like Him I
Shining all the time for Jesus.

> Shining all the time, shining all the time,
> Shining for Jesus, beams of love divine;
> Glorifying Him ev'ry day and hour,
> Shining all the time for Jesus.

2 Shining for Jesus when the way is
  bright;
Shining for Jesus in the darkest
  night;   [light;
Shining for Jesus, making burdens
Shining all the time for Jesus.

3 Shining for Jesus in a world of sin;
Shining for Jesus, bringing lost ones
  in;
Shining for Jesus, glorifying Him;
Shining all the time for Jesus.

4 Shining for Jesus while He gives me
  grace;   [race;
Shining for Jesus while I run the
Shining for Jesus till I see His face;
Shining all the time for Jesus.

666 MIGHTY army of the young,
  Lift the voice of cheerful song,
Send the welcome word along,
  Jesus lives!
Once He died for you and me,
Bore our sins upon the tree,
Now He lives to make us free,
  Jesus lives!

Wait not till the shadows lengthen, till you
    older grow ;   [go,
Rally now and sing for Jesus, ev'rywhere you
Lift your joyful voices high, ringing clear thro'
    earth and sky,
Let the blessed tidings fly, Jesus lives !

2 Tongues of children, light and free,
  Tongues of youth all full of glee,
  Sing to all on land and sea,
      Jesus lives !
  Light for you and all mankind,
  Sight for all by sin made blind,
  Life in Jesus all may find,
      Jesus lives !

3 Jesus lives, oh blessed words !
  King of kings, and Lord of lords !
  Lift the Cross and sheathe the swords,
      Jesus lives !
  See, He breaks the prison wall,
  Throws aside the dreadful pall,
  Conquers death at once for all,
      Jesus lives !

667 JESUS is our Shepherd,
      Wiping ev'ry tear ;
  Folded in His bosom,
    What have we to fear ? .
  Only let us follow
    Whither He doth lead,
  To the thirsty desert,
    Or the dewy mead.

2 Jesus is our Shepherd,
    Well we know His voice !
  How its gentle whisper
    Makes our heart rejoice !
  Even when He chideth,
    Tender is His tone ;
  None but He shall guide us,
    We are His alone.

3 Jesus is our Shepherd,
    For the sheep He bled ;
  Ev'ry lamb is sprinkled
    With the blood He shed.
  Then on each He setteth
    His own secret sign,
  " They that have My Spirit,
    These," saith He, " are Mine."

4 Jesus is our Shepherd,
  Guarded by His arm,
  Though the wolves may raven,
    None can do us harm ;
  When we tread death's valley,
    Dark with fearful gloom,
  We will fear no evil,
    Victors o'er the tomb.

668 GOLDEN harps are sounding,
      Angel voices ring,
  Pearly gates are opened,
    Opened for the King ;
  Christ, the King of Glory,
    Jesus, King of Love,
  Is gone up in triumph
    To His home above.

     All His work is ended
      Joyfully we sing,
     Jesus has ascended :
      Glory to our King !

2 He who came to save us,
  He who bled and died,
  Now is crown'd with glory
    At His Father's side ;
  Never more to suffer,
  Never more to die—
  Jesus, King of Glory,
    Is gone up on high.

3 Praying for His children
    In that blessed place,
  Calling them to glory,
    Sending them His grace ;
  His bright home preparing,
    Little ones, for you,
  Jesus ever liveth,
    Ever loveth too.

669 SAVIOUR, blessed Saviour,
      Listen while we sing,
  Hearts and voices raising
    Praises to our King.
  All we have to offer,
    All we hope to be ;
  Body, soul, and spirit,
    All we yield to Thee.

     Looking unto Jesus,
      Never need we yield,
     Over all the armour,
      Faith, the battle shield.

2 Nearer, ever nearer,
  Christ, we draw to Thee,
  Deep in adoration,
    Bending low the knee.
  Thou, for our redemption,
    Cam'st on earth to die ;
  Thou, that we might follow,
    Hast gone up on high.

3 Great, and ever greater,
    Are Thy mercies here ;
  True, and everlasting,
    Are the glories there ;

Where no pain or sorrow,
Toil, or care is known ;
Where the angel legions
Circle round Thy throne.

4 Onward, ever onward,
Journeying o'er the road
Worn by saints before us,
Journeying on to God.
Leaving all behind us,
May we hasten on ;
Backward never looking,
Till the prize is won.

5 Higher, then, and higher,
Bear the ransomed soul,
Earthly toils forgotten,
Saviour, to its goal ;
Where, in joys unthought of,
Saints with angels sing,
Never weary raising
Praises to their King.

670   JESUS loves me ! this I know,
For the Bible tells me so ;
Little ones to Him belong,
They are weak, but He is strong.

Yes, Jesus loves me !
Yes, Jesus loves me !
Yes, Jesus loves me !
The Bible tells me so.

2 Jesus loves me ! He who died
Heaven's gate to open wide ;
He will wash away my sin,
Let His little child come in.

3 Jesus loves me ! He will stay
Close beside me, all the way !
If I love Him, when I die
He will take me home on high.

671   I AM so glad that our Father
in heav'n
Tells of His love in the Book He has
giv'n ;
Wonderful things in the Bible I see ;
This is the dearest, that Jesus loves
me.

I am so glad that Jesus loves me,
Jesus loves even me.

2 Jesus loves me and I know I love
Him ;
Love brought Him down my lost
soul to redeem ;
Yes, it was love made Him die on
the tree ;   [me.
Oh, I am certain that Jesus loves

3 In this assurance I find sweetest rest,
Trusting in Jesus I know I am blest ;
Satan dismayed from my soul doth
now flee,   [me.
When I just tell Him that Jesus loves

4 Oh, if there's only one song I can
sing,   [King,
When in His beauty I see the great
This shall my song in eternity be,
" Oh, what a wonder that Jesus
loves me ! "

(Second Tune—" The Glory Song.")

672   I AM so glad that our Father
in heav'n
Tells of His love in the Book He has
giv'n ;
Wonderful things in the Bible I see ;
This is the dearest, that Jesus loves
me.

I am so glad...Jesus loves me,...
Jesus loves me,...Jesus loves me ;...
Wonderful things in the Bible I see,
This is the dearest, that Jesus loves me.....

2 Jesus loves me and I know I love
Him ;
Love brought Him down my lost
soul to redeem ;
Yes, it was love made Him die on
the tree ;   [me.
Oh, I am certain that Jesus loves

I am so glad...Jesus loves me,...
Jesus loves me,...Jesus loves me ;...
Yes, it was love made Him die on the tree ;
Oh, I am certain that Jesus loves me.

3 In this assurance I find sweetest rest,
Trusting in Jesus I know I am blest ;
Satan dismayed from my soul now
doth flee,   [me.
When I just tell him that Jesus loves

I am so glad...Jesus loves me,...
Jesus loves me,...Jesus loves me ;...
Satan dismayed from my soul now doth flee,
When I just tell him that Jesus loves me.

4 Oh, if there's only one song I can
sing,   [King,
When in His beauty I see the great
This shall my song in eternity be,
" Oh, what a wonder that Jesus loves
me ! "

I am so glad...Jesus loves me,...
Jesus loves me,...Jesus loves me ;...
This shall my song in eternity be,
" Oh, what a wonder that Jesus loves me ! "

673 TAKE up the battle-cry all
    along the line,
Victory by and by, victory divine ;
With your Commander nigh, foes in
    vain combine,
Raise aloft the banner, let it bear
    the sign—
" All the world for Jesus," let the chorus ring ;
" All the world for Jesus," crown Him King.
" All the world for Jesus," let the watchword be
" Forward go in Jesus' name to victory."

2 Truth's armour you may claim, faith
    will be your shield,
Fighting on in Jesus' Name, mighty
    pow'r you wield ;
Glory for God your aim, naught can
    make you yield,
Shout aloud the triumph sure to be
    revealed.

3 Soldiers, with courage go, go for-
    saking all ;
Onward, then, to meet the foe, soon
    the foe shall fall ;
Send mighty blow on blow—let no
    fear appal,   [call.
In the Name of Jesus sound afar the

674 AROUND the throne of God
    in heav'n
Thousands of children stand,
Children whose sins are all forgiv'n,
A holy, happy band :
Singing Glory, glory, glory ;
Singing Glory, glory, glory.

2 What brought them to that world
    above
That heav'n so bright and fair,
Where all is peace, and joy, and love ?
How came those children there ?
Singing Glory, glory, glory ;
Singing Glory, glory, glory.

3 Because the Saviour shed His blood
    To wash away their sin ;   [flood,
Bathed in that pure and precious
Behold them white and clean !
Singing Glory, glory, glory ;
Singing Glory, glory, glory.

4 On earth they sought the Saviour's
    grace,
On earth they loved His Name ;
So now they see His blessed face,
And stand before the Lamb.
Singing Glory, glory, glory ;
Singing Glory, glory, glory.

675 I THINK when I read that
    sweet story of old,
When Jesus was here among men,
How He call'd little children as
    lambs to His fold,
I should like to have been with
    Him then.
I wish that His hands had been
    placed on my head,
That His arms had been thrown
    around me ;
And that I might have seen His kind
    look when He said,   [Me."
" Let the little ones come unto

2 Yet still to His footstool in prayer I
    may go,
And ask for a share in His love ;
And if I thus earnestly seek Him
    below,
I shall see Him and hear Him
    above ;
In that beautiful place He has gone
    to prepare   [given ;
For all who are washed and for-
And many dear children are gather-
    ing there,
" For of such is the kingdom of
    heaven."

3 But thousands and thousands who
    wander and fall
Never heard of that heavenly
    home ;
I should like them to know there is
    room for them all,
And that Jesus has bid them to
    come.   [time,
I long for that blessed and glorious
The fairest and brightest and best,
When the dear little children of every
    clime
Shall crowd to His arms and be
    blest.

676 THERE'S a message of love,
    Come down from above,
To invite little children to heav'n ;
    In God's blessed book
    Poor sinners may look,
And see how all sin is forgiv'n.
    For there they may read
    How Jesus did bleed,
His life everlasting to give ;
    He cleanseth the soul,
    He maketh us whole,
That with Him in heav'n we may live

2 And then, when they die,
   He takes them on high,
To be with Him in heav'n above !
  For so kind is His heart,
  That He never will part,
From a child that has tasted His love.
   And oh ! what a delight
   In heav'n so bright,
When they see the dear Saviour's face,
   On His beauty to gaze,
   And sing to His praise,
And rejoice in His own boundless
   grace.

677 WE are little children, very
    young indeed,
But the Saviour's promise each of
  us may plead.
   If we seek Him early,
   If we come to-day,
  We can be His little friends,
   He has said we may.

2 Little friends of Jesus, what a happy
  thought !
What a precious promise in the Bible
  taught !

3 Little friends of Jesus, walking by
  His side,
With His arm around us, ev'ry step
  to guide.

4 We must love Him dearly with a
  constant love,
Then we'll go and see Him in our
  home above.

678 WE are but little children weak,
    Nor born in any high estate ;
What can we do for Jesus' sake,
  Who is so high and good and great?

2 O day by day, each Christian child
  Has much to do, without, within ;
A death to die for Jesus' sake,
  A weary war to wage with sin.

3 When deep within our swelling hearts
  The thoughts of pride and anger
  rise,
When bitter words are on our tongues
  And tears of passion in our eyes.

4 Then we may stay the angry blow,
  Then we may check the hasty
  word ;
Give gentle answers back again,
  And fight a battle for our Lord.

5 With smiles of peace and looks of
  love   [make,
  Light in our dwellings we may
Bid kind good humour brighten there,
  And still do all for Jesus' sake.

6 There's not a child so small and weak
  But has his little cross to take ;
His little work of love and praise
  That he may do for Jesus' sake.

679 YIELD not to temptation,
    For yielding is sin,
  Each vict'ry will help you
   Some other to win ;
  Fight manfully onward,
   Dark passions subdue,
  Look ever to Jesus,
   He'll carry you through.
   Ask the Saviour to help you,
   Comfort, strengthen and keep you ;
   He is willing to aid you,
   He will carry you through.

2 Shun evil companions,
   Bad language disdain,
  God's name hold in rev'rence,
   Nor take it in vain ;
  Be thoughtful and earnest,
   Kind hearted and true,
  Look ever to Jesus,
   He'll carry you through.

3 To him that o'ercometh
   God giveth a crown ;
  Thro' faith we shall conquer,
   Tho' often cast down ;
  He who is our Saviour,
   Our strength will renew,
  Look ever to Jesus,
   He'll carry you through.

680 THERE is a happy land,
    Far, far away,
  Where saints in glory stand,
   Bright, bright as day.
  O how they sweetly sing,
   " Worthy is our Saviour King ! "
  Loud let His praises ring,
   Praise, praise for aye.

2 Come to this happy land,
   Come, come away ;
  Why will ye doubting stand ?
   Why still delay ?
  O we shall happy be,
  When, from sin and sorrow free,
  Lord, we shall live with Thee,
   Blest, blest for aye.

3 Bright in that happy land
  Beams ev'ry eye ;
Kept by a Father's hand,
  Love cannot die :
On, then, to glory run ;
Be a crown and kingdom won ;
And, bright above the sun,
  Reign, reign for aye.

681 WHITHER, pilgrims, are you
          going,
  Going each with staff in hand ?
We are going on a journey,
  Going at our King's command.
Over hills, and plains, and valleys,
We are going to His palace,
We are going to His palace,
  Going to the better land.

2 Tell us, pilgrims, what you hope for,
  In that far-off, better land ?
Spotless robes and crowns of glory,
  From a Saviour's loving hand.
We shall drink of life's clear river,
We shall dwell with God for ever,
We shall dwell with God for ever,
  In that bright, that better land.

3 Pilgrims, may we travel with you
  To that bright and better land ?
Come and welcome, come and wel-
          come,
  Welcome to our pilgrim band.
Come, oh ! come, and do not leave
          us ;
Christ is waiting to receive us,
Christ is waiting to receive us,
  In that bright, that better land.

682 OUR God will guide us right,
          and, walking in the light,
  We shall win a crown of glory on
          that day,....
When Jesus calls His own together
          round the throne,
  Who keep along the middle of the
          King's highway.

The King's highway ! the King's highway !
Oh, turn aside from ev'rything that leads
          astray !
Our God will guide us right, and walking in the
          light,   [highway.
We'll keep along the middle of the King's

2 Wherever you may be, whatever you
          may see
  That would lead you into evil, say
          you " Nay ! "....

I will not turn aside, whatever may
          betide :
  I'll keep along the middle of the
          King's highway.

3 The meadows may be green where
          " byepath stile " is seen :
  " Turn aside ! " the little flowers
          seem to say ;....
Be sure you give no heed, they're
          trying to mislead ;
  Just keep along the middle of the
          King's highway.

4 For, on enchanted ground, there's
          danger all around,
  And a thousand pleasant voices
          bid you stay ;....
With fingers stop your ears, and
          never mind their jeers ;
  Just keep along the middle of the
          King's highway.

683 WHEN mothers of Salem
          Their children brought to Jesus,
The stern disciples drove them back,
  And bade them depart ;
But Jesus saw them ere they fled,
And sweetly smiled, and kindly said,
  " Suffer little children to come
          unto Me."

2 " For I will receive them,
  And fold them in My bosom ;
I'll be a Shepherd to those lambs,
  Oh, drive them not away !
For if their hearts to Me they give,
They shall with Me in glory live ;
  Suffer little children to come unto
          Me."

3 How kind was our Saviour
  To bid those children welcome !
But there are many thousands who
  Have never heard His Name ;
The Bible they have never read ;
They know not that the Saviour said,
  " Suffer little children to come
          unto Me."

4 Oh ! soon may the heathen
  Of ev'ry tribe and nation
Fulfil the blessed word, and cast
  Their idols all away ;
Oh ! shine upon them from above,
And show Thyself a God of love ;
  Teach the little children to come
          unto Thee.

684 I ONCE heard a sweet story of
wonderful love,
And it lifted the cross that I bore;
Made me think of the home and the
dear ones above:
I am longing to hear it once more.

I am longing to hear it once more;...
The story repeat o'er and o'er;...
It is rapture divine to know He is mine;
I am longing to hear it once more.

2 Tho' afar I had wandered in darkness
and sin, [poor,
And tho' helpless, and weary, and
This sweet story left light, hope, and
gladness within:
I am longing to hear it once more.

3 That sweet story of Jesus who died
on the tree
Will be told on eternity's shore;
How He came as a ransom for you
and for me:
I am longing to hear it once more.

685 WEARY child, thy sin forsaking,
Close thy heart no more;
From thy dream of pleasure waking,
Open wide the door.

While the lamp of life is burning,
And the heart of God is yearning,
To His loving arms returning,
Give thy wand'ring o'er.

2 To the Saviour's tender pleading
Close thy heart no more;
Now the call of mercy heeding,
Open wide the door.

3 To the Gospel invitation
Close thy heart no more;
To receive a full salvation,
Open wide the door.

4 To the joy that fadeth never
Close thy heart no more;
To the peace abiding ever
Open wide the door.

686 JESUS is all the world to me,
My life, my joy, my all;
He is my strength from day to day,
Without Him I would fall.
When I am sad, to Him I go,
No other one can cheer me so;
When I am sad He makes me glad,
He's my Friend.

2 Jesus is all the world to me,
My Friend in trials sore;
I go to Him for blessings, and
He gives them o'er and o'er.
He sends the sunshine and the rain,
He sends the harvest's golden grain;
Sunshine and rain, harvest of grain,
He's my Friend.

3 Jesus is all the world to me,
And true to Him I'll be;
O, how could I this Friend deny,
When He's so true to me?
Following Him I know I'm right,
He watches o'er me day and night;
Following Him by day and night,
He's my Friend.

4 Jesus is all the world to me,
I want no better friend;
I trust Him now, I'll trust Him when
Life's fleeting days shall end;
Beautiful life with such a Friend;
Beautiful life that has no end;
Eternal life, eternal joy,
He's my Friend.

687 THERE'S a sweet old story
which I long to hear,
When the night is long and dreary:
When I feel the power of the tempter
near,
And my soul is sad and weary.

'Tis the old, old story of His love,...
'Tis the sweet, old message from above;...
For no other I can find that can calm a
troubled mind,
Like the sweet old story of His love!...

2 There's a sweet old story that I love
to read,
When my spirit dreads the morrow;
When, to help me onward, strength
or cheer I need,
Or when comfort I would borrow.

3 There's a sweet old story that I love
to tell
To the heart by grief o'ertaken;
To the friendless brothers who in
darkness dwell,
And to those by hope forsaken.

688 WHAT shall I bring to the
Saviour?
What shall I lay at His feet?

I have no glittering jewels,
  Gold or frankincense so sweet.....

Gifts to the Saviour I'm bringing,
Love's richest treasures to lay
Low at His feet with rejoicing,
Ere yonder sunset to-day....

2 What shall I bring to the Saviour ?
  Lips His dear praises to sing ;
Feet that will walk in the pathway
  Leading to Jesus, our King.....

3 What shall I bring to the Saviour ?
  Love that is purest and best ;
Life in its sweetness and beauty,
  All for His service so blest.....

689 HOW oft I prayed for power,
       And tarried by the way ;
I wanted some great blessing
  To use each busy day.

But now He uses me,...
Praise God, He uses me,...
The blessed Holy Spirit uses me,...
But now He uses me....
Praise God, He uses me,...
The blessed Holy Spirit uses me.

2 I did not get the blessing
  Until the Blesser came,
Nor was I fit for service,
  Till filled with love's warm flame.

3 To-day my richest blessing
  Is doing His sweet Word,
My highest joy each moment,
  Is to be used of God.

690 BEFORE a Cross uplifted high,
       I stood alone one day ;
My soul was burdened with a guilt
  No tears could wash away.

Love,...mighty and wonderful,
Love,...so boundless and free !...
Love,...that suffered upon the Cross,
The love that died for me.

2 In grief and pain I wept aloud,
  In helpless agony ;
When from the Cross I heard One
    speak,
  "I gave My life for thee."

3 That voice, so sweet, entranced my
    soul,
  It gave me hope and cheer ;
Tho' trembling, I drew near the cross
  For I had naught to fear.

4 And there upon the cruel Cross
  My Saviour died that day ;
I looked, believed, and from my soul
  The burden roll'd away.

691 JESUS all my grief is sharing,
       He my mansion is preparing ;
When I'm trembling and despairing,
  He will surely hear my call ;
When the storms around me sweep-
    ing,
Tho' in helplessness I'm sleeping,
I am safe in His own keeping,
  This to me is best of all ;
  Best of all, best of all ;
I am safe in His own keeping,
  This to me is best of all.

2 Jesus loves and watches o'er me,
  With His grace He will restore me ;
Angel guards He sends before me,
  Lest in fatal snares I fall ;   [me,
With His friends He hath enrolled
By His might He will uphold me,
In His arms He will enfold me,
  This to me is best of all ;
  Best of all, best of all ;
In His arms He will enfold me.
  This to me is best of all.

3 Jesus loves and He will guide me,
  All I need He will provide me ;
In His bosom He will hide me
  When the woes of life appal ;
He will hear my feeblest sighing,
Needful grace to me supplying,
He'll be with me when I'm dying,
  This to be is best of all ;
  Best of all, best of all ;
He'll be with me when I'm dying,
  This to me is best of all.

692 I'VE a home fair and bright in
       yonder City,
  To its gates I am marching along ;
When my fighting for Jesus here is
    over,
  I shall then take my place with
    the throng
That face to face behold the
    Saviour,
  In whose praise is raised its song.

Up in the golden City
There's a mansion to me will be giv'n ;
I have riches I know that the world can't
    bestow,
I'm an heir of the wealth of heav'n.

2 It is true, on the way to yonder City,
I've to cross o'er a cold rolling
flood ;
But I trust Him to guide me by
whose pity
I've been led to the sin-cleanseing
blood ; [me,
As He has said, He'll never leave
I will trust my Friend, my God.

3 Do you know there's no place in
yonder City
For a soul that is burdened with
guilt ?
Do you know that no sin can ever
enter ?
Hasten then to the blood that was
spilt
To cleanse from sin, and with me
journey
To the City God has built.

693 HE is not a disappointment !
Jesus is far more to me
Than in all my glowing day-dreams
I had fancied He could be ;
And the more I get to know Him,
so the more I find Him true,
And the more I know that others
should be led to know Him too.

2 He is not a disappointment ! He has
saved my soul from sin ;
All the guilt and all the anguish,
which oppressed my heart within,
He has banished by His presence,
and His blessed kiss of peace
Has assured my heart for ever that
. His love will never cease.

3 He is not a disappointment ! He is
coming by and by.
In my heart I have the witness that
His coming draweth nigh.
All the scoffers may despise me, and
no change around may see,
But He tells me He is coming, and
that's quite enough for me.

4 He is not a disappointment ! He is
all in all to me—
Blessed Saviour, Sanctifier, the unchanging Christ is He !
He has won my heart's affections,
and He meets my every need ;
He is not a disappointment, for He
satisfies indeed.

694 HAVE you read the story of
the Cross,
Where Jesus bled and died ;
Where your debt was paid by His
precious blood [side ?
That flowed from His wounded
He died an atoning death for thee,
He died an atoning death ;
Oh, wondrous love ! it was for thee
He died an atoning death !

2 Have you read how they placed the
crown of thorns
Upon His lovely brow ?
When He prayed, forgive them, oh !
forgive,
They know not what they do.

3 Have you read how He saved the
dying thief
When hanging on the tree ?
Who looked with pitying eyes and
said,
Dear Lord, remember me.

4 Have you read that He looked to
heaven and said,
'Tis finished—'twas for thee ?
Have you ever said, I thank Thee,
Lord,
For giving Thy life for me.

695 WHEN I shall reach my home
in glory,
And see my Saviour face to face,
This shall be all my song and story,
A sinner saved by grace.
Saved by grace,...saved by grace,...
For ever I'll tell the sto - - ry,
How Jesus saved...me by His grace,...
And brought me to His glory.

2 I'll tell how by His blood He bought
me, [race ;
With all our lost and ransomed
And how so tenderly He sought me,
And saved me by His grace.

3 I'll tell them how His Spirit sealed
me, [trace ;
And cleansed me from each sinful
And how when sick and worn He
healed
And saved me by His grace.

4 I'll sing how lovingly He led me
At last to yonder heavenly place ;
And how He shepherded and fed me,
And kept me by His grace.

5 Yes, when I reach my home in glory,
    And see my Saviour face to face ;
This shall be all my song and story,
    A sinner saved by grace.

696   THE works and ways of God
               on high
I cannot solve—I do not try ;
But though I cannot these unfold,
One thing I know—to this I'll hold,
Though all the world beside deny—
    A sinner saved by grace am I.
    I cannot tell you why, nor how,
      For oh ! I do not understand ;
    I only say, " I know ! I know ! "
      On this unshaken ground I stand.

2 I know that my Redeemer lives,
  I know, I know that He forgives !
I know that I, who once was dead,
Am now alive in Christ, my Head.
Let all the world beside deny—
" I know I live ! " shall be my cry.

3 Now at His word the darkness flies,
And beams of sunlight flood my eyes,
I do not know ; enough for me
That I who once was blind now see !
Let all the world beside deny—
" I know I see ! " shall be my cry.

4 Beyond this mortal vale there stands
A house for me not made with hands ;
E'en now I see beyond the dome,
And occupy my heavenly home ;
Let all the world beside deny—
I know I have a home on high.

697   IN the heart of London city,
        'Mid the dwellings of the poor,
These bright golden words were
        uttered :
    I have Christ ! what want I more ?
    I have Christ !...what want I more ?...
    I have Christ !...what want I more ?...
    I have Christ !...what want I more ?...

2 Spoken by a lonely woman,
  Dying on a garret floor,
Having not one earthly comfort :
    I have Christ ! what want I more ?

3 Oh, her words will live for ever,
  I repeat them o'er and o'er ;
God delights to hear me saying :
    I have Christ ! what want I more ?

4 Oh, my dear, my fellow-sinners,
  High and low, and rich and poor,
Can you say, with deep thanksgiving :
    I have Christ ! what want I more ?

5 Look away from earth's attractions,
  All its joys will soon be o'er ;
Trust Him now, and say with glad-
        ness :
    I have Christ ! what want I more ?

698   MY Father is rich in houses
            and lands,
He holdeth the wealth of the world in
    His hands !
Of rubies and diamonds, of silver
    and gold,
His coffers are full, He has riches
    untold.
    I'm the child of a King !...
    I'm the child of a King !
    With Jesus my Saviour, I'm the child,
    I'm the child of a King !

2 My Father's own Son, the Saviour
    of men,
Once wandered o'er earth as the
    poorest of them ;   [high,
But now He is reigning for ever on
And will give me a home in heaven
    by and by.

3 I once was an outcast stranger on
    earth,   [birth !
A sinner by choice, and an alien by
But I've been adopted, my name's
    written down—
An heir to a mansion, a robe, and a
    crown !

4 A tent or a cottage, why should I
    care ?   [there !
They're building a palace for me over
Tho' exiled from home, yet still I
    may sing :   [King !
All glory to God, I'm the child of a

699   MY Father will not let me fall,
            His strong and loving arms
            enfold me ;
To Him I trust my life, my all,
    And know that He will safely hold
    me.
    Just as He promised, promised to do,
      When first to Him I trembling came ;
    Now I have trusted, proven Him true,
      Hallelujah to His Name.

2 My Saviour will not let me stray,
    The path He trod is plain before
    me ;
And He who said, " I am the Way,"
    Is watching, ever watching o'er me.

3 I trust Him as a little child,
   Content beneath His wings to
     hide me ;
Tho' all around is rough and wild,
   He walks the path of peace beside
     me.

4 His love will still remember me,
   In life, in death, in joy, and
     sorrow ;
Whate'er betide, He still will be
   My Guide to-day, my Hope to-
     morrow.

700 WHO is this that's waiting,
     waiting,
   Just outside the door ?
Who is He that's knocking, knocking,
   Has He knocked before ?
Rise and bid Him enter in,
   Peace and hope He'll bring ;
'Tis thy Saviour knocking, knocking,
   'Tis thy Lord and King.

   Let Him in ! Let Him in !
    He waits outside the door ;
   Let Him in ere He departs
    To return no more !

2 Don't you hear Him saying, saying,
   Come, O come to Me ;
'Twas for you that, dying, dying,
   I hung on the tree.
Come and see My hands, My side ;
   Look on Me and live ;
Though your sins be many, many,
   Pardon I can give.

3 Still His voice is calling, calling,
   Sweet the tones and low ;
Bid Him enter quickly, quickly,
   Ere He turns to go !
Must His pleading be in vain ?
   Must He, then, depart,
All because His pleading, pleading,
   Reaches not your heart !

4 Sometime you'll be waiting, waiting,
   Just outside the gate ;   [ing,
Sometime you'll be pleading, plead-
   Then 'twill be too late !
Now accept your Heavenly Guest !
   He'll forgive your sin !
While He still is waiting, waiting,
   Rise and let Him in !

701 JESUS is standing in Pilate's
     hall,
Friendless, forsaken, betrayed by all ;

Hearken, what meaneth the sudden
    call :
   What will you do with Jesus ?

  What will you do ? what will you do ?
    Neutral you cannot be,
  Some day your heart will be asking,
    What will He do with me ?

2 Jesus is standing on trial still ;
You can be false to Him if you will ;
You can be faithful thro' good or
    ill—
   What will you do with Jesus ?

3 Will you evade Him as Pilate tried ?
Or shall you choose Him whate'er
    betide ?
Vainly you struggle from Him to
    hide—
   What will you do with Jesus ?

4 Shall you, like Peter, your Lord
    deny ?   [fly ?
Or shall you scorn from His foes to
Daring for Jesus to live or die—
   What will you do with Jesus ?

5 "Jesus, I give Thee my heart to-day ;
Jesus, I'll follow Thee all the way."
Gladly obeying Him, will you say—
   "This will I do with Jesus."

702 SO strange it seemed and
     wondrous,
   When it first came to me,
The story of my Saviour,
   I asked, "Can such things be ?"
I felt my heart replying,
   "Oh, if I only knew !
The Cross, the thorns, the dying !
   O is it, is it true ? "

   I love to hear it spoken,
    I love to read it through ;
   But O for word or token
    To tell me it is true !

2 And when I heard the story
   Told o'er and o'er again,
How Jesus, now in glory,
   Was walking still with men ;
Was filling hearts with gladness,
   And scatt'ring sunshine thro' ;
My own heart longed in sadness
   To know if it were true !

3 Then softly was it spoken,
   " Come, lean upon My breast,
Ye weary ones, heart-broken,
   And I will give you rest."

My heart, so sad and lonely,
  A little closer drew ;
I cried, " O Lord, if only
  I felt and knew it true ! "

4 A voice came sweet and tender !
  It seemed to touch my woe ;
I felt my heart surrender—
  I cried, " O Lord, I know ! "
My Saviour, Thou hast spoken !
  The old, old story's new !
And Thou dost give the token !
  I know, I know it's true !

> My Saviour, O my Saviour !
> The old, old story's new !
> My strength, my joy for ever,
> I know, I know it's true.

703 WEARY and wand'ring and
        sunken in sin,
  Vile as a sinner could be,
Jesus beheld, and to Bethlehem
    came,
  Left His bright throne for me.

> All for me,...all for me ?
> Lord, was it all for me ?...
> From the throne to the manger, from there
>   to the Cross,
> Yes, it was all for me.

2 Footsore and weary He toil'd all
    the way,
  Even to Gethsemane ;
Oft I have met Him and heard His
    sweet voice
  Praying for me, for me.

3 Still I rejected your Saviour and
    mine,
  Till I beheld on the tree,
Suffering, dying, my Saviour and
    yours,
  Dying for you and for me.

704 WHO is this that cometh from
        Edom,
  Crimson red His garments dyed,
In His hands are cruel nail-prints,
  And a spear-wound in His side ?
Say, who is this " Man of Sorrows?"
  Why is He thus pierced and
    scarred ?
Why with face and form so kingly !
Why His beauteous visage marred?

> It is Christ,...the King of glo - - ry,
> Who His life...a ransom gave,...
> Bow before Him, and adore Him,
> Jesus Christ the mighty...to save....

2 Who is this, despised and rejected,
  Who the wine-press trod alone ?
Who is this by all forsaken,
  Left to comfort there are none ?
Who is this, oppressed, afflicted,
  Yet no murmur ever heard ;
As a Lamb led to the slaughter,
  Yet He answers not a word !

3 Who is this with bearing so kingly,
  And a crown His brow adorns,
Not of gold and gems befitting,
  But of mocking, cruel thorns ?
Why with many stripes thus beaten ?
Why thus scourged and spit upon ?
Why His anguish in the garden,
  Kneeling, praying all alone ?

4 Who is this on Calvary's mountain,
  Dying there such shameful death ?
Who for His tormentors praying,
  With His last expiring breath ?
Who is this that earth should tremble
  And the sun in darkness hide,
Rocks be rent and graves be opened,
  When He bowed His head and
    died ?

705 SEEK ye first, not earthly
        pleasure,
Fading joy and failing treasure,
But the love that knows no measure,
  Seek ye first, seek ye first.

2 Seek ye first, not earth's aspirings,
Ceaseless longing, vain desirings,
But your precious soul's requirings
  Seek ye first, seek ye first.

3 Seek ye first God's peace and blessing
Ye have all if this possessing ;
Come, your need and sin confessing,
  Seek Him first, seek Him first.

4 Seek Him first, then, when forgiven,
Pardon'd, made an heir of heaven,
Let your life to Him be given :
  Seek this first, seek this first.

5 Seek the coming of His kingdom ;
Seek the souls around to win them,
Seek to Jesus Christ to bring them :
  Seek this first, seek this first.

706 I WAS wandering and weary
       When my Saviour came unto
       me ;
For the ways of sin grow dreary,
  And the world has ceased to woo
    me :

And I thought I heard Him say,
As He came along His way :
: " O wand'ring souls, come near Me,
My sheep should never fear Me—
I am the Shepherd true ! "

2 At first I would not hearken,
And put off till the morrow;
But life began to darken,
And I was sick with sorrow ;
And I thought I heard Him say,
As He came along His way :

3 At last I stopp'd to listen—
His voice could not deceive me ;
I saw His kind eyes glisten,
So anxious to relieve me ;
And I thought I heard Him say,
As He came along His way :

4 I thought His love would weaken,
As more and more He knew me ;
But it burneth like a beacon, [me ;
And its light and heat go thro'
And I ever hear Him say,
As He goes along His way :

707 THE door of God's mercy is open
To all who are weary of sin,
And Jesus is patiently waiting,
Still waiting to welcome you in.
Come, says the Saviour, come enter the gate,
I watch by the portals both early and late,
Lest some precious soul, not far from the goal,
Should wander away into darkness and hate,
And miss it for ever, the pearly gate.

2 The world is e'er wantonly wooing
Your soul from the ways of the
blest,
But Jesus is tenderly bidding
You turn to His heavenly rest.

3 So many who hear the glad message
Will never its mandates obey,
But turn from the precious, dear
pleadings,
And wilfully wander away.

4 Sad hearts there will surely be
moaning
Outside of the gateway of life,
And praying to Him they rejected
When earth with gay pleasure
was rife.

5 The door of God's mercy is open,
Invitingly open to all,
Who list to the voice of the Master,
And hearing, shall heed His sweet
call.

708 JESUS was standing beside a
grave,
Weeping, but knowing His power to
save ;
" Take ye away now the stone from
the door,"
And Christ will His power display.
They roll'd the stone away, for Christ was there
that day,
And call'd upon a man to leave the darkened
grave.
We'll roll the stone away, for He is here to-day,
And waits to show His mighty power, His
power to save.

2 Jesus is speaking to you in song,
Asking why you have delayed so
long ?   [of sin,
While men are lying in grave-clothes
For whom Jesus died on the Cross.

3 Jesus is standing by hearts of sin,
Knocking and saying, " Let Me
come in."   [door,
Rouse, then, ye sleeper, and open the
For Jesus has power to save.

709 MY blessed Lord was cruci-
fied—
The day was dark, and grief was
wide ;   [vain,
For hope was crushed, and all seemed
Until that Saviour rose again.
Ring out the blessed news again !
Oh ! bear aloft the strain ;
The mighty Lord is ris'n in pow'r—
He died, but not in vain !

2 He brings His great salvation nigh,
And on His love bids us rely ;
He bought our peace thro' grief and
pain,
But oh ! He did not die in vain !

3 O, wondrous news of life and love !
That Jesus lives and reigns above !
He made the path to glory plain ;
Ah, no ! He did not die in vain.

710 JESUS is calling, is calling, is
calling,
Jesus is calling—
Open your heart's door wide and let
Him in.

711 ABOVE this earthly home of
ours,
Of chilling winds and fading flowers,

There is a home all bright and fair,
And all our hopes are centred there.

Oh happy home,...Oh mansions blest,...
Where all God's wea - - ry ones may rest ;
For in that bright...unclouded day,...
Our God shall wipe all tears away.

2 There we shall meet the lov'd and lost
Who over death's dark river cross'd ;
There we shall see our Saviour's face,
And praise the wonders of His grace.

3 Here we may suffer grief and pain,
And tears may flow like falling rain ;
But there, where shines eternal day,
God's hand shall wipe all tears away.

712 I HAVE a Friend, an ever-
          lasting Friend,
He is so kind, He is so good to me ;
He bore my sins, He suffered to the
   end,   [victory.
That I might win a glorious

Come to this Friend, He's waiting now for thee,
He'll be so kind, so loving, warm and true,
He'll break your bands, from sin He'll set you
   free,
He'll be an everlasting Friend to you.

2 This Friend of mine, O how He longs
      to give
The help you need in this dark
      world of sin ;
He bids you come, no longer sinful
      live,
And thro' His Name a crown of
      glory win.

3 Thro' ages past He's proved a
      glorious Friend,
None ever asked and were by Him
      denied ;
His blood was shed that you and I
      might spend   [side.
Eternity at His, our Saviour's

713 WHEN in His beauty my
          Saviour I see,
When I shall look on His face,
Tongue cannot tell of the joy it will
      be,
      Saved by His wonderful grace.....

Saved,...saved,...Saved by His wonderful grace!..
Saved,...saved,...Granted in heaven a place ;..
Saved,...saved,...Saved by His wonderful grace!..
Glory to Jesus, I know I am saved,
Saved by His wonderful grace !..

2 Long I had wander'd in pathways
      of sin,
Often His grace I had spurned ;
Often resisted His strivings within,
Ere to the Saviour I turn'd....

3 How I rejoice that salvation is free,
That I was not turn'd away ;
How I rejoice that my Saviour I'll see
Where I may praise Him for aye....

714 I TAKE my portion from Thy
          hand,
And do not seek to understand ;
For I am blind, while Thou dost see,
Thy will is mine, whate'er it be.

Whate'er it be ! whate'er it be !
I do not fear, whate'er it be !
Thy love divine sustaineth me ;
Thy will is mine, whate'er it be.

2 When darkness doth Thy face
      obscure,
And many sorrows I endure,
I think of Christ's Gethsemane ;
Thy will is mine, whate'er it be.

3 When tender joys to me are known,
I render thanks to Thee alone ;
I know my cup is filled by Thee ;
Thy will is mine, whate'er it be.

4 Thus calmly do I face my lot,
Accept it, Lord, and doubt Thee not ;
Lo ! all things work for good to me ;
Thy will is mine, whate'er it be.

715 GONE from my heart the
          world with all its charm,
Now thro' the blood I'm saved from
      sin's alarm ;
Down at the Cross my heart is
      bending low,
The precious blood of Jesus washes
      white as snow.

I love Him, I love Him,
Because He first loved me,
And purchased my salvation on Mount Calvary.

2 Once I was far away, deep down in
      sin,
Once was a slave to passions fierce
      within ;
Once was afraid to meet an angry
      God,
But now I'm cleansed from ev'ry
      stain thro' Jesus' blood.

3 Once I was bound, but now I am
 set free,
Once I was blind, but now the light
 I see ; [live,
Once I was dead, but now in God I
And tell the world around the peace
 that He doth give.

716 THERE'S a dear and precious
 book,
Though it's worn and faded now,
Which recalls the happy days of long
 ago ;
When I stood at mother's knee,
With her hand upon my brow,
And I heard her voice in gentle tones
 and low.

Blessed book,...precious book,...
On thy dear old tear-stained leaves I love to
 look ;... [narrow way
Thou art sweeter day by day, as I walk the
That leads at last to that bright home above.

2 There she read of Jesus' love,
As He blest the children dear,
How He suffered, bled and died
 upon the tree ;
Of His heavy load of care,
Then she dried my flowing tear
With her kisses as she said it was
 for me.

3 Well, those days are past and gone,
But their memory lingers still,
And the dear old Book each day has
 been my guide ;
And I seek to do His will,
As my mother taught me then,
And ever in my heart His words
 abide.

717 MY heart was oppressed with
 the load of my sin,
And it bent with the weight of
 its woe ; [burden fell off,
At a touch of His hand all the
Do you wonder my loving Him so?

My Saviour is precious to me,
My Saviour is precious to me,
And the more He is known by His loved
 and His own,
More precious He's certain to be.

2 Then He filled me with peace that
 the world knoweth not,
That is with me wherever I go ;
'Tis the very same calm that is
 filling His heart,
Do you wonder my loving Him so?

3 Then He shelters, and blesses, and
 watches o'er me, [low ;
Be my pathway the high or the
I am safe, for His arm is protecting
 His child,
Do you wonder my loving Him so?

4 Oh, will you not love Him who first
 loved you?
Just respond and His sweetness
 you'll know,
And never again will you want other
 love,
Nor will wonder my loving Him so.

718 OH, aching heart, with sorrow
 torn,
Thy Lord is near and knows ;
He knows it all—the feet way-worn,
The weary cares and woes,
The load of grief in anguish borne,
Thy Lord is near,....He knows.

He knows,...He knows,...
The Lord is near, He knows.

2 Oh, fainting soul, with doubts op-
 pressed,
Thy Lord is near and knows ;
He knows it all—how thou art
 pressed
On every side with foes ;
He waits to be thy cherished Guest ;
Thy Lord is near,....He knows.

3 Oh, weary head, that fain would rest,
Thy Lord is near and knows ;
He knows it all, and on His breast
Thou mayest now repose ;
Drop every care at His behest ;
Thy Lord is near,....He knows.

4 Oh, lonely one, live thou thy best,
Thy Lord is near and knows ;
He knows it all, sees ev'ry test,
Yes, every tear that flows ;
Rejoice, faint heart, His way is best ;
Thy Lord is near,....He knows.

719 I HAVE a Friend so precious,
 So very dear to me,
He loves me with such tender love,
 He loves so faithfully :
I could not live apart from Him,
 I love to feel Him nigh,
And so we dwell together,
 My Lord and I.

He knows how much I love Him,
  He knows I love Him well ;
But with what love He loveth me
  My tongue can never tell ;
It is an everlasting love
  In every rich supply,
And so we love each other,
    My Lord and I.

He knows how I am longing
  Some weary soul to win,
And so He bids me go and speak
  The loving word for Him ;
He bids me tell His wondrous love,
  And why He came to die,
And so we work together,
    My Lord and I.

So up into the mountains
  Of heaven's cloudless light,
Or away into the valleys
  Of darkness or of night,
Though round us tempests gather,
  And storms are raging high,
We'll travel on together,
    My Lord and I.

And when the journey's ended
  In rest and peace at last,
When every thought of danger
  And weariness is past,
In the Kingdom of the future,
  In the Glory by and by,
We'll live and reign together,
    My Lord and I.

720   JUST one touch as He moves
            along,
  Push'd and press'd by the jostling
            throng,
  Just one touch and the weak was
            strong,
    Cured by the Healer divine.
  Just one touch as He passes by,
  He will list to the faintest cry,
  Come and be saved while the Lord is nigh,
    Christ is the Healer divine....

2 Just one touch and He makes me
      whole,   [soul,
  Speaks sweet peace to my sin-sick
  At His feet all my burdens roll,
    Cured by the Healer divine.

3 Just one touch and the work is done,
  I am saved by the blessed Son,
  I will sing while the ages run,
    Cured by the Healer divine.
  G

4 Just one touch and He turns to me,
  O the love in His eyes I see !
  I am His, for He hears my plea,
    Cured by the Healer divine.

5 Just one touch, by His mighty power
  He can heal thee this very hour,
  Thou canst hear tho' the tempests
      low'r,
    Cured by the Healer divine.

721   ON the ocean of life we are
            sailing,
  For the Canaan above we are
      bound ;
  We are certain the port to be gaining,
  Since the heavenly Pilot we've
      found.
  Pil - - ot me,...pil - - ot me ;...
    Take the helm in Thine own hand,
    Bring my sinking barque to land.
  Pil - - ot me,...pil - - ot me,...pil - - ot me....

2 For He knows where the dangers are
      lurking,
  Where the rocks and the hidden
      reefs lie ;   [breaking,
  We are safe tho' the billows are
  And the hungry waves dash moun-
      tain high.

3 Soon the haven our barques will be
      nearing,
  The Jerusalem golden and fair ;
  Soon the lights of the city appearing,
  Soon the home of the ransomed
      we'll share.

722   OH, to be like Him,
            Tender and kind,
  Gentle in spirit,
    Lowly in mind ;
  More like to Jesus
    Day after day,
  Filled with His Spirit
    Now and alway.
  Yes, to be like Him, we must abide
  Near to our Saviour, close to His side.

2 Oh, to be like Him,
    Quick to obey,
  Childlike and truthful,
    Ready to say,
  " I and my Father
    Purpose have one,
  Thine, not my will,
    Ever be done."

3 Oh, to be like Him,
  Tempted in vain,
  Dwelling with sinners,
  Yet without stain ;
  Giving our life-work
  Sinners to save,
  Triumphing over
  Death and the grave.

723 WHERE shall I flee for refuge
  Hiding when storms are near ?
Where find a place of safety,
  Dwelling without a fear ?

  Jesus alone can save me,
  All of my joys increase ;
  From ev'ry storm He'll shield me,
  Giving my soul sweet peace.

2 Softly I hear Him calling,
  " Come unto Me and rest ;
Here in My arms find shelter,
  Close to My loving breast."

3 Burdens oft-times oppress me,
  Burdens so hard to bear ;
Oh, then, how sweet His whisper,
  " Cast upon Me thy care."

4 Thus would I ever journey,
  On toward my home above ;
Resting alone on Jesus,
  Whom, tho' unseen, I love.

724 I ENTERED once a home of
  care,
Old age and penury were there,
  Yet peace and joy withal ;
I ask'd the lonely mother whence
Her helpless widowhood's defence,"
  She told me, " Christ was all."

  Christ is all, all in all,
  Yes, Christ is all in all.

2 I stood beside a dying bed
Where lay a child with aching head,
  Waiting for Jesus' call ;
I mark'd his smile, 'twas sweet as
  May,
And as his spirit passed away,
  He whisper'd, " Christ is all."

3 I saw the martyr at the stake,
The flames could not his courage
  shake,
  Nor death his soul appal ;
I asked him whence his strength
  was giv'n,
He look'd triumphantly to heav'n,
  And answered, " Christ is all."

4 I saw the Gospel herald go
  To Afric's sand and Greenland's
  snow,
  To save from Satan's thrall.
No home or life he counted dear,
'Midst wants and perils own'd no
  fear,
  He felt that " Christ is all."

5 I dream'd that hoary time had fled
And earth and sea gave up their dead
  A fire dissolved this ball ;
I saw the Church's ransom'd throng
I heard the burden of their song,
  'Twas " Christ is all in all."

6 Then come to Christ, oh, come to-
  day,
The Father, Son, and Spirit say,
  The Bride repeats the call,
For He will cleanse your guilty
  stains,   [pains
His love will soothe your weary
  For " Christ is all in all."

725 THERE'S no love to me like
  the love of Jesus,
Ever, always just the same ;
E'en tho' of this world you may be
  most lowly,   [Name.
  Jesus still loves you, bless His

  There never was one like Jesus,
  Ever always true is He ;
  There never was one like Jesus,
  There's no love like His love to me.

2 When far, far away, and in condem-
  nation,
Feeling no one cared for me,
There came a sweet voice, I shall
  ne'er forget it—   [Thee."
  " Jesus, thy Saviour, still loves

3 O wonderful love is the love of Jesus,
  Who on Calvary's cruel tree
Was wounded and died to make full
  atonement
For a poor sinner, lost, like me.

726 A MESSAGE sweet is borne to
  me
On wings of joy divine,
A wondrous message, glad and free,
  That thrills this heart of mine.

  O glorious song,...that all day long...
  With tuneful note is ringing ;
  I'm saved by grace...amazing grace,....
  And that is why I'm singing.

2 I'm saved by grace, by grace alone,
  Thro' Christ whose love I claim,
No other could for sin atone,
  Hosanna to His Name.

3 I hear the message that I love
  When morning dawns anew,
I read it in the sun above,
  That shines across the blue.

4 I hear it in the twilight still,
  And at the sunset hour—
I'm sav'd by grace ! what words can
  thrill
With such a magic power.

5 Oh, wondrous grace for all mankind,
  That spreads from sea to sea !
It heals the sick and leads the blind,
  And sets the pris'ner free.

6 The soul that seeks it cannot fail
  To see the Saviour's face,
And Satan's power cannot prevail
  If we are saved by grace.

727 IT pleased the Lord to bruise
  His only Son
    On Calvary,....
That He might ransom sinners such
  as you,
    And set you free.....
He hid His face from Jesus, whom
  He lov'd
    So tenderly,....
With all His heart in yearnings deep
  and true,
    On Calvary.....

2 Although the piercing wail went up
  on high
    From Calvary,....
"My God, oh, why hast Thou forsaken Me
    On Calvary ? "....
The heav'ns return'd nor echo, groan
  nor sigh
    On that dark day,....
And all that He might freely pardon
  me
    On Calvary.....

3 And canst thou, sinner, stand beneath the Cross
    Of Calvary,....
To see His life's blood dropping
  surely down
    Unheedingly ;....

And treat His cruel suffering as dross
    On Calvary,....
While He is wearing sorrow's heavy
  crown
    In agony.....

4 The Cross unfolds the wondrous love
  divine,
    On Calvary,....
And shows in woe love's majesty
  supreme
    On Calvary.....
Then yield to Him that burden'd
  heart of thine
    At Calvary,....
And then the Cross will be thy theme
  throughout
    Eternity.....

728 MY stubborn will at last hath
  yielded ;
I would be Thine, and Thine alone;
And this the pray'r my lips are
  bringing,
Lord, let in me Thy will be done.
  Sweet will of God, still fold me closer,
  Till I am wholly lost in Thee.

2 I'm tired of sin, footsore and weary,
  The darksome path hath dreary
  grown,
But now a light has ris'n to cheer me;
  I find in Thee my Star, my Sun.

3 Thy precious will, O conqu'ring
  Saviour,
  Doth now embrace and compass
  me ;
All discords hushed, my peace a
  river,
  My soul a prisoned bird set free.

4 Shut in with Thee, O Lord, for ever,
  My wayward feet no more to roam ;
What pow'r from Thee my soul can
  sever ?
  The centre of God's will my home.

729 O GOLDEN day, when light
  shall break
  And dawn's bright glories shall
  unfold,
When He who knows the path I take
  Shall ope for me the gates of gold.
Earth's little while will soon be past,
  My pilgrim song will soon be o'er,

The grace that saves shall time out-
last,
   And be my theme on yonder shore.

Then I shall know, as I am known,
And stand complete before the throne ;
Then I shall see my Saviour's face,
And all my song be, " Saving grace."

2 Life's upward way, a narrow path,
   Leads on to that fair dwelling
      place,
Where safe from sin, and storm, and
   wrath,   [grace.
   They live who trust redeeming
Sing, sing, my heart, along the way,
   The grace that saves will keep and
      guide,
Till breaks the glorious crowning day
   And I shall cross to yonder side.

3 I dimly see my journey's end,
   But well I know who guideth me.
I follow Him, that wondrous Friend,
   Whose matchless love is full and
      free.
And when with Him I enter in,
   And all the way look back to trace,
The conqueror's palm I then shall
   win   [grace.
Thro' Christ and His redeeming

730   FAR away my steps have wan-
      dered,
   On the rugged mountain's brow ;
But to Thee my heart is crying,
   Gentle Shepherd, save me now !

Save me now ! save me now !
Gentle Shepherd, save me now !
Unto Thee my heart is crying,
Gentle Shepherd save me now !

2 Thou hast borne my weight of sorrow
   At Thy feet I humbly bow ;
And my heart with Thee is pleading,
   Gentle Shepherd, save me now !

3 Though Thy love I long have
    slighted,
   Though ungrateful I have been,
To Thy fold my faith has brought
   me ;
   Let my weary soul come in.

4 Though Thy love I long have
    slighted,
   O'er my wasted years I weep ;
In Thy blessed arms of mercy,
   Shield and save Thy wand'ring
    sheep.

731   THO' the angry surges roll
      On my tempest-driven soul,
I am peaceful, for I know,
   Wildly tho' the winds may blow,
I've an anchor safe and sure,
   That can evermore endure.

And it holds, my anchor holds ;
Blow your wildest, then, O Gale,..
On my barque so small and frail ;
I shall never, never fail,
For my an - - chor...holds,...my anchor holds.

2 Mighty tides about me sweep,
   Perils lurk within the deep ;
Angry clouds o'ershade the sky,
   And the tempest rises high ;
Still I stand the tempest's shock,
   For my anchor grips the rock.

3 Troubles almost whelm the soul ;
   Griefs like billows o'er me roll ;
Tempters seek to lure astray ;
   Storms obscure the light of day ;
I can face them and be bold,
   I've an anchor that shall hold.

732   O CONDESCENSION wonder-
      ful !
   O boundless love surpassing
    thought !
That Christ the mighty Counsellor,
   From heaven to earth salvation
    brought !

O love divine ! O matchless grace !
O mercy flowing full and free !
With wondrous love and winning voice,
We hear Him whisper, " Come to Me."

2 O joy to know that He is mine !
   This wondrous Friend, beyond
    compare !
O joy above all human joy,
   He will a place for me prepare !

3 O peace that passeth human thought!
   The peace of God so freely giv'n !
The world cannot this peace destroy,
   This peace that fills the soul with
    heaven !

733   I KNOW that afar in God's
      boundless realm,
   Perhaps 'mid the starry spaces,
Lies the promised home of the saints
   redeemed,
   Replete with celestial graces ;

In dreams I have walked on the
    streets of gold,
  As I sought for my own fair
    dwelling,
And voices I knew and loved of old
  I've heard in the music swelling.

> That beautiful city is home to me,
>   Each day it is growing dearer ;
> And voices that call from beyond the sea
>   Are drawing me nearer and nearer.

2 That beautiful city with jasper walls,
    Ne'er closes its pearly portals,
  And the healing pow'r of its holy
    Light
  Sweeps over the blest immortals ;
  There sorrow and tears shall be
    wiped away
  In the dawn of an endless morning,
  Our triumphs of faith like stars shall
    shine,
  Bright crowns for the soul's
    adorning.

3 The longings of life shall be satisfied,
    The fetters of earth be broken,
  And the words imprisoned within
    the soul
  With rapture shall then be spoken ;
  The music that sorrow hath hushed
    awhile,
  And the silence of life's sad story
  Shall leap into songs of perfect joy,
  Attuned to eternal glory.

734 THERE is a land mine eye
    hath seen
  In visions of enraptur'd thought,
So bright that all which spreads
    between
  Is with its radiant glories fraught.

> Oh, land of love,...of joy and light,...
> Thy glories gild...earth's darkest night ;...
> Thy tranquil shore,...we, too, shall see,...
> When dawn shall break...and shadows flee.

2 A land upon whose blissful shore
    There rests no shadow, falls no
    stain ;
  There those who meet shall part no
    more,
  And those long parted meet again.

3 Its skies are not like earthly skies,
    With varying hues of shade and
    light !
  It hath no need of suns to rise
    To dissipate the gloom of night.

4 There sweeps no desolating wind
    Across the calm, serene abode ;
  The wand'rer there a home may find
    Within the paradise of God.

735 LIKE a shepherd, tender, true,
    Jesus leads,....Jesus leads,....
Daily finds us pasture new,
    Jesus leads,....Jesus leads ;....
If thick mists....are o'er the way,....
    Or the flock....'mid danger feeds,...
He will watch them lest they stray,
    Jesus leads,....Jesus leads....:

2 All along life's rugged road,
    Jesus leads,....Jesus leads,....
Till we reach yon blest abode,
    Jesus leads,....Jesus leads,....
All the way...before, He's trod,....
    And He now...the flock precedes,...
Safe into the folds of God
    Jesus leads,....Jesus leads.....

3 Thro' the sunlit ways of life
    Jesus leads,....Jesus leads,....
Thro' the warrings and the strife,
    Jesus leads,....Jesus leads ;....
When we reach...the Jordan's tide,...
    Where life's bound'ry....line re-
    cedes,....
He will spread the waves aside,
    Jesus leads,....Jesus leads.....

736 WHEN angry waves about me
    roll,
  And hide my path across life's sea,
No fear alarms my trusting soul,
  For well I know who pilots me.

> Yes, well I know...who pilots me...
> Across life's ev - - er troubled sea ;...
> The winds may rave...and waves may swell,...
> While Jesus pi - - lots, all is well....

2 Day after day, tho' tossed about,
    And often dang'rous rocks I see,
There comes to me no fear nor doubt,
  For well I know who pilots me.

3 Tho' each new day brings trials sore,
    Tho' rougher still the ocean be,
I know that I shall reach the shore,
  For well I know who pilots me.

4 My Saviour's love still guides me on,
    My only chart and compass He ;
I'll trust Him till the journey's done,
  For well I know who pilots me.

737 THERE was One who was
　　willing to die in my stead
　That a soul so unworthy might live
And the path of the Cross He was
　　willing to tread,
　　All the sins of my life to forgive.

They are nail'd to the Cross, they are nail'd
　to the Cross,
O how much He was willing to bear !
With what anguish and loss, Jesus went to
　the Cross !
And He carried my sins with Him there !

2 He is tender and loving and patient
　　with me,　　　　　　　　[dross,
While He cleanses my heart of its
But "there's no condemnation"—I
　　know I am free,
　　For my sins are all nail'd to the
　　　Cross.

3 I will cling to my Saviour and never
　　depart,
　I will joyfully journey each day,
With a song on my lips and a song
　　in my heart,　　　　　　[away.
　That my sins have been taken

738 BEYOND the sea....that rolls
　　between....
　This world of care....and things un-
　　seen....
　There is a land....of endless day,....
　Where all our tears....are wiped
　　away....

Beyond the sea..the restless, rolling sea,..
I hear my loved..ones gently calling me...
I soon shall leave the troubled shores of time...
And dwell for aye..in that celestial clime....

2 Beyond the sea....lies heav'n's fair
　　shore,....　　　　　　[o'er ;....
　Where all of sin....and earth are
　Where care and toil....have passed
　　away ;....　　　　　　　[stray.....
　Where weary feet....no more shall

3 No more shall beat....the flood of
　　years....　　　　　　[worn ;....
　Across these forms....so frail and
　No more shall roll...the sea of tears...
　Across these hearts....by anguish
　　torn....

4 Beyond the sea....there's rest and
　　peace,....　　　　　　[come ;....
　There Jesus bids....His children
　Beyond the sea....the tempests
　　cease,....　　　　　　[home."....
　There angels sing....a " welcome

739 I NEVER can forget the day
　　I heard my mother kindly say :
" You're leaving now my tender
　　care ;
Remember, child, your mother's
　　pray'r."

Whene'er I think of her so dear,
I feel as if she still were here ;
A voice comes floating on the air,
Reminding me of mother's pray'r.

2 I never can forget the voice
　That always made my heart rejoice ;
Tho' I have wandered, God knows
　　where,
　Still I remember mother's prayer.

3 Tho' years have gone, I can't forget
　Those words of love, I hear them yet ;
I see her by the old armchair,
　My mother dear, in humble pray'r.

4 I never can forget the hour
　I felt the Saviour's cleansing pow'r ;
My sin and guilt He cancell'd there ;
'Twas there He answer'd mothers'
　　pray'r.

O praise the Lord for saving grace !
We'll meet up yonder, face to face,
The home above together share
In answer to my mother's pray'r.

740 WHEN I'm sad and heavy
　　laden,
Burdened with the weight of sin,
　Jesus is the very Friend I need ;
To the bloodstained Cross He points
　　me,
And He gives me peace within,
　Jesus is the very Friend I need.

O He is the best of friends,
And His goodness never ends,
　And His love will ev'ry human thought
　　exceed ;
Let me love Him more and more,
Till I stand on glory's shore ;
　O Jesus is the very Friend I need.

2 When I'm struggling with tempta-
　　tion,
When my strength shall almost fail,
　Jesus is the very Friend I need ;
For His arm will bring deliv'rance,
And His grace will still prevail,
　Jesus is the very Friend I need.

3 When I drink the cup of sorrow,
When I tread the path of grief,
　Jesus is the very Friend I need ;

In His Word is consolation,
In His presence sweet relief,
  Jesus is the very Friend I need.

4 When I reach the silent river,
When I wait beside the tide,
  Jesus is the very Friend I need ;
He will bear me o'er the billows
To the radiant morning side,
  Jesus is the very Friend I need.

741   THOU my ransom price hast paid,
  Blessed Son of God,
Since on Thee my heart is stayed,
  Keep me under the blood.

> Keep me under the blood, dear Lord,
>   Calvary's crimson flood ;
> Not mine own, but Thine alone,
>   Keep me under the blood.

2 At the Cross where first I knelt,
  Full of sinful pride,
Where I first salvation felt,
  Let me still abide.

3 Where to self and sin I died,
  Where, the nails were driven,
Let me still for cleansing hide
  In Thy dear side riven.

4 Shouting with my latest breath
  Praises to our God,
Who my soul has saved and kept
  By His precious blood.

742   WHEN I was but a little child, how well I recollect,
How I would grieve my mother with
  my folly and neglect ;
And now that she has gone to heaven
  I miss her tender care ;
O Saviour, tell my mother, I'll be
  there.

> Tell mother I'll be there, in answer to her
>   pray'r ;
> This message, blessed Saviour, to her bear :
> Tell mother I'll be there, heav'n's joys with
>   her to share ;
> Yes, tell my darling mother I'll be there.

2 Tho' I was often wayward, she was
  ever kind and good,
So patient, gentle, loving, when I
  acted rough and rude :
My childhood griefs and trials she
  would gladly with me share ;
O Saviour, tell my mother I'll be
  there.

3 When I became a prodigal, and left
  the old roof tree,
She almost broke her loving heart
  in mourning after me.
And day and night she prayed to
  God to keep me in His care ;
O Saviour, tell my mother I'll be
  there.

4 One day a message came to me, it
  bade me quickly come,
If I would see my mother ere the
  Saviour took her home ;
I promised her, before she died, for
  heaven to prepare,   [there.
O Saviour, tell my mother I'll be

743   I PRAISE the Lord that one like me
For mercy may to Jesus flee ;
He says that whosoever will
May seek and find salvation still.

> My Saviour's promise faileth never,
> He counts me in the Whosoever.

2 I was to sin a wretched slave,
But Jesus died my soul to save ;
He says that whosoever will
May seek and find salvation still.

3 I look by faith and see this word
Stamp'd with the blood of Christ,
  my Lord ;
He says that whosoever will
May seek and find salvation still.

4 I now believe He saves my soul,
His precious blood hath made me
  whole ;
He says that whosoever will,
May seek and find salvation still.

744   SOME day 'twill all be over—
  The toils and cares of life ;
Some day the world be vanquished
  With all this mortal strife ;
Some day, the journey ended,
  I'll lay my burden down ;
Some day, in realms supernal,
  Receive, at last, my crown.

> Some day,...some happy day,...
> The Lord will wipe all tears away,...
> And I shall go to dwell with Him,....
> To dwell with Him...some happy day..

2 Some day I'll see the mansions
  Of heaven's city fair ;
Some day I'll greet with pleasure
  The dear ones waiting there ;

Some day I'll hear the voices
　Of God's angelic throng;
Some day I'll join the chorus
　In heaven's immortal song.

3 Some day I'll see the Saviour,
　　And know Him face to face;
　Some day receive, unmeasured,
　　The blessings of His grace;
　Some day He'll smile upon me
　　From that white throne above;
　Some day I'll know the fulness
　　Of His undying love.

745 BROTHER, don't stay away,
　Brother, don't stay away,
Brother, don't stay away, don't stay
　away.
My Lord says there's room enough,
Room enough in the heavens for you,
My Lord says there's room enough,
　don't stay away.

746 HE who hath led will lead,
　　All through the wilderness,
He who hath fed will surely feed;
　He who hath blessed will bless;
He who hath heard thy cry,
　Will never close His ear;
He who hath marked thy faintest
　　sigh
Will not forget thy tear.
　He loveth always, faileth never,
　So rest on Him to-day, for ever.

2 He who hath made thee whole
　Will heal thee day by day;
He who hath spoken to thy soul
　Hath many things to say.
He who hath gently taught,
　Yet more will make thee know;
He who so wondrously hath wrought
　Yet greater things will show.

3 He who hath made thee nigh,
　Will draw thee nearer still;
He who hath given the first supply
　Will satisfy and fill.
He who hath given thee grace,
　Yet more and more will send;
He who hath set thee in the race
　Will speed thee to the end.

4 He who hath won thy heart
　Will keep it true and free;
He who hath shown thee what thou
　　art,
Will show Himself to thee.

He who hath bid thee live,
　And made thy life His own,
Life more abundantly will give,
　And keep it His alone.

747 WHEN your spirit bows to
　　　sorrow
From the load it bears,
Go and tell your heart to Jesus,
　Don't you know He cares?
　Yes, there is One who bears your burdens,
　Ev'ry sorrow shares;
　Go and tell it all to Jesus—
　　Don't you know He cares?

2 Have your feet become entangled
　In the tempter's snares?
There is One who died to save you,
　Don't you know He cares?

3 Have you been by grief o'ertaken,
　Stricken unawares?
Yet ye will not be forsaken,
　Don't you know He cares?

4 Is your body filled with anguish,
　With the pain it bears?
Think of how the Saviour suffered,
　Don't you know He cares?

5 Loss of friends and loss of fortune—
　Life a dark look wears;
Yet the Saviour still is with you,
　Don't you know He cares?

6 So amid life's cares and struggles,
　Blending songs with prayers—
Always put your trust in Jesus,
　Don't you know He cares?

748 ONE thing I of the Lord
　　　desire,
　For all my path hath miry been;
Be it by water or by fire,
　Oh make me clean, oh make me
　　clean!
　So wash me, Thou,...without, within,...
　Or purge with fire,...if that must be!..
　No matter how,..if only sin..
　Die out in me,..Die out in me...

2 If clearer vision Thou impart,
　Grateful and glad my soul shall be;
But yet to have a purer heart
　Is more to me, is more to me.

3 Yea, only as this heart is clean
　May larger vision yet be mine,
For mirror'd in its depths are seen
　The things divine, the things
　　divine.

4 I watch to shun the miry way,
  And staunch the springs of guilty
      thought ;
  But, watch and struggle as I may,
  Pure I am not, pure I am not.

749 THE trusting heart to Jesus
          clings,
  Nor any ill forebodes,
But at the Cross of Calv'ry sings,
  Praise God for lifted loads !

> Singing I go along life's road,
> Praising the Lord, praising the Lord,
> Singing I go along life's road,
> For Jesus has lifted my load.

2 The passing days bring many cares,
  "Fear not," I hear Him say ;
And when my fears are turned to
      prayers,
  The burdens slip away.

3 He tells me of my Father's love,
  And never-slumb'ring eye ;
My everlasting King above
  Will all my need supply.

4 When to the throne of grace I flee,
  I find the promise true,
The mighty arms upholding me
  Will bear my burdens too.

750 ERE you left the homestead
          in the vanished long ago,
When your heart was happy and
      your soul was pure as snow,
You were bade to Jesus' feet, His
      shelt'ring love to know ;
  Don't forget the promise made to
      mother.

Don't forget those tender hands that soothed
      your cares away ;
Don't forget that gentle face, those tresses thin
      and grey ;   [you to-day ;
And don't forget her Saviour, who is calling
Don't forget the promise made to mother.

2 When you sought the world, she bade
      you take this faithful Friend,
  Begged you to confess Him, and in
      Him your soul defend ;
  Oft you vowed to claim Him and to
      trust Him to the end,
    Don't forget the promise made to
        mother.

3 Far from grace you wander'd in the
      weary passing years,
  Patiently she suffered and endured
      her grief and fears ;

Many times you told her you would
    heed the pray'rs and tears ;
  Don't forget the promise made to
      mother.

4 Once again you promised when her
    pilgrim work was done,
When she went in triumph to receive
    her golden crown ;
When she said, " Thro' Christ alone
    were life and vict'ry won ; "
  Don't forget the promise made to
      mother.

751 I READ that whosoever
          May from wrath flee ;
God will reject me never,
  For that means me.

> For that means me,
>   Yes, that means me ;
> When I read " whosoever,"
>   That means me.

2 His blood is efficacious,
    His love is free ;
To sinners He is gracious,
  And that means me.

3 Christ died for ev'ry nation,
    On Calv'ry's tree ;
He died for our salvation,
  And that means me.

4 I read the promise given
    That o'er death's sea,
We'll live with Him in heaven,
  And that means me.

752 THE sun will never set
          In Summer-land ;
No eyes with tears are wet
    In Summer-land ;
No shade of dark'ning night
Will shut the view from sight,
Nor e'er becloud the light,
    In Summer-land.

2 No one will lose the way
    In Summer-land ;
Nor ever go astray
    In Summer-land ;
No mountain hard to climb,
Yet all is grand, sublime,
With endless summer clime,
    In Summer-land.

3 No death is ever known
    In Summer-land ;
For life is on the throne
    In Summer-land ;

No mourning for the dead,
No heavy hearts, like lead,
But endless joy instead,
  In Summer-land.

753 SOMEWHERE the sun is
    shining,
Somewhere the song-birds dwell ;
Hush, then, thy sad repining,
God lives, and all is well.

Some - - where,...some - - where,
Beautiful Isle of Somewhere !
Land of the true where we live anew,
Beautiful Isle of Somewhere !

2 Somewhere the day is longer,
  Somewhere the task is done :
Somewhere the heart is stronger,
  Somewhere the guerdon won.

3 Somewhere the load is lifted,
  Close by an open gate ;
Somewhere the clouds are rifted,
  Somewhere the angels wait !

754 WHEN the world and sin
    oppose,
We will follow Jesus ;
He is greater than our foes,
We will follow Jesus.
On His promise we'll depend,
He'll be with us to the end,
He will guard us and defend :
  We will follow Jesus.

755 BOTH weak and blind, dear
    Lord, I am,
For now Thy face I cannot see,
But I can hear Thy gentle voice
Speak words of love to me.

O some day...I shall see,...
  And some day...clasp Thy hand....
Yes, some day...see Thy face,...
  When in Thy courts I stand.

2 But I can feel Thy gentle touch,
  And I can read Thy blessed Word,
And with Thy mighty throbbing love
  My lonely heart is stirred.

3 Till then, dear Lord, but lead me on,
  And guide me in the better way,
Lest, groping in the darkness here,
  My feet shall go astray.

4 And when at last my journey's o'er,
  Earth's heavy burdens are laid
    down ;   [joy,
When tears are changed to pearls of
My cross to jewelled crown.

756 OH, I can't tell it all, of the
    wonderful love,
How, when lost in my sins, Jesus
  found me ;
With a heart full of love, how He
  came from above,
Threw His strong arms of mercy
  around me.

Oh, I can't tell it all ; no, I can't tell it all ;
  But my heart is so full of His glory,
That wherever I go in this wide world below,
  I am telling the wonderful story.

2 Oh, I can't tell it all, how He freely
    forgave ;
How the blood flowed with wonderful healing ;
O'er my lost, guilty soul, how it
  cleansed and made whole,
While low at the Cross I was
  kneeling.

3 Oh, I can't tell it all, what a Friend
    He has been,
Now He's borne all my sorrows
  and sadness ;
How He saves me to-day, bids the
  clouds chase away,
How He turns all my mournings
  to gladness.

4 Oh, I can't tell it all, but His love
    you may know,
You may have Him, this wonder-
  ful Saviour ;
You may taste of His bliss, you may
  say, I am His,
And He is my portion for ever.

5 Oh, I can't tell it all, but as long as
    I've breath
I will still tell the wonderful story ;
When my life work is done and a
  crown I have won,
I will tell it for ever in glory.

757 AFTER the earthly shadows
    have lifted,
And o'er the hill-tops morning I
  see,
Sweetest of prospects, I shall behold
  Him,
Jesus, the Saviour of sinners like
  me.

When I behold Him, Christ, in His beauty,
  When with the ransom'd His face I shall see
O how my heart in rapture will praise Him,
  Praise Him for saving a sinner like me.

2 Helpless He found me, lifted me to
    Him ;
    Whisper'd of pardon abundant
    and free ;
    Breath'd He His peace o'er my sin-
    stricken spirit ;
    Pointed my vision to Calvary's
    tree.

3 Now in His presence daily I'm living,
    Walking by faith where mine eyes
    cannot see ;
    For He is guiding home to that city,
    Built for His lov'd ones—saved
    sinners like me.

758   HOLY Bible, book divine,
    Precious treasure, thou art
    mine ;
    Mine to tell me whence I come,
    Mine to tell me what I am.

    Mine,....mine,...book divine,
    Precious treasure, thou art mine ;
    O thou holy book divine,
    Precious treasure, thou art mine !

2 Mine to chide me when I rove,
    Mine to show a Saviour's love ;
    Mine thou art to guide and guard,
    Mine to punish or reward.

3 Mine to Comfort in distress,
    Suff'ring in this wilderness ;
    Mine to show by living faith,
    Man can triumph over death.

4 Mine to tell of joys to come,
    And the rebel sinner's doom ;
    O thou holy book divine,
    Precious treasure, thou art mine !

759   WHAT hinders your coming to
    Jesus,
    What hinders your coming to-day?
    He offers His grace and His pardon,
    Tell Jesus what stands in the way.

    What is it that hinders your coming ?
    You may find this salvation to-day ;
    The Saviour is ready and waiting,
    O why do you longer delay ?

2 If pleasures and earthly enjoyment
    Have hindered your coming before
    O tarry no longer, but prove Him,
    Who offers you joy evermore.

3 The fearful, the troubled and doubt-
    ing,
    May lovingly lean on His breast ;
    O trust Him who offers salvation,
    Come now to His arms and be blest

4 What hinders your coming to Jesus?
    The fear that you may not hold
    out ?
    His mercy endureth for ever,
    O how can you linger in doubt ?

760   FAR from home and kindred,
    Wandering away,
    Where is he I think of,
    Pray for day by day ?
    Once home's brightest sunshine,
    Once its joy and light,
    Still his mother's darling,
    Where is he to-night ?

    For the Shepherd, Jesus,
    Leaves the rest behind,
    Seeks the lost and wand'ring,
    Seeks until He find.

2 Far he may be straying,
    From the heavenly fold,
    Yet the tender Shepherd,
    With a love untold,
    And a great compassion
    Filling all His mind,
    Will be following after,
    Seeking till He find.

3 Ah ! no heart can harden
    So He cannot teach ;
    And no sheep can wander
    Where He cannot reach ;
    So I keep on praying,
    Wheresoe'er he be,
    Bring him home, Good Shepherd,
    Bring him back with Thee.

4 May the bells of heaven
    Ring for him with joy ;
    May rejoicing angels
    Smile upon my boy ;
    May the Father meet him
    Coming back alone,
    Saying, " Loved and lost one,
    Welcome, welcome home ! "

761   I WAS far away from Jesus,
    dead in trespasses and sin,
    And I thought for one so vile no
    hope could be ;
    But the blessed Lord of Glory
    stooped and raised me to Him-
    self,   [me.
    And He put His loving arms around

    He put His loving arms around me,
    He put His loving arms around me,
    I look'd into His face, it beamed with tender
    grace,
    As He put His loving arms around me.

2 Then He whispered to me pardon
    thro' the all atoning blood
  Which He shed for my transgres-
    sions on the tree ;
And the blessed peace of heaven
    came into my weary soul,
  As He put His loving arms around
    me.

3 Day by day He guides and keeps me
    and in the blessed narrow way,
  From the ban of sin and death He
    makes me free ;
There's no evil can befall me while
    I'm resting in His grace,   [me.
And He has His loving arms around

4 In the hour of deepest trial, when all
    earthly comfort fails,
  And no cheering ray of sunshine I
    can see ;
Then to Him I bring my sorrow, and
    He wipes away my tears,   [me.
  As He puts His loving arms around

5 Oh, this blessed life in Jesus ! sinner,
    won't you hear His call ?
  From the power of sin's dominion
    He can free ;
Yield thy heart to Him this moment
    and with joy thou'lt surely find,
  That He'll put His loving arms
    around thee.

He'll put His loving arms around thee,
He'll put His loving arms around thee,
Look up into His face, it beams with tender
    grace,
And He'll put His loving arms around thee.

762 WITH ev'ry power, with heart
    and soul,
  I belong to Jesus !
He shall my ev'ry thought control,
  I belong to Jesus !

    I belong to Jesus !
    I belong to Jesus !
    I belong to Jesus,
    He belongs to me.

2 What though temptations sore beset,
  I belong to Jesus !
What though earth's cares annoy
    and fret,
  I belong to Jesus !

3 In vain the world my heart allures,
  I belong to Jesus !
In weakness this my soul assures,
  I belong to Jesus !

4 No threat'ning danger then I see,
  I belong to Jesus !
Through time and through eternity,
  I belong to Jesus !

763 WHEN weary and fainting
    and ready to die,
To the Rock in the desert for safety
    I fly ;
There 'neath its cool shelter from
    storms I would hide,   [abide.
My soul is refresh'd as in Him I

O come, all ye weary, and blissfully prove,
That Christ is the Rock, and His shadow is love.

2 When thirsty and parched with the
    heat of the day,
To the Rock that was smitten I'll
    haste me and say,
" Give me a cool drink from Thy
    bountiful store,"
And quickly and freely the life
    waters pour.

3 Though billows of sorrow around me
    may roll,
And dangers of midnight may
    trouble my soul,
I'll haste to the Rock that is higher
    than I,
And safely I'll rest till the night
    passeth by.

764 I BELONG to the King, I'm
    a child of His love,
  I shall dwell in His palace so fair ;
For He tells of its bliss in yon
    heaven above,
  And His children its splendour
    shall share.

I belong to the King, I'm a child of His love,
  And He never forsaketh His own ;
He will call me some day to His palace above,
  I shall dwell by His glorified throne.

2 I belong to the King, and He loves
    me, I know,
  For His mercy and kindness so free
Are unceasingly mine, wheresoever
    I go,
  And my refuge unfailing is He.

3 I belong to the King, and His pro-
    mise is sure,   [last
  That we all shall be gathered at
In His kingdom above, by life's
    water so pure,   [past.
  When this life with its trials is

765 LORD, Thou hast granted
  salvation to me,
  What wilt Thou have me to do ?
From Satan's bondage at last I am
  free,
  What wilt Thou have me to do ?

What wilt Thou have me to do ?
Where wilt Thou have me to go ?
Jesus, my Master, Thy will shall be mine,
  What wilt Thou have me to do ?

2 Since I am saved by the Crucified
  One,
  What wilt Thou have me to do ?
I would point others to God's only
  Son,
  What wilt Thou have me to do ?

3 Pardon is granted thro' Him who
  hath died,
  What wilt Thou have me to do ?
I am so happy with Thee at my side,
  What wilt Thou have me to do ?

4 Ready and willing Thy voice to obey,
  What wilt Thou have me to do ?
Bid me to follow Thee day unto day,
  What wilt Thou have me to do ?

766 I SHALL lay the cross aside,
  Some day, some glad day ;
Safely pass to Canaan's side,
  Some day, some glad day ;
If I live a life of pray'r,
And the cross for Jesus bear,
I a glorious crown shall wear,
  Some day, some glad day.

2 I the sinner's Friend shall see,
  Some day, some glad day ;
See the wounds once made for me,
  Some day, some glad day ;
I shall press close to His side,
Who for me was crucified,
And shall then be satisfied,
  Some day, some glad day.

3 I shall meet the friends of yore,
  Some day, some glad day ;
And with them the Lamb adore,
  Some day, some glad day ;
There at Jesus' sacred feet
Saints of ev'ry clime I'll meet,
Hold with them communion sweet,
  Some day, some glad day.

4 I shall lean on Jesus' breast,
  Some day, some glad day ;
Find a sweet, a perfect rest,
  Some day, some glad day ;

On that bright eternal shore
All our sorrows will be o'er,
We shall meet to part no more,
  Some day, some glad day.

767 HAVE you accepted the friend-
  ship of Jesus ?
  Do you walk with Him day by day
Resting secure in His blessed assur-
  ance,
  " Lo, I am with you alway ? "

By and by,...by and by,...
  They who walk with Him here below,
In His glorified likeness awaking,
  As they are known, shall they know.

2 Dear as a mother, or sister, or
  brother,
  To His infinite heart of love
Is he that doeth the will of the
  Father,
  Seeking for strength from above.

3 Servants no longer, but friends He
  doth call us,
  If we do what His love commands,
Yesterday, now, and for ever His
  promise
  Fixed and unchangeable stands.

768 LEAD me gently home, Father,
  Lead me gently home,
When life's toils are ended,
  And parting days have come ;
Sin no more shall tempt me,
  Ne'er from Thee I'll roam,
If Thou'lt only lead me, Father,
  Lead me gently home.

Lead me gently home, Father,
  Lead me gently,
Lest I fall upon the wayside,
  Lead me gently home....

2 Lead me gently home, Father,
  Lead me gently home ;
In life's darkest hours, Father,
  When life's troubles come,
Keep my feet from wand'ring,
  Lest from Thee I roam,
Lest I fall upon the wayside,
  Lead me gently home.

769 JESUS of Nazareth, Healer of
  men,
  Curer of halt and of blind ;
Worker of wonders again and again,
  Seeking the sad ones to find.

Jesus of Nazareth, tell it again,
  Died on the Cross for sinful men.

2 Jesus of Nazareth, Curer of sin,
  Seeker for lost and defiled ;
Striving so kindly the straying to
  win,
Loving each penitent child.

3 Jesus of Nazareth, dying for all,
  Hanging in pain on the tree,
Suff'ring so meekly that we who may
  call,
    Pardon thro' Him may have free.

770 JUST as I am I come to Thee,
  Myself I cannot better make ;
The precious blood my only plea,
  Oh, save me for Thy mercy's sake.

    Just as...I am,...
      Just as I am I come to Thee,...
    Oh hear me, bless me, save me, Lord,
      Just as I am I come to Thee.

2 Just as I am, yet this I know,
  The blood will all-sufficient be ;
I shall be whiter than the snow,
  Made fully whole in trusting Thee.

3 Just as I am, I come to-day,
  My hungry soul cries out for Thee ;
I can no longer stay away,
  Thine, wholly Thine, I long to be.

4 Just as I am, my Life, my Love,
  My soul here finds a perfect rest ;
While, like the weary, wand'ring
  dove ;
    Safe folded in Thy love I rest.

771 OH, awful load for that bow'd
  Head,   [form,
Terrific weight for that marr'd
He bore *your* sins, *your* burden
  dread,
    And brav'd *your* judgment's fear-
      ful storm.

    Thy death, Lord Jesus, evermore,
    Shall be our song on yonder shore ;
    We'll praise the blessed One who bore
    Our load of sin upon the tree.

2 Transferred to Him, the guiltless, see
  Your guilt, in blood your debt was
    paid ;
Behold, to set the captive free,
  Jesus the great sin-off'ring made.

3 Believe, believe, thou guilty one,
  That all thy sins' deserved doom
Was borne by Christ ; God's Holy
  Son   [tomb.
  For thee has bow'd Him to the

772 THERE is singing up in heaven
  such as we have never known,
Where the angels sing the praises of
  the Lamb upon the throne ;
Their sweet harps are ever tuneful
  and their voices always clear,
Oh, that we might be more like them
  while we serve the Master here.

    Holy, holy, is what the angels sing.
    And I expect to help them make the courts
      of heaven ring ;
    But when I sing redemption's story they will
      fold their wings,   [vation brings.
    For angels never felt the joys that our salva-

2 But I hear another anthem blending
  voices clear and strong,
" Unto Him that hath redeemed us
  and has bought us," is the song ;
We have come thro' tribulations to
  this land so fair and bright,
In the fountain freely flowing He
  hath made our garments white.

3 Then the angels stand and listen, for
  they cannot join that song,
Let the sound of many waters, by
  that happy, blood-washed throng ;
For they sing about great trials,
  battles fought and vict'ries won,
And they praise their great Redeemer, who hath said to them,
  " Well done."

4 So, although I'm not an angel, yet I
  know that over there
I will join a blessed chorus that the
  angels cannot share ;
I will sing about my Saviour, who
  upon dark Calvary,
Freely pardoned my transgressions,
  died to set a sinner free.

773 YEARS I spent in vanity and
  pride,
Caring not my Lord was crucified ;
Knowing not it was for me He died
  On Calvary.

    Mercy there was great and grace was free,
    Pardon there was multiplied to me,
    There my burdened soul found liberty,
      At Calvary.

2 By God's Word at last my sin I
  learned,   [spurned,
Then I trembled at the law I'd
Till my guilty soul imploring, turned
  To Calvary.

3 Now I've given to Jesus ev'rything,
Now I gladly own Him as my King,
Now my raptured soul can only sing
Of Calvary.

4 Oh! the love that drew salvation's
plan,
Oh! the grace that brought it down
to man,
Oh! the mighty gulf that God did
span
At Calvary.

774 MY Father has many dear
children ;
Will He ever forget to keep me ?
He gave His own Son to redeem them
And He cannot forget to keep me.

He'll never forget to keep me,...
He'll never forget to keep me,...
He gave His own Son to redeem me,
And He cannot forget to keep me.

2 Our Father remembers the sparrows,
Their value and fall He doth see ;
But dearer to Him are His children,
And He'll never forget to keep me.

He'll never forget to keep me,...
He'll never forget to keep me,...
But dearer to Him are His children,
And He'll never forget to keep me.

3 The words of the Lord are so price-
less,
How patient and watchful is He ;
Tho' mother forget her own offspring,
Yet He'll never forget to keep me.

He'll never forget to keep me,...
He'll never forget to keep me,...
Tho' mother forget her own offspring,
Yet He'll never forget to keep me.

4 O brother, why don't you accept
Him ?
He offers salvation so free ;
Repent and believe and obey Him,
And He'll never forget to keep
thee.

He'll never forget to keep thee,...
He'll never forget to keep thee,...
Repent and believe and obey Him,
And He'll never forget to keep Thee.

775 WHAT were we when mercy
found us ?
Captives unto death and sin ; [us,
Clouds and darkness closed around
All was hopeless night within.

We were lost, but Jesus found us,
Burst the bonds of death that bound us,
Wrapt the robe of grace around us,
And the heirs of glory crowned us.

2 What are we since mercy found us ?
Blameless, spotless in His sight ;
Sons and saints His Word has
crowned us,
Called to walk with Him in light.

3 What we shall be ? That's a story
Never uttered or expressed !
We shall see Him in His glory,
And be folded to His breast.

776 UNANSWERED yet ? The
prayer your lips have pleaded
In agony of heart these many
years ?
Doth faith begin to fail ? Is hope
departing ?
And think you all in vain those
falling tears ?
Say not the Father hath not heard
your prayer,
You shall have your desire, sometime, somewhere.

2 Unanswered yet ? tho' when you
first presented
This one petition at the Father's
throne,
It seemed you could not wait the
time of asking,
So urgent was your heart to make
it known.
Tho' years have passed since then,
do not despair,
The Lord will answer you sometime, somewhere.

3 Unanswered yet ? Nay, do not say
" ungranted ; "
Perhaps your part is not yet
wholly done ;
The work began when first your
prayer was uttered,
And God will finish what He has
begun ;
If you will keep the incense burning
there,
His glory you shall see sometime,
somewhere.

4 Unanswered yet ? Faith cannot be
unanswered ;
His feet are firmly planted on the
Rock ;

Amid the wildest storms she stands
   undaunted,
  Nor quails before the loudest
   thunder shock.
She knows Omnipotence has heard
   her prayer,
  And cries, " It shall be done,"
   sometime, somewhere.

777 COME home ! come home !
     You are weary at heart,
For the way has been dark,
And so lonely and wild ;
  O prodigal child !
Come home ! O come home !

2   Come home ! come home !
For we watch and we wait,
And we stand at the gate,
While the shadows are piled ;
  O prodigal child !
Come home ! O come home !

3   Come home ! come home !
From the sorrow and blame,
From the sin and the shame,
And the tempter that smiled,
  O prodigal child !
Come home ! O come home !

4   Come home ! come home !
There is bread and to spare,
And a warm welcome there ;
Then, to friends reconciled,
  O prodigal child !
Come home ! O come home !

778 THERE is something strangely
    tender
  In His parting words so sweet,
" Do not let your heart be troubled,
  For we by and by shall meet
In the home of many mansions
  Which I go now to prepare,
And when I am ready, dear ones,
  I will come and take you there."
" Ah," He whisper'd when He left them,
  " I am coming back again,
And will take you to your new home,
  Ever near Me to remain."

2 Ah, those words, so strangely tender,
  Still keep echoing all round,
And tho' they have gone to glory,
  And have reached the hallow'd
    ground,   [them,
The sweet promise has not failed
  They are with their Lord to-night,
We shall find them ready waiting,
  Just within the gates of light.

3 Don't you hear the words so tender ?
  Don't they echo in your heart ?
Don't they woo you from this poor
    life,
  That with which you soon must
    part ?
Those who wait His coming glorious
  Then will form His royal train,
Oh, the rapturous hour of meeting
  When the Lord comes back to
    reign.

779 I LOVE to think my Father
    knows
Why I have missed the path I chose,
And that I soon shall clearly see
The way He led was best for me.

He knows it all,...He knows it all,...
My Father knows,...He knows it all ;...
Thy bitter tears,...how fast they fall !
He knows, my Father knows it all.

2 I love to think my Father knows
The thorns I pluck with ev'ry rose,
The daily griefs I seek to hide
From the dear souls I walk beside.

3 I love to think my Father knows
The strength or weakness of my foes,
And that I need but stand and see
Each conflict end in victory.

780 MY soul is so happy in Jesus,
    For He is so precious to me ;
His voice it is music to hear it,
  His face it is heaven to see.

I am happy in Him,...
I am happy in Him ;...
My soul with delight He fills day and night,
  For I am happy in Him.

2 He sought me so long ere I knew
    Him,   [fold ;
  When wand'ring afar from the
Safe home in His arms He hath
    brought me,
  To where there are pleasures
    untold.

3 His love and His mercy surround me,
  His grace like a river doth flow ;
His Spirit, to guide and to comfort,
  Is with me wherever I go.

4 They say I shall some day be like
    Him,
  My cross and my burden lay down ;
Till then I will ever be faithful,
  In gathering gems for His crown.

781 HOW I praise Thee, precious
    Saviour,
That Thy love laid hold of me ;
Thou hast saved and cleansed and
    filled me,
That I might Thy channel be ;

Channels only, blessed Master,
   But with all Thy wondrous power,
Flowing through us, Thou canst use us
   Ev'ry day and ev'ry hour.

2 Just a channel, full of blessing,
    To the thirsty hearts around ;
To tell out Thy full salvation,
    All Thy loving message sound.

3 Emptied that Thou shouldst fill me,
    A clean vessel in Thine hand ;
With no pow'r but as Thou givest
    Graciously with each command.

4 Witnessing Thy power to save me,
    Setting free from self and sin ;
Thou hast bought me to possess me,
    In Thy fulness, Lord, come in.

5 Jesus, fill now with Thy Spirit
    Hearts that full surrender know ;
That the streams of living water
    From our inner man may flow.

782 I AM on the Gospel highway,
    Pressing forward to the goal,
Where for me a rest remaineth,
    In the home-land of the soul ;
Ev'ry hour I'm moving onward,
    Not a moment to delay ;
I am going home to glory
    In the good old-fashioned way.

In the good old-fashioned way,
In the good old-fashioned way,
   I am going home to glory
In the good old-fashioned way.

2 From the snares of sinful pleasure,
    Here my feet are always free ;
Tho' the way may be called narrow,
    It is wide enough for me ;
It was wide enough for Daniel,
    And for David in his day ;
I am glad that I can follow
    In the good old-fashioned way.

3 Many friends have gone before me,
    They have laid their armour down ;
With the pilgrims and the martyrs,
    Have obtained a robe and crown ;
On this road they fought their
    battles,
    Shouting vict'ry day by day ;

I shall overcome and join them
    In the good old-fashioned way.

4 Just a few more steps to follow,
    Just a few more days to roam ;
But the way grows more delightful
    As I'm drawing nearer home ;
When the storms of life are over,
    And the clouds have rolled away,
I shall find the gates of heaven
    In the good old-fashioned way.

Then palms of victory, crowns of glory,
Palms of victory I shall wear.

783 I'LL cling closer to Jesus ;
    I'll cling closer to Him ;
I'll cling closer to Jesus,
    The mighty to save.

784 DO you know the world is
      dying
    For a little bit of love ?
Ev'rywhere we hear their sighing
    For a little bit of love ?
For the love that rights a wrong,
Fills the heart with hope and song ;
They have waited, oh, so long !
    For a little bit of love.

For a little bit of love,
For a little bit of love ;
They have waited, oh, so long,
   For a little bit of love.

2 From the poor of ev'ry city,
    For a little bit of love,
Hands are reaching out in pity
    For a little bit of love ;
Some have burdens hard to bear,
Some have sorrows we should share ;
Shall they falter and despair
    For a little bit of love ?

For a little bit of love,
For a little bit of love ;
Shall they falter and despair
   For a little bit of love ?

3 Down before their idols falling,
    For a little bit of love,
Many souls in vain are calling
    For a little bit of love ;
If they die in sin and shame,
Someone surely is to blame
For not going, in His Name,
    With a little bit of love.

With a little bit of love,
With a little bit of love ;
For not going, in His Name,
   With a little bit of love.

4 While the souls of men are dying
  For a little bit of love,
While the children, too, are crying
  For a little bit of love ;
Stand no longer idly by,
You can help them if you try ;
Go then, saying, " Here am I,"
  With a little bit of love.

> With a little bit of love,
> With a little bit of love :
> Go then, saying, " Here am I,"
> With a little bit of love.

785 ONLY one word for the Master,
  Lovingly, quietly said :
Only a word ! Yet the Master heard,
  And some fainting hearts were fed.

2 Only a cry from the sinner,
  Bitterly earnest and wild ;
" Help, Lord, I die ! " rose in agony,
  And the Saviour saved His child.

3 Only an hour with the children,
  Pleasantly, cheerfully given ;
Still seed was sown in that hour
  alone,   [heaven.
Which would bring forth fruit for

786 THERE is a land mine eyes
  shall see   [down ;
When I shall lay life's armour
But all its bliss is not for me,
  If I must wear a starless crown.

> A starless crown, when life is done,
> No glitt'ring gems which I have won !
> Forbid it, Lord, that there should be
> A starless crown in Heav'n for me.

2 The gains of earth are all but loss—
  Eternal joys are all for me,
When I by faith uplift the cross,
  And lead one soul, dear Lord, to
    Thee.

3 Forbid it, Lord, that I should be
  Content to live for self alone ;
Oh, may some soul I win for Thee
  Adorn my crown when life is done.

787 ONCE upon the tide I drifted,
  With no guide to yonder
  shore ;
But I've found a side once rifted,
  Where I'm safe for evermore.

> I am anchored, safely anchored,
> Anchored, never more to roam,
> Anchored by the side of Jesus,
> Anchored in the soul's bright home.

2 Let the storms sweep o'er life's ocean,
  They can do me no more harm ;
Anchored far from their commotion,
  I am resting 'neath His arm.

3 Here my peace flows like a river,
  Here my soul o'erflows with song ;
Prayer and praises to the Giver
  Fill my glad heart all day long.

4 When this life below is ended,
  I shall anchor on that shore ;
When my praises will be blended
  With ten thousand thousand more.

788 FAR away in the depths of my
  spirit to-night
Rolls a melody sweeter than psalm ;
In celestial-like strains it unceasingly
  falls
O'er my soul like an infinite calm.

> Peace ! peace ! wonderful peace,
> Coming down from the Father above,
> Sweep over my spirit for ever, I pray,
> In fathomless billows of love !

2 What a treasure I have in this
  wonderful peace,   [soul,
Buried deep in the heart of my
So secure that no power can mine it
  away,
While the years of eternity roll !

3 I am resting to-night in this wonder-
  ful peace,
Resting sweetly in Jesus' control ;
For I'm kept from all danger by
  night and by day,
And His glory is flooding my soul.

4 And methinks when I rise to that
  city of peace,   [see,
Where the Author of peace I shall
That one strain of the song which
  the ransomed will sing
In that heavenly kingdom will be :

5 Ah, soul ! are you here without
  comfort and rest,   [of time ?
Marching down the rough pathway
Make Jesus your Friend ere the
  shadows grow dark ;
O accept of this peace so sublime.

789 I CANNOT drift beyond Thy
  love,
Beyond Thy tender care ;
Where'er I stray, still from above
Thine eye beholds me there.

I cannot drift so far away
  But what Thy love divine
Upon my path, by night and day,
  In mercy sweet doth shine.

2 I cannot drift beyond Thy sight,
  Dear Lord, the thought is sweet;
Thy loving hand will guide aright,
  My weary, wand'ring feet.
When rough and dark my lonely way
  I shall not be forgot,   [day
Thro' all life's changeful, shadow'd
  Thou wilt forsake me not.

3 I cannot drift away from Thee,
  No matter where I go;
Still Thy dear love doth gladden me,
  Thou all my way dost know.
Where'er I journey Thou art there,
  In wind and wave I hear
Thy voice, in tones of music rare,
  And know that Thou art near.

790   MY soul in sad exile was out
       on life's sea,
So burden'd with sin and distress'd
Till I heard a sweet voice saying,
  "Make Me your choice;"
And I entered the "Heaven of
  Rest."

I've anchored my soul in the Haven of Rest,
  I'll sail the wide seas no more;
The tempest may sweep o'er the wild, stormy
    deep,
  In Jesus I'm safe evermore.

2 I yielded myself to His tender
  embrace,
  And faith taking hold of the Word,
My fetters fell off, and I anchor'd
  my soul;
  The "Haven of Rest" is my Lord.

3 The song of my soul, since the Lord
  made me whole,
Has been the old story so blest,
Of Jesus, who'll save whosoever will
  . have
  A home in the "Haven of Rest."

4 How precious the thought that we
  all may recline,
  Like John, the beloved and blest,
On Jesus' strong arm, where no
  tempest can harm,
  Secure in the "Haven of Rest."

5 Oh, come to the Saviour, He
  patiently waits
  To save by His power divine;

Come, anchor your soul in the
  "Haven of Rest,"
  And say, "My beloved is mine."

791   LIKE a bird on the deep, far
       away from its nest,
  I have wander'd, my Saviour,
    from Thee;
But Thy dear loving voice called me
  home to Thy breast,
  And I knew there was welcome
    for me.

Welcome for me, Saviour, from Thee;
A smile and a welcome for me,
Now, like a dove, I rest in Thy love,
And find a sweet refuge in Thee....

2 I am safe in the ark; I have folded
  my wings
  On the bosom of mercy divine;
I am filled with the light of Thy
  presence so bright,
  And the joy that will ever be mine.

3 I am safe in the ark; and I dread
  not the storm,
  Tho' around me the surges may
    roll;
I will look to the skies, where the
  day never dies,
  I will sing of the joy in my soul.

792   I KNOW my heavenly Father
       knows
The storms that would my way
  oppose,
But He can drive the clouds away,
And turn my darkness into day.

He knows,....He knows,....
The storms that would my way op - - pose,
  He knows,.....He knows,....
And tempers ev'ry wind....that....blows.

2 I know my heavenly Father knows
  The balm I need to soothe my woes;
And with His touch of love divine,
He heals this wounded soul of mine.

3 I know my heavenly Father knows
  How frail I am to meet my foes;
But He my cause will e'er defend,
Uphold and keep to me the end.

4 I know my heavenly Father knows
  The hour my journey here will close,
And may that hour, O faithful Guide,
Find me safe sheltered by Thy side.

793 I HAVE giv'n up all for Jesus,
This vain world is nought
to me,
All its pleasures are forgotten
In rememb'ring Calvary ;
Though my friends despise, forsake
me,
And on me the world looks cold,
I've a Friend that will stand by me
When the pearly gates unfold.

Life's morn will soon be waning,
And its evening bells be toll'd,
But my heart will know no sadness
When the pearly gates unfold.

2 When the voice of Jesus calls me,
And the angels whisper low,
I will lean upon my Saviour,
Through the valley as I go ;
I will claim His precious promise,
Worth to me the world of gold,
" Fear no evil, I'll be with thee
When the pearly gates unfold."

3 Just beyond the waves of Jordan,
Just beyond its chilling tide,
Blooms the tree of life immortal,
And the living waters glide ;
In that happy land of spirits
Are there stores of bliss untold,
And the angels are awaiting
Where the pearly gates unfold.

794 WHEN this passing world is
done,
When has sunk yon glowing sun,
When we stand with Christ in glory,
Looking o'er life's finished story,

Then, dear Lord, shall I fully know,
Not till then, how much I owe ;
Then, dear Lord, shall I fully know,
Not till then, how much I owe.

2 When I stand before the throne,
Dressed in beauty not my own ;
When I see Thee as Thou art,
Love Thee with unsinning heart,

3 When I hear the wicked call
On the rocks and hills to fall ;
When I see them start and shrink
On the fiery deluge brink,

4 When the praise of heav'n I hear,
Loud as thunders to the ear ;
Loud as many waters' noise,
Sweet as harp's melodious voice,

795 JUST when I am dishearten'd,
Just when with cares op-
press'd,
Just when my way is darkest,
Just when I am distress'd,
Then is my Saviour near me,
He knows my ev'ry care ;
Jesus will never leave me,
He helps my burdens bear.

His grace is enough for me, for me,
His grace is enough for me ;
Thro' sorrow and pain, thro' loss or gain,
His grace is enough for me.

2 Just when my hopes have vanish'd,
Just when my friends forsake,
Just when the fight is thickest,
Just when with fear I shake ;
Then comes a still small whisper,
" Fear not, my child, I'm near,"
Jesus brings peace and comfort,
I love His voice to hear.

3 Just when my tears are flowing,
Just when with anguish bent,
Just when temptation's hardest,
Just when with sadness rent ;
Then comes a thought of comfort,
" I know my Father knows,"
Jesus has grace sufficient
To conquer all my foes.

796 BOW'D beneath your burden,
is there none to share ?
Weary with the journey, is there
none to care ?
Courage, way-worn trav'ler, heed
your Lord's commands,
There's a thought to cheer you,
Jesus understands.

Yes,...He understands,
All His ways are best,
Hear,...He calls to you,
" Come to Me and rest."
Leave the unknown future in the Master's
hands,
Whether sad or joyful, Jesus understands.

2 Ev'ry heavy burden He will gladly
share ;
Are you sad and weary ? Jesus has
a care :
Well He knows the pathway o'er
life's burning sands,
Courage, fainting pilgrim, Jesus
understands.

Tho' temptation meet you, Jesus
  can sustain,
Life has vexing problems which He
  can explain ;
Serve Him where He sends you, tho'
  in distant lands ;
Do not doubt or question, Jesus
  understands.

Weary heart, He calls you, " Come
  to Me and rest,"
Does the path grow rugged ? yet
  His way is best ;
Leave the unknown future in the
  Master's hands,
Whether sad or joyful, Jesus under-
  stands.

797 I'M pressing on the upward
          way,
New heights I'm gaining ev'ry day ;
Still praying, as I onward bound,
" Lord, plant my feet on higher
  ground."

    Lord, lift me up and let me stand,
    By faith, on heaven's table-land ;
    A higher plane than I have found,
    Lord, plant my feet on higher ground.

My heart has no desire to stay
Where doubts arise and fears dismay ;
Tho' some may dwell where these
  abound,
My pray'r, my aim is higher ground.

I want to live above the world,
Tho' Satan's darts at me are hurled ;
For faith has caught the joyful soun 1
The song of saints on higher ground.

I want to scale the utmost height,
And catch a gleam of glory bright ;
But still I'll pray till heav'n I've
  found,
"Lord, lead me on to higher ground."

798 O HOUSE of many mansions,
          Thy doors are open wide,
And dear are all the faces
  Upon the other side ;
Thy portals, they are golden,
  And those who enter in
Shall know no more of sorrow,
  Of weariness and sin.

    O house of many mansions,
      Thy doors are open wide,
    And dear are all the faces
      Upon the other side.

2 O house of many mansions,
    My weary spirit waits,
And longs to join the ransom'd
    Within thy pearly gates,
Who enter thro' thy portals,
    The mansions of the blest ;
Who come to thee aweary,
    And find in thee their rest.

3 O house of many mansions,
    O house not made with hands,
I sigh for thee while waiting
    Within these border lands ;
I know that but in dying
    Thy threshold is cross'd o'er ;
There shall be no more sorrow
    In thy for-ever-more.

799 HOW dear to my heart is the
          story of old,
The story that ever is new,
The message that saints of all ages
    have told,
The message so tender and true.

    The story that never grows old,....
    Though over and over 'tis told,....
    The story so dear, bringing heaven so near,
    Sweet story that never grows old.

2 It came to my heart when, all fet-
    tered by sin,
    I sat in the prison of doubt ;
Like angel of old, the glad story
    came in
And led me triumphantly out.

3 It comes to my soul when the temp-
    ter is nigh
    With snares for my way-weary
    feet ;
It tells of the rock that is higher
    than I,
And leads to its blissful retreat.

4 When sorrow is mine, and on pillows
    of stone
    My aching head seeks for repose,
This story brings comfort and peace
    from the throne,
    My desert blooms forth like the
    rose.

5 When down in the " valley and
    shadow of death,"
    I enter the gloom of the grave,
I'll tell the old story with life's latest
    breath,
    Of Christ and His power to save.

800 THE Lord hath declared, and
the Lord will perform ;
" Behold ! I am near to deliver,
A refuge and fortress, a covert in·
storm ; "
He keepeth His promise for ever.

For ever ! for ever ! O not for a day !
He keepeth His promise for ever !
To all who believe, to all who obey,
He keepeth His promise for ever !

2 Who seek Him shall find Him, shall
find Him to-day,
The word is to all, " whosoever ! "
No soul that entreateth He turneth
away ;
He keepeth His promise for ever.

3 Tho' often my toil seems but labour
in vain,
I leave with the Lord my endeavour !
I patiently wait for the sunshine and
rain,
He keepeth His promise for ever.

4 My heart may sink low in the depths
of its woe,
But never, He tells me, O never !
The frail, bruised reed will He break
and I know
He keepeth His promise for ever.

5 The bonds that unite us in earth's
dearest ties,
The rude hand of Time will dis-
sever ;   [skies ;
But we shall renew them again in the
He keepeth His promise for ever.

801 THEY shall be comforted ;
sorrowing heart,
Soon every cloud will for ever depart;
Joy, wondrous joy, in that beautiful
day,
When God shall wipe ev'ry tear-drop
away.

Never a sorrow, never a fear,
Never a shadow, never a tear,
They shall be comforted in that sweet day,
When God shall wipe ev'ry tear-drop away.

2 They shall be comforted, Jesus says
so,   [know ;
True and eternal His promise we
Gentle His smile, and how tender
His voice,
Bidding His children in Him to
rejoice.

3 They shall be comforted ; yea even
here,
Blessed the mourner whom Jesus
shall cheer ;
Sunbeams of glory thro' time's
fleeting show'rs,   [ours !
Heaven around us—this Saviour is

4 They shall be comforted ; rise then
and shine,
Shine in the beauty of love so divine ;
Let others find there the " still
waters " flow,   [so.
They may be comforted, Jesus says

802 BEHOLD the precious Lamb of
God,
Who died upon the tree,
That guilty sinners, such as I,
Might thro' His grace be free.

Thy bound - - - less love I'll sing,
Thy grace....so full and free,
'Tis under Thy protecting wing
My soul delights to be !

2 Behold the healing streams of grace
That from His side did flow,
I plunged beneath the crimson flood
That washes white as snow.

3 Behold the Cross He bore for me,
Whereby He saved my soul ;
His matchless grace shall be my
theme
While countless ages roll.

803 I HAVE perfect peace to-day,
All my sins are washed away ;
Hiding 'neath the crimson blood,
I am reconciled to God.

Under the blood, under the blood,   [blood
Pardoning and cleansing I found under the
Under the blood, under the blood,
There I for ever will hide, under the blood.

2 What a work the Lord has done !
What a work of grace begun !
All my sins are cover'd o'er ;
He remembers them no more.

3 Wondrous is God's grace to me,
Making me for ever free,
Sanctifying me to God,
Thro' the all-prevailing blood.

4 So in gladness I go on,
Till the Master's work is done,
Trusting in atoning blood,
Walking in the love of God.

304 PEACE like a river is flooding
    my soul,
Since Christ, my Saviour, maketh
  me whole ;   [be—
Sweet peace abiding my portion shall
Jesus, my Saviour, is precious to me.

    Pre - - cious to me,.....
    Pre - - cious is He ;.....
Jesus shall ever..be pre - - cious to me...

2 Joy is abounding—my heart gaily
    sings,
Cleave I the heavens, mount up on
  wings ;   [free—
Christ hath exalted, my soul He set
Jesus, my Saviour, is precious to me.

3 Oh, precious Jesus, how lovely Thou
  art !
Come, and abiding, rule in my heart ;
Break ev'ry fetter, Thy face let me
  see,   [me.
Then Thou shalt ever be precious to

305 I KNOW not the hour of His
    coming,
  Nor how He will speak to my
    heart ;
Or whether at morning or mid-day
  My spirit to Him will depart.

But I know..I shall wake in the likeness
  Of Him..I am longing to see ;
I know..that mine eyes shall behold Him,
  Who died..for a sinner like me.

2 I know not the bliss that awaits me,
  At rest with my Saviour above ;
I know not how soon I shall enter
  And bathe in the ocean of love.

3 Perhaps in the midst of my labour
  A voice from my Lord I shall hear ;
Perhaps in the slumber of mid-night,
  Its message may fall on my ear.

4 I know not, but oh I am watching,
  My lamp ever burning and bright !
I know not if Jesus will call me
  At morning, at noon, or at night.

306 I CANNOT tell thee whence it
    came,
  This peace within my breast ;
But this I know, there fills my soul
  A strange and tranquil rest.

There's a deep, settled peace in my soul,...
There's a deep, settled peace in my soul,...
Though the billows of sin near me roll,
  He abides, Christ abides.

2 Beneath the toil and care of life
  This hidden stream flows on ;
My weary soul no longer thirsts,
  Nor am I sad and lone.

3 I cannot tell the half of love,
  Unfeigned, supreme, divine,
That caused my darkest, inmost self,
  With beams of hope to shine.

4 I cannot tell thee why He chose
  To suffer and to die ;
But if I suffer here with Him,
  I'll reign with Him for aye.

307 IN land or store I may be poor ;
    My place unknown, my name
    obscure ;
Of this I have the witness sure ;
  O bless the Lord, I've Jesus.

What tho' the world its gifts deny,
I've riches more than gold can buy—
The key to treasures in the sky !
  O bless the Lord, I've Jesus !

2 On life's rough sea how frail my
    barque !
But in the storm and densest dark
I have a safe and trusted ark :
  O bless the Lord, 'tis Jesus !

3 When shadows deep around me fall,
And gloom and fear my soul enthrall,
There is an arm beneath them all :
  O bless the Lord, 'tis Jesus !

4 Soon will this fleeting life be o'er ;
O then, upon the other shore
I'll be with Him for evermore,
  For evermore with Jesus !

308 LIFE wears a different face to
    me
    Since I found my Saviour ;
Rich mercy at the Cross I see,
  My dying, living Saviour.

    Golden sunbeams round me play,
Jesus turns my night to day,
Heaven seems not far away,
    Since I found my Saviour.

2 He sought me in His wondrous love,
    So I found my Saviour ;
He brought salvation from above,
  My dear, almighty Saviour.

3 The passing clouds may intervene
    Since I found my Saviour ;
But He is with me though unseen,
  My ever-present Saviour.

4 A strong hand kindly holds my own
    Since I found my Saviour ;
It leads me onward to the throne,
    Oh, there I'll see my Saviour !

809 IF I could only tell Him as I
    know Him,
    My Redeemer who has brightened
    all my way ;
If I could tell how precious is His
    presence,
I am sure that you would make
    Him yours to-day.

Could I tell..it, could I tell..it,
How the sunshine of His presence lights my
    way;
  I would tell..it, I would tell..it,
And I'm sure that you would make Him yours
    to-day.

2 If I could only tell you how He loves
    you,
    And if we could thro' the lonely
    garden go,   [pardon,
If I could tell His dying pain and
    You would worship at His
    wounded feet, I know.

3 If I could tell how sweet will be His
    welcome
    In that home whose matchless
    beauty ne'er was told ;
The Father's mansions stand by
    living waters,
    And the trees of healing shades
    the streets of gold.

4 But I can never tell Him as I know
    Him :
    Human tongue can never tell all
    love divine ;   [Him ;
I only can entreat you to accept
    You can know Him only when you
    make Him thine.

810 OH, bless the Lord, He cleansed
    my soul,
And filled my lips with singing ;
He came in my poor, sinful heart,
    And set the joybells ringing.

Oh, praise the Lord, He first loved me,
  I feel new life upspringing ;
He came in my poor, sinful heart,
  And set the joybells ringing.

2 He placed my feet upon the Rock,
    The only sure foundation ;
He shows me wonders of His grace,
    The blessings of salvation.

3 His promise is " for all the days."
    His love for me is caring ;
While in the " Father's House "
    above,
    A mansion He's preparing.

4 His love is calling, seeking still,
    Come, ev'ry burden bringing ;
The touch of Christ within you
    heart
    Will set the joybells ringing.

811 FOR God so lov'd this sinfu
    world,
    His Son He freely gave,
That whosoever would believe,
    Eternal life should have.

'Tis true, O yes, 'tis true,....
  God's wonderful promise is true :....
For I've trusted, and tested, and tried it,
  And I know God's promise is true.....

2 I was a wayward, wand'ring child,
    A slave to sin and fear,
Until this blessed promise fell
    Like music on my ear.

3 The " whosoever " of the Lord,
    I trusted was for me ;
I took Him at His gracious word,
    From sin to set me free.

4 Eternal life begun below
    Now fills my heart and soul :
I'll sing His praise for evermore,
    Who has redeemed my soul.

812 *Special Solo, for words see No
573.*

813 JUST to trust in the Lord, jus
    to lean on His Word,
Just to feel I am His ev'ry day ;
Just to walk by His side with Hi
    Spirit to guide,
Just to follow where He leads th
    way.

Just to say what He wants me to say,...
  And be still when He whispers to me ;...
Just to go where He wants me to go,...
  Just to be what He wants me to be.

2 When my way darkest seems, whe
    are blighted my dreams,
Just to feel that the Lord knoweth
    best ;
Just to yield to His will, just to trus
    and be still,
    Just to lean on His bosom an
    rest.

Then my heart will be light, then my
    path will be bright,
If I've Jesus for my dearest friend;
Counting all loss but gain, such a
    friend to obtain,   [end.
    True and faithful He'll be to the

314 ON the Cross my Saviour
         bought me,
In the wilderness He sought me,
To His blessed fold He brought me,
    For He loves even me,
    He loves even me;
To His blessed fold He brought me,
    Jesus loves even me.

Soft as ev'ning dewdrops falling,
Is His voice so sweetly calling,
More and more my soul enthralling,
    For He loves even me,
    He loves even me;
More and more my soul enthralling,
    Jesus loves even me.

Since that happy day He found me,
Everlasting arms surround me;
With His mercies He hath crowned
    me,
    For He loves even me,
    He loves even me;   [me,
With His mercies He hath crowned
    Jesus loves even me.

All my needs to Him I'm bringing,
To His keeping hand I'm clinging,
And my heart for joy is singing,
    For He loves even me,
    He loves even me;
And my heart with joy is singing,
    Jesus loves even me.

Tho' the ills of life may grieve me,
Yet I know He'll never leave me,
To His glory He'll receive me,
    For He loves even me,
    He loves even me;
To His glory He'll receive me,
    Jesus loves even me.

315 THERE'S One above all
         earthly friends,
Whose love all earthly love tran-
    scends,
It is my Lord and Christ divine,
My Lord, because I know He's mine.

I know He's mine,.. this Friend so dear,..
He lives with me,.. He's ever near ;..
Ten thousand charms..around Him shine,..
And, best of all, I know He's mine.

2 He's mine because He died for me,
  He saved my soul, He set me free ;
  With joy I worship at His shrine,
  And cry, " Praise God, I know He's
    mine."

3 He's mine because He's in my heart,
  And never, never will we part ;
  Just as the branch is to the vine,
  I'm joined to Christ ; I know He's
    mine.

4 Some day upon the streets of gold
  Mine eyes His glory shall behold,
  Then, while His arms around me
    twine,
  I'll cry for joy, " I know He's mine."

816 I WAS poor as the poorest out-
         cast from the fold,
    I sank by the wayside with hunger
       and cold ;
    But He bade me look up, all His
       riches behold ;
    O the wealth of the world is Jesus.

I was poor as the poorest outcast from the fold,
But He gave me great treasures of silver and
    gold,
And a mansion above that will never grow old,
    For the wealth of the world is Jesus.

2 I was poor as the poorest, I shrank
       from the throng,   [me long ;
  I hid in the darkness that dwelt with
  But He came like the morning, with
       sunlight and song,
    Now the light of my life is Jesus.

3 I was poor as the poorest, I wandered
       alone.   [stone ;
  No dwelling had I, and my pillow a
  But I heard someone whisper, " I'll
       make thee My own " ;
    Now the peace of my heart is Jesus.

4 I was poor as the poorest, no riches
       had I,
  But Jesus, my Saviour, came down
       from the sky,
  And He went to the Cross, there to
       suffer and die,   [Jesus.
    And my soul was redeemed by

5 I was poor as the poorest till Jesus
       stooped low,
  And washed me and cleansed me as
       white as the snow ;
  I have bathed in the blood, I am
       under the flow,
    O the power to save is Jesus.

817 IN looking through my tears
     one day
  I saw Mount Calvary ;
  Beneath the Cross there flowed a
     stream
  Of grace enough for me.....

  Grace is flowing from Calvary,....
     Grace as fathomless as the sea,....
  Grace for time and eternity,....
     Grace enough for me !

2 While standing there my trembling
     heart,
  Once full of agony,
  Could scarce believe the sight I saw
  Of grace enough for me....

3 While I beheld my ev'ry sin
  Nailed to the cruel tree,
  I felt a flood go thro' my soul
  Of grace enough for me....

4 When I am safe within the veil,
  My portion there will be
  To sing thro' all the years to come
  Of grace enough for me....

818 WHERE shall I go, Lord,
     where shall I go ?
  Wisdom to guide me Thou wilt
     bestow ;
  Help me to go, Lord, where Thou
     dost lead,
  Trusting Thy promise, " Grace for
     all need."

  What shall it be,..Lord, what shall it be ?..
    How can I serve..Thee, serve Thee best ?..
  Speak unto me, Lord, speak unto me,
    Help me to shrink from no test.

2 What shall I say, Lord, what shall I
     say ?   [day ;
  Thou art my Teacher, *teach* me to-
  Only and ever help me to be
  Speaking for Thee, Lord, speaking
     for Thee.

3 What shall I read, Lord, what shall
     I read ?
  Here Thy protection ever I need ;
  Led by Thy Spirit sent from above,
  E'en through temptation safely I'll
     move.

4 Purchased by Thee, Lord, now I am
     Thine,
  Time, thought, and effort never-
     more mine ;   [be
  Thou hast redeem'd me, help me to
  Shining for Thee, Lord, *only* for Thee.

819 THE way of the cross mear
     sacrifice,
  As to God you yield your all.
  To be laid on the altar, the place o
     death,
  Where fire will surely fall.

  'Tis the way of the Cross, are you willing fo
     this ?
  What does bearing the Cross mean to you ?
  You who've given yourself, your all to God !
     To God are you wholly true ?

2 As the voice of song and prayer w
     raise,
  How easy to say, " We give all ! "
  Till some rougher cross lies jus
     before,
  And sterner is duty's call.

3 Do not falter then, or, true to death
  Just die on the cross in the way,
  Till the fulness of life from th
     Living One
  Is filling you day by day ?

4 'Tis the plan of life, for you die t
     live—
  One with Jesus crucified ;   [you
  With the life alone to be liv'd thro
  Of the risen, the glorified.

820 TO me, dear Saviour, yes, tc
     me,
  Speak out Thy utmost will,
  What Thy great love doth bid me do
  I surely can fulfil.

  There is not in my heart left one treasure,
     dear Lord,
  That I would not yield gladly to Thee,
  Only let in Thy mercy, Thy pleadings be
     heard,
  They shall gladly be answered by me.

2 To me, dear Saviour, yes, to me,
  Thy gracious pardon show,
  That not one sin I've ever sinned
  May unforgiven go.

3 To me, dear Saviour, yes, to me,
  The floodgates open wide,
  That even I may stoop and wash
  Within the crimson tide.

4 To me, dear Saviour, yes, to me,
  To me, the least of all,
  With all my consciousness of guilt,
  Thou hast for me a call.

5 To me, dear Saviour, yes, to me,
  Thy saving power be given,
  Then shall I know why I have lived,
  And what on earth is heaven.

821 NO, no, no, He never will for-
        sake me,
No, no, no, no evil can o'ertake me ;
  His love will ever last,
  Till all of earth is past,
Oh, no, He never will forsake me.

2 No, no, no, He never will deceive me,
No, no, no, His words shall never
      grieve me ;
  I know His love is true,
  And what He says He'll do,
Oh, no, He never will deceive me.

3 No, no, no, He never will desert me,
No, no, no, no grief can ever hurt me ;
  For on His throbbing breast
  I can most sweetly rest,
Oh, no, He never will desert me.

4 No, no, no, He never will reject me,
No, no, no, His blood will e'er pro-
      tect me ;
  And when before His throne
  I shall not stand alone,
No, no, He never will reject me.

822   TELL me about the Master !
        I am weary and worn to-
        night,
The day lies behind me in shadow,
  And only the ev'ning is light !
Light with a radiant glory
  That lingers about the West,
My poor heart is a-weary, a-weary,
  And longs like a child for rest.

2 Tell me about the Master !
  Of the wrongs He for us forgave ;
Of love and of tender compassion,
  Of love that was mighty to save ;
Sad is my heart and a-weary
  Of woes and the trials of life,
Of the wrongs that are stalking in
      noonday,
  Of falsehood, and sin, and strife.

3 Yet what I know of sorrow
  And temptations that oft befall,
The infinite Master had suffered,
  And knoweth and pitieth all.
Tell me the sweetest old story
  That falls on each wound like balm
And my heart that was bruised and
      broken,
  Shall grow well, and strong, and
      calm.

823   IF waves of affliction should
        over thee roll,
Tho' tempests around thee may
      sweep,
No storms on life's ocean can injure
      thy soul,
  The Saviour has promised to keep.
Hold thy faith steady, be not afraid,
Jesus will keep ev'ry promise He's made.

2 Whene'er thou art weary, and long
      seems the road,
  If laden with care thou art press'd,
Thy Saviour has promised to carry
      thy load,
  Has promised to give thee His rest.

3 If thou hast been praying for more
      of His grace,
  Hast pray'd to know more of His
      will,
  Hast pray'd to be held in His loving
      embrace,
  He's promised such pray'rs to
      fulfil.

4 Thy dear, loving Saviour has gone to
      prepare
  A mansion in glory for thee,
He's promised to take thee to live
      with Him there,
  If thou only faithful wilt be.

824   IN tender compassion and
        wonderful love,   [high ;
  The Father looks down from on
He knoweth the raven hath need of
      its food,
  And heareth in mercy its cry.
The raven He feedeth, then why should I fear ?
To the heart of the Father His children are
    dear ;
So, if the way darkens or storms gather o'er,
I'll simply look upward and trust Him the more.

2 His arm is abundantly able to save,
  His eye is a guide to my feet ;
Since love sought and found me, I
      constantly dwell
  With Him in companionship sweet

3 No need have I ever to trouble my
      breast,
  Or fear what the morrow may
      bring ;
The heart of the Father is planning
      my way,
  And I am a child of a King.

825 THO' your sins may be red
and like scarlet,
Outnumb'ring the sands on the
shore,
Yet thro' Christ and His infinite
mercy
They're cleans'd and remember'd
no more.

Remember'd no more,
Remember'd no more,
Yet thro' Christ and His infinite mercy,
Your sins are remember'd no more.

3 Hear the voice that in love now
entreats you
To enter the wide-open door
That will lead to the kingdom of
heaven,
Where sins are remember'd no
more.

3 At the door of your heart Christ is
knocking,
He often has knock'd there before,
Let Him in, He'll forgive your transgressions,
And they'll be remember'd no
more.

826 WHEN my heart is sad with
life's cares and toils,
I will hush my troubled spirit's
anxious cry,
For the day is coming fast when my
cares shall all be past,
I shall see Him, I shall see Him
by and by.

I shall see Him ! My Redeemer !
O my heart, be brave, be strong !..
I shall see Him, and I'll praise Him,
With an everlasting song.

2 When the path is rough and the way
is hard,
And no resting for my weary feet
is nigh ;
I will bravely press along, singing
still my hopeful song,
I shall see Him, I shall see Him
by and by.

3 When the day grows dark, and the
clouds o'erhang,
And they close out all the sunshine from the sky ;
Tho' in darkness I abide, He is still
my faithful Guide,
I shall see Him, I shall see Him
by and by.

4 Then, my heart be brave, and my
soul rejoice,
For His promise standeth sure—
on it rely ;
And for all the care and pain there
shall be eternal gain,
When I see Him, when I see Him
by and by.

827 BLEST revelation, wondrous
salvation,
God in love doth for the lost of
earth provide ;
Sins like a mountain, lost in the
fountain,
Calv'ry's stream for ever flows, a
cleansing tide.

Safe in the hollow of His hand,....
Safe in the hollow of His hand,....
To His promise clinging, evermore I'm singing ;
I am safe within the hollow of God's hand.

2 Nothing can harm me, naught can
alarm me,
Fiercely tho' the tempest rage o'er
sea and land ;
Waking or sleeping, safe in His
keeping,
Kept within the hollow of His
mighty hand.

3 Come, all ye burdened and heavy
laden,
Without doubting all your cares
upon Him roll ;
Gracious for ever, strong to deliver,
Ye shall surely find sweet rest unto
your soul.

828 AFTER the sowing of sin is all
done,
After the glory of earth has been won,
After the sands of thy life have all
run,
Oh, what shall thy reaping be ?

Sowing, sowing, sowing in Satan's might ;
Reaping, reaping, reaping eternal night.

2 After the pleasures of sin are all past,
After the wealth of the world is
amassed,
When the death-angel you face at
the last,
Oh, what shall thy reaping be ?

Sowing, sowing, sowing in Satan's might ;
Reaping, reaping, reaping eternal night.

3 Come to the Saviour of sinners, come
  home !
Why will you longer so aimlessly
  roam ?   [come,
While He is pleading, O wanderer,
  The Master is waiting for thee.
Come home, come home, like as a weary dove,
Come home, come home, unto thy Father's
  love.

4 Cease from thy waywardness, Jesus
  invites ;
List to the Bride who with pleading
  unites,   [incites,
While the blest Spirit to prayer now
  The Master is waiting for thee.
Come home, come home, like as a weary dove,
Come home, come home, unto thy Father's
  love.

829 O TELL me more of Christ,
  my Saviour ;
On this glad theme dwell o'er and
  o'er ;   [favour,
His boundless grace, His saving
  His precious name, O tell me more !
  O tell me more ! so much I need
  His power to keep, His hand to lead ;
  O tell me more of Him I love,
  Until I see His face above,...

2 O tell me more of love's sweet story,
  If you would cheer and comfort me
How Jesus wept, the King of glory,
  Those tender tears of sympathy.

3 O tell me more ! How waves of
  sorrow
Shall hear His voice say, " Peace,
  be still ; "
How after night, bright dawns the
  morrow,   [will.
To those who trust His blessed

4 O tell me more ! And I repeating
  The happy news, shall spread the
  joy ;   [pleting,
Come, blessed Lord, Thy work com-
Till songs of praise our lips employ.

830 IS there a heart that is willing
  to lay
Burdens on Jesus' breast ?
He is so loving, and gentle, and
  true—
Come unto Him and rest.
  Lord, it is I who need Thy love,
  Need Thy strength and power ;
  Oh, keep me, use me, and hold me fast,
  Each moment, each day, each hour.

2 Is there a heart that is lonely to-day,
  Needing a faithful Friend? [side,
Jesus will always keep close by your
  Loving you to the end.

3 Is there a heart that has failed to
  o'ercome
Sin with its mighty power ?
Jesus is stronger than Satan and sin,
  Trust Him this very hour.

4 Is there a heart that is longing to
  bring
Blessing to some lost soul ?
Jesus is willing the weakest to use,
  Let Him thy life control.

831 I CANNOT breathe enough of
  Thee,
O gentle breeze of love ;
More fragrant than the myrtle tree
The Rose of Sharon is to me,
  The Balm of Heaven above.

2 I cannot gaze enough on Thee,
  Thou Fairest of the Fair ;
My heart is filled with ecstasy,
As in Thy face of radiancy
  I see such beauty there.

3 I cannot work enough for Thee,
  My Saviour, Master, Friend ;
I do not wish to go out free,
But ever, always willingly,
  To serve Thee to the end.

4 I cannot sing enough of Thee,
  The sweetest name on earth,
A note so full of melody
Comes from my heart so joyously,
  And fills my soul with mirth.

5 I cannot speak enough of Thee,
  I have so much to tell ;
Thy heart it beats so tenderly
As Thou dost draw me close to Thee,
  And whisper, " All is well."

832 FILLED with my sin to the
  Saviour I came,
This power has changed me, all praise
  to His Name ;
Grace all sufficient He gives me each
  day,   [way.
Trusting I follow where He leads the
Oh,..what a change,..since He came into my
  heart,
Oh,..what a change,..since He bade sin depart,
Oh,..what a change,..Jesus wrought in my
  soul,   [whole..
Oh,..what a change, since His blood makes me

2 Changed all my grief to a heart full
    of song,
And now I'm confiding in Him all
    day long ;   [shown,
Tender compassion and love He has
Cleansed me and healed me, and
    called me His own.

3 When thro' the portals of glory I've
    passed,
I then shall be changed to His image
    at last ;   [shine,
I shall be like Him in beauty to
Ever to live in His presence divine.

833   ALL for Jesus ! all for Jesus !
       All my being's ransom'd
       pow'rs ;
All my thoughts and words and
    doings,
All my days and all my hours.
All for Jesus ! all for Jesus !
All my days and all my hours.

2 Let my hands perform His bidding,
Let my feet run in His ways ;
Let my eyes see Jesus only ;
Let my lips speak forth His praise.
All for Jesus ! all for Jesus !
Let my lips speak forth His praise.

3 Worldlings prize their gems of beauty,
Cling to gilded toys of dust,
Boast of wealth, and fame, and
    pleasure ;
Only Jesus will I trust.
Only Jesus ! only Jesus !
Only Jesus will I trust.

4 O what wonder ! how amazing !
Jesus, glorious King of kings,
Deigns to call me His beloved,
Lets me rest beneath His wings.
All for Jesus ! all for Jesus !
·Resting now beneath His wings.

834 IF you are sad and weary, and
       burdened down with care,
And feel that you have wandered
    from the right ;
Tho' all your life seems dreary, your
    load seems hard to bear,
Just tell Him you are coming
    home to-night.
Just tell Him you are coming home to-night,
Just tell Him you are coming home to-night;
If, weary and distressed, you long for peace and
    rest,
Just tell Him you are coming home to-night.

2 The Saviour loves you dearly, and
    longs your soul to win,
His precious love would make
    your burden light ;
Heed now His tender pleading, and
    turn away from sin,
Just tell Him you are coming
    home to-night.

3 He offers you forgiveness, and peace,
    and joy, and rest,
He wants to make your pathway
    fair and bright ;
His loving arms are open to fold you
    to His breast,
Oh, tell Him you are coming home
    to-night.

835   MASTER, speak ! Thy servant
       heareth,
Waiting for Thy gracious Word ;
Longing for Thy voice that cheereth,
Master, let it now be heard.
I am list'ning, Lord, for Thee :
What hast Thou to say to me ?

2 Speak to me by name, O Master,
Let me know it is to me ;
Speak, that I may follow faster,
With a step more firm and free,
Where the Shepherd leads the flock,
In the shadow of the Rock.

3 Master, speak ! tho' least and lowest,
Let me not unheard depart ;
Master, speak ! for oh, Thou knowest
All the yearning of my heart.
Knowest all its truest need ;
Speak ! and make me blest indeed.

4 Master, speak ! and make me ready,
When Thy voice is truly heard,
With obedience glad and steady,
Still to follow ev'ry word.
I am list'ning, Lord, for Thee ;
Master, speak, oh, speak to me !

836   SHOULD the new dawn
       breaking, a burden bring,
That your soul deems hard to bear,
Seek a boon of grace for a little space;
There is always time for pray'r.
There is always time in the morning's prime,
    And the golden noon-tide fair ;
There is always time 'neath the even-chime,
    There is always time for pray'r.

2 With a lift of heart let the day begin,
And a moment respite spare,

Ere you press along with the toiling
    throng ;
  There is always time for pray'r.

3 When your weary feet falter on the
    path,
  Tho' to pause you do not dare,
  Would you find the stress of the
    noon grow less ?
  There is always time for pray'r.

4 When the late light dies with the
    setting sun,
  Would you taste a balm for care ?
  With a lift of heart let the day
    depart ;
  There is always time for pray'r.

837 MY soul crieth out for the
        Spirit,   [know
  I'm hung'ring and thirsting to
  The fulness of blessing He giveth ;
  Now fill me while humbly I bow.

  Come in, come in ! Holy Spirit,
    Thy work of great blessing begin ;
  By faith I lay hold of Thy promise,
    And claim complete vict'ry o'er sin.

2 O Spirit of God and of Jesus,
  Blest Trinity, come and possess
  My body, my soul, and my spirit,
  And fill me with Thy holiness.

3 My body make meet for Thy temple;
  My heart make Thou whiter than
    snow ;
  My spirit make loving and gentle—
  Oh, fill me, while humbly I bow.

4 Oh, ye that are thirsting for fulness,
  Make room for Him by forsaking all sin ;
  Surrender to Him your whole nature,
  By faith let the Spirit come in.

838 WHEN the waves are rolling
        fast,
  And I face the threat'ning blast,
  And a dark, forbidding cloud my
    barque enfolds ;
  Tho' the billows round me roll,
  There's a calm within my soul,
  Hallelujah ! praise the Lord, my
    anchor holds.

I can face the tempest's shock, for I'm anchored
    to the Rock,
  And His mighty arm my feeble strength
    upholds ;
Tho' the billows round me roll, there's a calm
    within my soul,
  Hallelujah ! praise the Lord, my anchor holds.

2 Satan tries by ev'ry art,
  And with many a fiery dart,
  To affright me from the Christ my
    faith beholds ;
  But I trust Him more and more,
  And I've proved Him o'er and o'er,
  Hallelujah ! praise the Lord, my
    anchor holds.

3 I am waiting for a day   [away,
  When the storms have passed
  And the haven of sweet rest my eye
    beholds ;
  When my voyage is complete,
  And I bow at Jesus' feet,
  Praise the Lord for evermore, my
    anchor holds.

839 SOMEBODY did a golden
        deed,
  Proving himself a friend in need ;
  Somebody sang a cheerful song,
  Bright'ning the skies the whole
    day long—
  Was that somebody you ?

2 Somebody thought 'tis sweet to live,
  Willingly said, " I'm glad to give ; "
  Somebody fought a valiant fight,
  Bravely he lived to shield the right—
  Was that somebody you ?

3 Somebody idled all the hours,
  Carelessly crushed life's fairest
    flowers ;
  Somebody made life loss, not gain,
  Thoughtlessly seemed to live in
    vain—
  Was that somebody you ?

4 Somebody filled the day with light,
  Constantly chased away the night ;
  Somebody's work bore joy and peace,
  Surely his life shall never cease—
  Was that somebody you ?

840 O SOFTLY the Spirit is
        whisp'ring to me,
  With tender compassion, with pity-
    ing plea ;
  I hear His beseeching, and earnestly
    pray,
  That Jesus will make me a blessing
    to-day.

  Lord, make..me a blessing to-day,
  A blessing to some one, I pray ;..
  In all that I do, in all that I say,
  O make me a blessing to-day.

2 Some heart may be longing for only
    a word,
Whose love by the Spirit is quickened
    and stirred ;
Now grant, blessed Saviour, this
    service to me,
Of speaking a comforting message
    for Thee.

3 Some soul may be plung'd in the
    darkest despair,
Whose shadows would melt in the
    sunlight of pray'r ;
O give me, dear Saviour, I humbly
    implore,
The sweet consolation that soul to
    restore.

841 IN the warfare that is raging
      For the truth and for the
      right,
When the conflict fierce is raging
    With the powers of the night ;
God needs workers, brave and true:...
May He, then, depend on you ?

    May the Lord..depend on you ?....
    Loyalty..is but His due,..
    Say, O spirit, brave and true,....
    That He may depend on you.

2 See, they come on sable pinions,
    Come in strong Satanic might—
Powers come and dark dominions
    From the regions of the night.
God requires the brave and true :....
May He, then, depend on you ?

3 From His throne the Father sees us ;
    Angels help us to prevail ;
And our leader true is Jesus,
    And we shall not, cannot fail ;
Triumph crowns the brave and true,..
May the Lord depend on you ?

842 SAVED by grace, oh, wonder-
      ful story,
    Jesus, the Saviour, has come from
      on high ;
Saved by grace, an heir to His glory,
    I shall inherit it by and by.

    Saved by grace, Oh, wonderful story !
    Sing it o'er and o'er again ;
    Saved by grace, oh, tell of His glory !
    Jesus is coming, coming again.

2 Saved by grace, and justified freely,
    Jesus, the Crucified, rose from the
    grave ;

Saved by grace, oh, marvellous
    dealing ;
Life everlasting to me He gave.

3 Saved by grace, and sanctified
    through Him,
Christ, the Ascended, now pleads
    for His own ;
Saved by grace, I sing hallelujah !
    I shall behold Him upon His
    throne.

843 JESUS the Saviour, dying on
      Calv'ry,
Purchased my pardon, setting me
    free ;   [Him,
Love so abundant, should I not serve
When He so gladly suffer'd for me?

    Lord,..I am Thine,..Saviour Divine !..
    Oh,..what a joy..just to know..Thou art
    mine !..

2 Oh, what a Saviour, tender and
    loving,
    Guarding my footsteps lest I
    should stray ;
Love so abundant, leading me ever
    Out of the darkness into the day.

3 Constant Companion, leaving me
    never,
    Bidding me follow close by His
    side ;
He is my Refuge, safely I shelter,
    Knowing He loves me whate'er
    betide.

844 I HAVE a mighty Saviour,
      His love is all my song,
And since His grace redeemed me
    I praise Him all day long.

    He brought me out of darkness,
    He turned my night to day,
    For when I knew His pard'ning love
    The sin clouds rolled away.

2 No friend so kind and tender,
    And none so true as He ;
Unworthy of His goodness,
    His grace my song shall be.

3 I would that you might know Him
    As Friend and Saviour too ;
For what He is to others
    He'll surely be to you.

4 Some day in realms of glory
    I'll see Him face to face,
And sing through endless ages
    Of His redeeming grace.

845 MY times are in my heav'nly
        Father's hands,
    Their changeful scenes I should
        not fear ;
  The reason why, He fully under-
        stands,
    He will not cause a needless tear.

My times are in His hands...
What's best for me He understands,...
I'll ever trust in His unchanging love,
  'Twill lead me to my home above.

2 My times are in my heav'nly Father's
      hands,
  The joy He sends a blessing brings ;
  His light will sparkle on life's golden
      sands ;   [wings.
  I'll hide beneath His shelt'ring

3 My times are in my heav'nly Father's
      hands,
  Used for His glory may they be ;
  Until in that most beautiful of lands,
  I'll sing of Him who died for me.

846 I HAD heard the Gospel call,
        Off'ring pardon free for all,
  And I hearkened to the blessed in-
        vitation ;
  Laid my sins at Jesus' feet,
  Tasted there redemption sweet,
  And He saved me with an utter-
        most salvation.

Jesus saves,...Jesus saves,...
Jesus saves me with an uttermost salvation ;
Tho' I cannot tell you how,
  Jesus fully saves me now,
With a full, and free, an uttermost salvation.

2   Now the load of sin is gone,
    And by faith I travel on,
  And I rest no longer under con-
      demnation ;
  For the blood has been applied,
  And my soul is satisfied
  With this full and free, this utter-
      most salvation.

3   From the mire and from the clay
    Jesus took my feet away,
  And He placed them on the Rock,
    the sure Foundation ;
  Whether now I live or die,
  This shall be my constant cry,
  Jesus saves me with an uttermost
    salvation.
H

847 LORD, fill us with Thy Spirit's
        might,
  That we may live as in Thy sight,
  And teach us how to pray aright ;
    We ask in Jesu's Name.

2 Lord, cleanse our hearts from ev'ry
      sin,
  And let Thy love so dwell within
  That Thou canst use our lips to win
  Some souls for Jesu's Name.

3 As we for others intercede,
  Lord, let Thy power be felt indeed,
  And some from Satan's grasp be
    freed ;
    We ask in Jesu's Name.

4 On all children lay Thy hand,
  That each may live as Thou hast
    planned,
  To serve in home or foreign land ;
    We ask in Jesu's Name.

To be sung at the close of the meeting.

5 The prayers that we have offered,
    Lord,
  " In faith," according to Thy Word,
  We thank Thee, Father, Thou hast
    heard,
    And praise in Jesu's Name. AMEN.

848 BE careful what you sow,
        For seed will surely grow ;
    The dew will fall,
      The floods will come,
    The clouds grow dark,
      And then the sun,
  And he who sows good seed to-day
    Shall reap good seed to-morrow ;
  And he who sows good seed to-day
    Shall reap with joy to-morrow.

Be careful what you sow,...
For seed will surely grow...
And he who sows good seed to-day
Shall reap with joy to-morrow.

2 Be careful what you sow,
  For seed will surely grow ;
    Where it may fall
      You cannot know,
    In sun or shade,
      'Twill surely grow,
  And he who sows good seed to-day
    Shall reap good seed to-morrow ;
  And he who sows good seed to-day
    Shall reap with joy to-morrow.

3 Be careful what you sow,
   The weeds you plant will grow ;
     The scattered seed
       From thoughtless hand
     Must gathered be,
     By God's command ;
   And he who sows wild oats to-day
     Must reap the crop to-morrow ;
   And he who sows wild oats to-day
     Shall reap with tears to-morrow.

4 Then let us sow good deeds,
   And not the briars and weeds ;
     Then harvest time
       Its joys shall bring,
     And when we reap
     Our hearts shall sing ;
   And he who sows good seed to-day
     Shall reap good seed to-morrow ;
   And he who sows good seed to-day
     Shall reap with joy to-morrow.

849 JESUS, Thy strength we need,
    Sowing Thy precious seed ;
   In thought, or word, or deed,
    Oh, lead us by Thy hand.

2 May we this hour be led
   In righteous paths to tread ;
   And, by Thy manna fed,
    Oh, lead us by Thy hand.

3 As this brief fleeting day
   Passes so swift away,
   May we from Thee not stray—
    Oh, lead us by Thy hand.

4 And when the hour draws nigh
   When death shall dim our eye,
   Take us to Thee on high—
    Oh, lead us by Thy hand.

850 WHEN the storm is raging and
    the heart is sad,
   Listen for the whispers of Jesus ;
  Surely you will hear them, and
    they'll make you glad,
   Listen for the whispers of Jesus.

  Listen....listen !....
  Listen for the whispers of Jesus ! [glad,
Surely you will hear them and they'll make you
  Listen for the whispers of Jesus !

2 When beneath a burden you are
    bending low,
   Listen for the whispers of Jesus ;
  When your friends forsake you and
    the sad tears flow,
   Listen for the whispers of Jesus.

3 When the night seems endless, when
    for courage pressed,
   Listen for the whispers of Jesus ;
  When the soul is weary and you sigh
    for rest,
   Listen for the whispers of Jesus.

851 O'ER death's sea in yon blest
    city,
   There's a home for ev'ry one ;
  Purchased with a price most costly,
   'Twas the blood of God's dear Son.

  In that city, bright city,
    Soon with loved ones I shall be :
  And with Jesus live for ever,
    In that city beyond death's sea.

2 Here we've no abiding city,
   Mansions here will soon decay
  But that city God's built firmly
   It can never pass away.

3 I have lov'd ones in that city,
   Those who left me years ago ;
  They with joy are waiting for me,
   Where no farewell tears e'er flow.

4 T'ward that pure and holy city,
   Oft my longing eyes I cast ;
  Jesus whispers sweetly to me,
   Heav'n is yours when earth is past.

852 "IT is finished ! " Jesus cries,
    I will trust ! I will trust !
  As He bows His head and dies !
   I will trust ! I will trust !
  All my load on Him was laid ;
  And my debt He freely paid ;
  He my peace with God has made ;
   I will trust ! I will trust !

  I will trust !...I will trust !....
    And I will not be afraid !....
  I will trust !....I will trust !....
    And I will not be afraid !

2 Jesus, hear my cry to Thee,
   I will trust ! I will trust !
  Thou alone art all my plea ;
   I will trust ! I will trust !
  In Thy hands I leave my case,
  Trusting fully in Thy grace ;
  All my hope in Thee I place ;
   I will trust ! I will trust !

3 Wherefore should I doubt or fear ?
   I will trust ! I will trust !
  Thou, my Lord, art ever near ;
   I will trust ! I will trust !

May I close to Thee abide,
Ever keeping near Thy side,
There from ev'ry storm to hide ;
    I will trust ! I will trust !

853   I'VE been redeemed, all glory
           to the Lamb,
Jesus has loved me, I'm saved, I
    know I am ;
O wondrous love that caused my
    Lord to die,
Now I will serve Him, then reign
    with Him on high.

I've been redeemed, yes, I have been redeemed,
  Glory to Jesus ! 'tis sweet for me to know ;
I've been redeemed, yes, I have been redeemed,
  O hallelujah ! my soul is white as snow.

2 O sinner, listen, I once was lost like
    you,
But Jesus found me, and saved me
    thro' and thro' ;
Now He is waiting for you to make a
    start,
Come to Him quickly and choose
    the better part.

3 I'm so glad I've found the way of life,
Free from all sorrow, from sin, and
    from strife ;
I am so glad I'm in this holy way,
O hallelujah ! I'm happy night and
    day.

4 I'm going home, all glory to the
    Lamb,
Jesus will take me now just as I am ;
Soon I'll be there with friends who've
    gone before ;
O happy meeting ! we'll meet to
    part no more.

854   NEVER alone in this earthly
           way,
Somebody cares, Somebody cares ;
I have a Helper each busy day ;
Somebody cares, 'tis Jesus.
Somebody cares when the clouds
    hang low,
Cares when my heart is o'erwhelmed
    with woe,
Cares, and is marking my path below ;
Somebody cares, 'tis Jesus.

Some - - body cares for me,
Some - -body cares for me,
In all my life His kind hand I see,
Somebody cares, 'tis Jesus.

2 When I am singing a happy song,
    Somebody cares, Somebody cares ;
When I am fighting against the
        wrong,
    Somebody cares, 'tis Jesus.
Somebody cares when I stand alone,
Cares when the pleasures of earth are
    gone,
Cares when my false hopes with
    wings have flown ;
    Somebody cares, 'tis Jesus.

3 When I am weary and long for rest,
    Somebody cares, Somebody cares ;
When by the tempter I'm sorely
        pressed,
    Somebody cares, 'tis Jesus.
Somebody cares, and, whate'er
    betide,   [side,
Walks ev'ry hour by the Christian's
Love so amazing will e'er abide,
    Somebody cares, 'tis Jesus.

855   DAY is dying in the west,
           Heav'n is touching earth with
               rest,
Wait and worship while the night
Sets her evening lamps alight
    Through all the sky.

Holy, Holy, Holy, Lord God of Hosts !
Heav'n and earth are full of Thee ;
Heav'n and earth are praising Thee,
    O Lord, most high !

2 While the deep'ning shadows fall,
Heart of love enfolding all,
Thro' the glory and the grace
Of the stars that veil Thy face,
    Our hearts ascend.

3 When for ever from our sight
Pass the stars, the day, the night,
Lord of angels, on our eyes
Let eternal morning rise,
    And shadows end.

856   CAME He to Bethlehem's
           manger,
Infant, yet glorious Lord ;
Stood He in Temple and uttered
    Wondrous and mystical word ;
Toiled He in workshop, and lowly,
    Bore He the burden of life ;
Calmly, and sweetly, and purely,
    Mixed He in anger or strife.

Love brought Him down from the glory,
  Love made Him come from the sky,
Love is His heart for the sinner,
  Led Him to suffer and die.

2 Passed He the fiery temptation,
    Was He the homeless and lone,
    Was He despised and rejected,
    Claimed He dark sorrow His own ;
  Came He to Olivet's garden,
    Drank He the dregs of the cup,
  Say, was that holy cheek sullied,
    Gave He His precious life up.

3 Went He to Pilate and Herod,
    Bore He the lash and the nail,
  Prayed He His Father to pardon,
    Died He with agony's wail ;
  Lay He in grave of the stranger,
    Rose He in majesty grand,
  Went He to claim as a victor
    Trophies as countless as sand.

857   GOD will take care of me ;
      Here will I rest,
    Trusting His promise true,
      Safe on His breast.
    Changeful may be my lot,
    His mercy changeth not ;
    No child of His forgot,
      In Jesus blest.

2 God will take care of me ;
      Hushing my fear ;
    When dangers round I see,
      His voice I hear ;
    Then let my soul be brave,
    High though the wind and wave,
    Greater His power to save,
      Tenderly near.

3 God will take care of me ;
      Holding the helm ;
    Storms that may sweep the sea
      Will not o'erwhelm.
    Soon, ev'ry billow pass'd,
    I shall my anchor cast,
    Safe, safe at home at last,
      In joy's bright realm.

858 THERE'S joy in the home-land,
      there's plenty and peace,
  A welcome for souls gone astray ;
  Glad songs over sinners returning to
      God !—
    Tell someone the story to-day.

Tell someone the story to-day,....
  Tell someone,...tell someone ;..
Tell someone the story, 'twill add to His
    glory :
  Tell someone the story to-day.

2 The sinful and weary find pardon
      and rest,
    The lame may be healed in the
      way ;
  Believing in Jesus, each soul may be
      blest—
    Tell someone the story to-day.

3 For love like the Master's, for wis-
      dom to win,
    For patience and tenderness, pray ;
  And, weeping, go forth to the high-
      ways of sin—
    Tell someone the story to-day.

4 The parting commandment of Jesus,
      your King,
    Be earnest and swift to obey ;
  To help the Good Shepherd His
      " other sheep " bring,
    Tell someone the story to-day.

859 I HAVE a dear Saviour who
      loves me, I know,
  And whose will I delight to do.
  He's present to cheer me wherever
      I go—
    Was there ever a Friend so true ?

Was there ever a Friend so true ?
  Was there ever a Friend so, true ?..
I often have proved Him, I ever will love Him ;
  Was there ever a Friend so true ?

2 This wonderful Friend is a helper
      indeed ;
  He has promised to lead me thro',
  And closer He comes than a brother
      in need—
    Was there ever a Friend so true ?

3 He soothes me in sorrow with songs
      in the night,
  And inspires me with hopes anew ;
  He fills me with courage my battles
      to fight—
    Was there ever a Friend so true ?

4 His love is a fountain of blessing so
      pure,
  Ever flowing for me, for you ;
  His pow'r is unfailing, His promise
      is sure—
    Was there ever a Friend so true ?

860 BECAUSE of His love the
      Saviour died,
  For sin of the world was crucified ;

With His own blood our ransom paid,
And for our souls deliv'rance made.

Because of His love, His sacrifice !
Because of His love, oh, what a price !
He suffered and died, was crucified,
Because of His love, because of His love.

2 Because of His love, oh, blessed
        thought,
  Were wonderful deeds of mercy
        wrought ;
  The wind and wave obey'd His will,
  Hush'd by His wondrous "Peace,
        be still."

3 Because of His love, His blest com-
        mand,
  We'll send the glad word to ev'ry
        land ;
  His Name above all names we'll sing,
  And crown Him Saviour, Priest,
        and King.

861 SHOW me the way, dear
        Saviour !
  The shadows are falling fast.
  And through the clouds above me
        No ray of light is cast ;
  The storm is wildly raging,
        The thunders loudly roar,
  The restless waves are dashing
        Against the wreck-strewn shore.

  Show me the way, dear Saviour,
      That Thou wouldst have me go,
  Show me the way, dear Saviour,
      For Thou alone dost know.

2 Show me the way, dear Saviour !
      The night is so wild and dark ;
  I cannot stem the current
      Unless Thou guide my barque ;
  Oh, fiercer grows the tempest,
      And wilder rolls the sea ;
  Help ! help me, O my Saviour,
      I trust alone in Thee.

3 Show me the way, dear Saviour !
      My courage is failing fast ;
  My storm-toss'd barque is sinking
      But I'll be saved at last.
  Come nearer, nearer to me,
      And speak the word of peace
  That stills the angry waters,
      And bids the tempest cease.

862 IS it nothing to you that
        heaven's King
  Came down to this world of woe,

That He suffered and bled, and rose
        from the dead,
  That eternal life you might know?

  Is it nothing to you that grace is free,
  And that God in His love doth call ?
  Is it nothing to you ? Is it nothing to you ?
  Is it nothing, nothing to you ?

2 Is it nothing to you that by and by
      You must travel death's dark vale,
  Where Jordan's waves the pathway
        laves,
      And all but Christ doth fail ?

3 Is it nothing to you that some sweet
        day,
      In the heavenly land so fair,
  You may join the song that the ran-
        somed throng
      Are for ever singing there ?

863 ARE you with some sorrow
        burdened,
      On your way no ray of light ?
  Strain your ear, all heaven's watch-
        ing ;
      God can give you songs by night.

  Weary soul,..cease your repin - - ing,
      Burdened one.. God's ways are right,
  Ev'ry cloud..has silver lin - - ing ;
      God can give..you songs by night..

2 Paul and Silas, prison-fastened,
      Shook the jail with earthquake
        might ;
  Bands were rent and doors were
        opened ;
      God had given songs by night.

3 It is oft in saddest moments
      That our souls take highest flight ;
  And to strains of sweetest music
      God doth set the songs by night.

864 O SO long was my barque
        toss'd about on life's sea,
  But I've anchored in Jesus at last ;
  And I heard a sweet voice gently
        calling to me,
      And I've anchored in Jesus at last.

All my doubtings are over, my struggling is past
And the load of my sin at His feet I have cast,
I have anchor'd in Jesus at last....

2 Safely moor'd to the Rock which no
        tempest can shake,
      I have anchored in Jesus at last ;

Tho' the billows in fury around me
   may break,
   I have anchored in Jesus at last.
3 In the harbour of faith there is
   safety and rest,
   I have anchored in Jesus at last;
And a deep settled peace now is
   filling my breast,
   I have anchored in Jesus at last.
4 Deeper groweth my peace as I'm
   nearing the shore,
   I have anchored in Jesus at last;
And by simply believing I'm safe
   evermore,
   I have anchored in Jesus at last.

865   GIVE me a sight, O Saviour,
     Of Thy wondrous love to me,
Of the love that brought Thee down
   to earth,
   To die on Calvary.
   Oh, make me understand it,
    Help me to take it in,..
   What it meant to Thee, the Holy One,
   To bear away my sin.

2 Was it the nails, O Saviour,
   That bound Thee to the tree ?
Nay, 'twas Thine everlasting love,
   Thy love for me, for me.

3 Oh, wonder of all wonders,
   That through Thy death for me,
My open sins, my secret sins,
   Can all forgiven be.

4 Then melt my heart, O Saviour,
   Bend me, yea, break me down,
Until I own Thee Conqueror,
   And Lord and Sov'reign crown.

866   JUST beyond the river Jordan,
     Just across its chilling tide,
There's a land of life eternal,
   Thro' its vales sweet waters glide.
By the crystal river flowing
   Grows the tree of life so fair ;
Many loved ones wait our coming
   In the Upper Garden there.
We..shall meet them some bright morning,..
Rest - - ing by the waters fair ;..
They..are waiting for our coming,..
In..the Upper Garden there...

2 Growing in the Upper Garden,
   " Flowers the earth too rudely
    pressed,"
In that land shall reach perfection
   By the heav'nly Gard'ner dressed ;

Where the flowers bloom for ever,
   Death can find no entrance there ;
All is life and light eternal.
   All is joy beyond compare.

3 There the buds from earth trans-
    planted
   For our coming watch and wait ;
In the Upper Garden growing,
   Just within the golden gate ;
Though our hearts may break with
    sorrow,
   By the grief so hard to bear,
We shall meet them some glad
    morning
   In the Upper Garden there.

867   SHE came to Jesus, one of old
     Who sent her He has not
     revealed ;
This only are we plainly told,
   How she by simple faith was
    healed.
   Oh ! touch Him too, oh ! touch Him too,
   There's virtue still in Christ for thee ;
   His blood can cleanse, His power can save,
   Though crimson-dyed your sins may be.

2 She heard, she came, she touch'd the
    hem
   Of His loose garment in the way ;
Immediately through her weak frame
   She felt the thrill of health that
    day.

3 I came with all my guilt and sin ;
   Knelt in contrition at His feet ;
The Holy Spirit entered in,
   And wrought in me a change
    complete.

4 Oh come to Him, and rest assured,
   Whate'er thy sin He'll welcome
    thee ;
Who ever came to Him was cured,
   And from all doubts and fear set
    free.

868   A   HOMELESS   Stranger
     amongst us came,
   To this land of sin and mourning ;
He walked in a path of sorrow and
    shame,   [scorning ;
   Thro' insult, and hate, and
A Man of Sorrows, of toils, of tears,
   An outcast man and lonely ;
But He looked on me, and thro'
    endless years,
   Him must I serve, Him only.

2 And then from this sad and sorrowful
      land,
   This land of tears, He departed ;
   But the light of His eyes, and the
      touch of His hand,
   Had left me broken-hearted ;
   And I clave to Him as He turn'd
      His face
   From the land that was mine no
      longer,
   The land I'd loved in the golden days
      Ere I knew the love that was
      stronger.

3 And I must abide where He abode,
      And follow His steps for ever ;
   His people, my people ; His God,
      my God,
      In the land beyond the river ;
   His face in glory I'll soon behold,
      And dear ones who've gone before
      me.
   With the blood-bought throng in
      that heavenly fold
   I'll sing redemption's story !

869   O SHIPWRECKED soul, far
            out on sin's dark wave,
   With no help near, no life-line
      thrown to save ;
   No boat to launch, no crew with
      courage brave ;
      Thy only help is Jesus.
   Jesus has conquer'd the storm-toss'd sea,
   Walk'd the wild billows of Galilee ;
   He is the Saviour for you, and me ;
      Jesus, only Jesus.

2 O shipwrecked soul, no wave can
      drown the voice
   Of Him who speaks to make thy
      soul rejoice ;
   'Midst tempest swirl, make Jesus
      now thy choice ;
      Thy only help is Jesus.

3 O shipwrecked soul, He waits with
      pitying eye,
   Behold thee ; He'll hear thy helpless
      cry ;
   O venture now, trust fully, He is
      nigh ;
      Thy only help is Jesus.

870   A LAMP in the night, a song
            in time of sorrow ;
   A great glad hope, which faith can
      ever borrow,

To gild the passing day with the
      glory of the morrow,
   Is the hope of the coming of the
      Lord.
   Blessed hope,..blessed hope,..
   Blessed hope of the coming of the Lord ;
   How the aching heart it cheers ;
   How it glistens through our tears ;
   Blessed hope of the coming of the Lord.

2 A star in the sky, a beacon bright to
      guide us ;
   An anchor sure to hold when storms
      betide us ;
   A refuge for the soul, where in quiet
      we may hide us,
      Is the hope of the coming of the
      Lord.

3 A call of command, like trumpet
      clearly sounding,
   To make us bold when evil is sur-
      rounding ;
   To stir the sluggish heart, and to
      keep in good abounding,
      Is the hope of the coming of the
      Lord.

4 A word from the One to all our
      hearts the dearest,
   A parting word to make Him aye
      the nearest ;
   Of all His precious words, the
      sweetest, brightest, clearest,
      Is the hope of the coming of the
      Lord.

871   WHERE He may lead me I
            will go,
   For I have learned to trust Him so
   And I remember 'twas for me,
   That He was slain on Calvary.
   Jesus shall lead me night and day,
   Jesus shall lead me all the way :
   He is the truest Friend to me,
   For I remember Calvary.

2 O I delight in His command,
   Love to be led by His dear hand,
   His divine will is sweet to me,
   Hallowed by blood-stained Calvary.

3 Onward I go, nor doubt nor fear,
   Happy with Christ, my Saviour,
      near ;
   Trusting some day that I shall see
   Jesus, my Friend of Calvary.

872 EV'RY *step* with Jesus
　　Thus we love to go,
Down life's shady pathway
Into ev'ning's glow.

> Ev'ry power for Jesus,
> 　Brain and heart and will,
> Used at highest pressure
> 　Till the pulse be still;
> Crown of Glory waiting,
> 　On the further shore,
> Sing with glad rejoicing,
> 　Praises evermore.

2 Ev'ry *day* with Jesus
　When the morning breaks,
Whispering life's secrets
　Ere the road we take.

3 Ev'ry *nerve* for Jesus
　Strained in mighty toil,
Just to bring the Master
　Heaps of golden spoil.

4 Ev'ry *man* for Jesus,
　What a mighty throng,
Then would swell the chorus
　Of the victor's song!

CHOIR PIECES

873 WILL you come and help us
　　in our work,
　　For Jesus' sake?
Will you fight with enemies that lurk,
　For Jesus' sake?
The pow'rs of evil stronger grow,
Within, without, we meet the foe;
Will you lend a hand to strike a blow,
　For Jesus' sake?

> For Jesus' sake, for Jesus' sake,
> What will you do for Jesus' sake?
> Let each one bring some worthy thing
> 　For Jesus' sake.

2 Will you make the homes of darkness
　　bright
　　For Jesus' sake?
Will you be an ever-shining light
　For Jesus' sake?
Against all forms of deadly sin,
Against all evil thoughts within,
Will you strike as one who means to
　win
　　For Jesus' sake?

3 Will you curb the quick and angry
　　word
　　For Jesus' sake?
Will you bear the yoke of our dear
　Lord
　　For Jesus' sake?
When work is hard and duty dry,
And easy seems the tempting lie,
Will you speak the truth, although
　you die,
　　For Jesus' sake?

4 Will you turn from every evil way
　For Jesus' sake?
Will you climb up higher day by day
　For Jesus' sake?

Amid the stress of earthly strife,
Amid a world with evil rife,
Will you try to live the higher life,
　For Jesus' sake?

874 HAVE you toiled all night near
　　the shore in vain?
　Push away from the shore, launch
　　out;
Where the flood is deep cast your
　　nets again,
　Push away from the shore, launch
　　out;
There a blessing waits for your souls
　　to take,　　　　　[strand
　Haste away from the barren,
Toil no more in vain where the
　　surges break,
　Launch out is your Lord's com-
　　mand.

> Launch out,...launch out,...
> Push away from the shore, launch out,...
> God's grace flows free, like a mighty sea,
> And the Master calls, "Launch out!"

2 Have your souls grown faint with
　　the vigil long?
　Push away from the shore, launch
　　out;
Put your trust in Christ, He will
　　make you strong,
　Push away from the shore, launch
　　out;
Be no more content with a meagre
　　share
　From your Father's abundant
　　store;
Ask Him largely now, He will hear
　　your pray'r,
　And give till you want no more.

3 Jesus bids to-day ev'ry weary soul
　　Push away from the shore, launch
　　　out ;
　Hear His loving voice, He will make
　　you whole,
　　Push away from the shore, launch
　　　out ;
　Leave the shore of sin with its
　　shallowness,
　It has nothing of life to give ;
　Look to Jesus now, who alone can
　　bless,
　　Launch out on His grace and live.

875　ARE you sowing the seed of
　　　　the kingdom, brother,
　In the morning bright and fair ?
　Are you sowing the seed of the
　　kingdom, brother,
　In the heat of the noonday's glare ?

For the harvest time is coming on,..
　And the reapers' work will soon be done,...
Will your sheaves be many, will you garner any
　For the gath'ring at the harvest home ?

2 Are you sowing the seed of the
　　kingdom, brother,
　In the still and solemn night ?
　Are you sowing the seed of the
　　kingdom, brother,
　For a harvest pure and white ?

3 Are you sowing the seed of the
　　kingdom, brother,
　All along the fertile way ?
　Would you glean golden sheaves in
　　the harvest, brother,
　Come and join the ranks to-day.

876　PRAISE the Lord with heart
　　　　and voice,
　Joyfully serving your King,
　Come and worship at His throne,
　　Lovingly, gratefully sing ;
　Happy ev'ry hour, trusting in His
power,
　　Unto the Giver of our salvation
　　　praises bring.

　　Praise Him ! sing with melody,
　　　Heart and voice.
　　Praise Him everlastingly,
　　　Come, rejoice ;
　　Hail Him, Lord, most glorious,
　　Mighty One victorious,
　　　Praise His Holy Name,
　　Praise Him, heav'nly company,
　　　Angels bright.

　　Crown Him now and evermore,
　　　Lord of light :
　　Praise Him, all creation,
　　God of our salvation,
　　Boundless in majesty,
　　King eternal ;
　　　Praise His Name.

2 Praise the dear Redeemer's Name,
　　Crown Him with beauty and light,
　Just and true are all His ways,
　　Wonderful, boundless His might ;
　Glad hosannas swelling, loud His
　　goodness telling,
　　Fountain of blessing our joy
　　　eternal, day and night.

3 Praise the Lord with heart and voice,
　　Ever adoringly raise
　Hallelujahs sweet and strong,
　　Unto the " Ancient of Days ; "
　Shout with acclamation, hail Him
　　all creation,
　　Worship Jehovah, O come rejoic-
　　　ing, sound His praise.

877　CHRIST, our mighty Captain,
　　　　leads against the foe ;
　We will never falter when He bids
　　us go ;
　Tho' His righteous purpose we may
　　never know,
　　Yet we'll follow all the way.

Forward ! forward ! 'tis the Lord's command,
Forward ! forward ! to the promised land ;
Forward ! forward ! let the chorus ring :
We are sure to win with Christ, our King !

2 Satan's fearful onslaught cannot
　　make us yield,
　While we trust in Christ, our Buckler
　　and our Shield ;
　Pressing ever on—the Spirit's sword
　　we wield,
　　And we follow all the way.

3 Let our glorious banner ever be un-
　　furled—
　From its mighty stronghold evil
　　shall be hurled ;
　Christ, our mighty Captain, over-
　　comes the world,
　　And we follow all the way.

4 Fierce the battle rages, but 'twill not
　　be long,
　Then triumphant shall we join the
　　blessed throng,　　　　[song—
　Joyfully uniting in the victor's
　　If we follow all the way.

878 LIFE-TIME is working time,
Spend no idle days ;
Jesus is calling thee
On the harvest ways.
Working with a willing hand,
Sing a song of praise ;
Work, ever work for Jesus !

..Swiftly the hours of labour fly,..
Freighted with love let each pass by !..
There is joy in labour for the struggling
    neighbour,
Work, ever work for Jesus !

2 Life-time is working time,
Learn where duty lies ;
Grasp ev'ry passing day
As a precious prize,
Glad to help the sorrowing,
Glad to sympathise ;
Work, ever work for Jesus !

3 Life-time is working time,
Do thy honest part ;
Though in discouragements
Bear a cheerful heart.
Trusting Jesus as Thy Friend,
Ne'er from Him depart,
Work, ever work for Jesus !

879 STANDING in the market
places all the season through,
Idly saying, " Lord, is there no work
    that I can do ? "
O how many loiter, while the Master
    calls anew—
    " Reapers ! reapers ! Who will
    work to-day ? "

Lift..thine..eyes and look upon the fields
    that stand..
Ripe..and..ready for the willing gleaner's
    hand..
        Rouse ye, O sleepers !
        Ye are needed as reapers !
Who will be the first to answer, " Master,
here am I ?"..
Far..and..wide the ripened grain is bending
    low,..
In..the..breezes gently waving to and fro,..
        Rouse ye, O sleepers !
        Ye are needed as reapers,
And the golden harvest days are swiftly
    passing by.

2 Ev'ry sheaf you gather will become
    a jewel bright
In the crown you hope to wear in
    yonder world of light.

Seek the gems immortal that are
    precious in His sight !
    " Reapers ! reapers ! Who will
    work to-day ? "

3 Morning hours are passing, and the
    ev'ning follows fast ;
Soon the time for reaping will for
    evermore be past ;
Empty-handed to the Master will
    you go at last ?
    " Reapers ! reapers ! Who will
    work to-day ? "

880 COME to the ark of refuge,
Come to the place of rest ;
Safe in this quiet harbour,
Naught can thy peace molest ;
Come with thy guilt to Jesus,
Weary and sore distrest ;
List to His plea,
" Come unto Me,
And I will give you rest."....

O message of mercy !
    Unbounded, unknown !
He died to redeem thee ;
    O make Him now thine own !
By faith in His mercy,
    By trust in His grace ;
With saints in His kingdom,
    He'll give thy soul a place.

2 Come to the heart that loves thee,
Come to the soul's true home,
Come while the Lord invites thee,
Come while there yet is room ;
Tell Him thy ev'ry sorrow,
Nought from this Friend with-
    hold ;
He'll hear thy prayer,
Thy burden bear :
Trust in His love untold.....

3 Christ is the soul's sure refuge ;
When breaks the world's fierce
    blast,
He will protect His children
Till all is overpast ;
When storms without are raging,
Rest and be not afraid ;
Look to the Lord,
Hope in His Word,
Trust and be undismayed.....

881 O LISTEN to our wondrous
    story,
Once we dwelt among the lost ;

Yet Jesus came from heav'n's glory,
    Saving us at awful cost.

Who saved us from eternal loss ?
Who but God's Son upon the Cross !
What did He do ? He died for you !
Where is He now ? Believe it, thou !
In Heaven interceding !

2 No angel could our place have taken,
    Highest of the high though He ;
Nail'd to the Cross, despis'd for-
    saken,
    Was one of the Godhead three !

3 Will you surrender to this Saviour ?
    Now before Him humbly bow ?
You, too, shall come to know His
    favour,
    He will save, and save you now !

882 I MUST needs go home by the
        way of the Cross,
    There's no other way but this ;
I shall ne'er get sight of the Gates of
    Light,
    If the way of the Cross I miss.

The way of the Cross leads home,..
The way of the Cross leads home ;..
It is sweet to know, as I onward go,
The way of the Cross leads home.

2 I must needs go on in the blood-
    sprinkled way,
    The path that the Saviour trod,
If I ever climb to the heights sub-
    lime,
    Where the soul is at home with
        God.

3 Then I bid farewell to the way of the
    world,
    To walk in it never more ;
For my Lord says, " Come ! " and
    I seek my home,
    Where He waits at the open door.

883 I LOVE the Gospel story,
        'Tis God's redeeming love,
It comes with light and glory
    From Him who reigns above.
I love the blessed story,
    Its theme the Lamb of God,
Who left His home in glory,
    For me to shed His blood.

I love the Gospel story,
    It never can grow old ;
It helps me on to glory,
    The more I hear it told.

2 I love the Gospel story,
    It keeps me ev'ry hour ;
For Christ, the Prince of Glory,
    Imparts His saving pow'r.
I love the blessed story,
    'Tis manna to my soul ;
The balm of life and glory,
    It makes my spirit whole.

3 I love the Gospel story,
    It cheers me day by day ;
My hope, my joy, my glory,
    I own its gentle sway.
I love the blessed story,
    My portion evermore ;
'Twill be my theme in glory,
    When earthly cares are o'er.

884 DEAR Lord, I need Thy saving
        care about....me ;
    Into Thine arms of refuge would
        I flee ;....
I could not live, I dare not die with-
    out....Thee,
    In mercy then abide, abide with
        me.....

Abide with me—I need Thee ev'ry hour ;..
Abide with me, I fear the tempter's pow'r,..
Abide with me, in sunshine and in show'r,
In life,..in..death,..O Lord, abide with me.

2 When foes without, and foes within
    assail....me,
    And I am tossed upon a troubled
        sea ;....
When, in my weakness, hope and
    courage fail....me,
    In mercy then abide, abide with
        me.....

3 When o'er my way the sun is brightly
    shin - - ing,
    My Counsellor, my Guide and
        Keeper be,....
And in the hour of sorrow and re-
    pin - - ing,
    In mercy then abide, abide with
        me.....

4 When I am near the dark and un-
    known riv - - er,
    Lord, who in earth or heav'n can
        save but Thee ?....
'Tis Thou alone hath power to de-
    li - - ver,
    In mercy then abide, abide with
        me....

885 BY the way of the Cross we're
    going,
Home to the land above ;
We will fear not the hosts of evil,
Kept by a Father's love.

Home,....home, home,....
    Home to the Land above,..
    By the way of the Cross we're going,
    Home to the land of love.

2 By the way of the Cross we're going ;
    Jesus has gone before ;   [steps,
We will follow our Master's foot-
Home to the golden shore !

3 By the way of the Cross we're going ;
    Rough though the path may be ;
There's a hand that will guide us
    safely
Home, blessed Lord, to Thee !

886 WHO are the soldiers of Jesus
    Christ ?
    Who who are they ?
What is the fight that they wage on
    earth ?
    Why do they watch and pray ?
Ah ! they are God's own children ;
    He is near them,
    He will cheer them ;
Truth is the cause for which they
    strive
    In battle fray.

They are stepping bravely onward,
    They are eager with the hope of youth,
    They never fear the foe,
    But strike a gallant blow
    For God and the cause of truth ;
    They are ever climbing homeward,
    They are looking unto higher things,
    Free as the flag that waves o'erhead,
    Soldiers of the King of kings.

2 Who are the soldiers of Jesus Christ ?
    Who, who are they ?
Are they the heroes of earthly war,
    Eager to smite and slay ?
No, they are something nobler ;
    And the story
    Of their glory
Rings with the power of faith and
    love,
    That lights their way.

3 Who are the soldiers of Jesus Christ ?
    Who, who are they ?
Are they the lovers of empty joys,
    Things that will pass away ?

No, they would lead for ever
    Lives of beauty,
    Lives of duty,
Lives that are hid with Christ in God,
    No more to stray.

4 Who are the soldiers of Jesus Christ ?
    Who, who are they ?
Are they the rich and the great of
    earth,
    Holding a mighty sway ?
No, in a grander kingdom,
    Ever fairer,
    Ever rarer,
Bright with the crown of endless life,
    They'll shine like day.

887 "LOYALTY unto Christ" the
    trumpet now is sounding,
And the echoes answer from the
    fields of sin ;
    Nations are awakening,
    Idol thrones are shaking,
For the great Millennium is coming
    in.
    Like a mighty army,
The heralds of the Cross are march-
    ing over land and sea ;
    Bearing through the darkness
The light that leadeth to salvation
    full and free.

Long and loud, " Loyalty unto Christ " we
    sing ;
    Till ev'ry human tongue,
    Shall hear His praises sung !
Let the hills, valleys and desert places ring,
With " Loyalty unto Christ our Lord and
    King."..

2 " Loyalty, faith and works," in holy
    consecration,
Shall the scattered nations unto Him
    restore ;
    Then the world shall own Him,
    And with joy enthrone Him,
King of kings and Lord of lords for
    evermore.
    See the darkness rifting !
The Gospel light of truth is spreading
    to the perfect day !
    Clouds are backward drifting !
Renew endeavour ! for the King
    prepare the way !

3 " Loyalty unto Christ ! " O what a
    mighty power,
Where the hosts of God united in
    His Name !

Then would angels greet us,
Christ Himself would meet us,
And baptise us with the Pentecostal
    flame.
Then would come the triumph,
And Christ be known and lov'd, His
    praise be sung from shore to
    shore ;
Earth would then, in glory,
Become the kingdom of the Lord
    for evermore.

888   WHAT are you seeking day by
    day,
Working with heart and hand ?
Is it for honour in the fray ?
    Is it for wealth or land ?
Turn from the eager longing thirst,
    Turn from the world's great strife,
Seek ye the Kingdom of Heaven first,
    Seek ye eternal life.

For the kingdom of Heav'n is better
   Than pearls of a priceless worth,..
Than treasures great, or pomp of state,
   Than the kingdom of all the earth.
It ever abideth within you,
   This home of the life divine,
Let the dark clouds roll from your heart
   and soul,
   Let the Light of the Kingdom shine.

2 What are you seeking day by day ?
    Is it for something new ?
Is it for pleasures bright and gay,
    Brief as the morning dew ?
Seek ye the kingdom evermore,
    Joys shall be added then,
Greater than all that you felt before,
    Ever renew'd again.

3 What are you seeking day by day,
    Comrade so brave and true ?
Is it for some great thing to say ?
    Some noble deed to do ?
Give to the Master heart and hand,
    Follow in truth and love,
So shall you share in His work and
    stand
    Crown'd in the life above.

4 Enter the kingdom, child of truth,
    Seeking the Saviour's face ;
Enter the kingdom, maid and youth,
    Come in your strength and grace ;
Enter the kingdom one and all,
    Cease from the path to stray,
Hear ye the voice of the Master, call
    " I am the Living Way."

889   HARK ! 'tis the clarion sound-
    ing the fight,
Turn from each siren charmer.
Banners are waving, swords gleam-
    ing bright,
Gird on the heavenly armour.
Stern is the conflict, fierce the foe ;
Cowards and traitors will backward
    go !
Brave men are wanted, hearts all
    aglow,
    Wanted to battle for Jesus.

Soldiers of God, we join you to-day,
   Join in our grand endeavour,
Soldiers of God, advance to the fray,
   For the truth is triumphant for ever.

2 Haste to the rescue, souls in their
    need
    Loud for relief are calling ;
Must they for ever hopeless plead ?
    None hear the cry appalling ?
Broken in spirit, wounded by sin,
Foemen around them, and fear
    within ;   [win ;
Speed ye to help them freedom to
    Speed with the Gospel of Jesus.

3 Soon 'twill be over, danger all past ;
    Ended the marches dreary.
After the warfare, rest comes at last,
    Sweet rest for soldiers weary.
Crown after conflict ; ease after
    pain ;
Parting shall never be known again ;
Joy everlasting all shall obtain ;
    All who are faithful to Jesus.

890   OH, Christian, rise and shine,
    and give God the glory ;
Christian, rise and shine, and give
    God the glory (*Repeat*) ;
    Christian, rise, rise and shine.
Do you want to be a really happy
    Christian (*Repeat*),
Do you want to be a really happy
    Christian, full of joy, joy divine?
Yes, I want to be a really happy
    Christian (*Repeat*),
Yes, I want to be a really happy
    Christian, full of joy, joy divine !
Then you must rise and shine, and
    give God the glory (*Repeat*) ;
You must rise and shine, and give
    God the glory ;
    You must rise, rise and shine.

891 ON to the front, for the fight
is on !
This is not the time for dreaming !
See ! on the breeze of the early dawn,
Banners of the foe are streaming !
Into position for battle drawn,
And with weapons brightly gleam-
ing,
Now from the hill-top of vantage
ground,
Loud their battle cries resound.

Onward to the conflict !....
Fearless, like a soldier true ;..
Press into the bat - - tle,..
Your Commander calls for you.

2 On to the front, nor the danger fear,
Satan's forces cannot harm you ;
Let not the hordes that are pressing
near
In their proud array alarm you ;
Be not dismayed by the foeman's
cheer,
Let no evil power disarm you ;
Trust in the Lord for your strength
to win
Over all the ranks of sin.

3 On to the front ! He who smote the
sea,
And its angry waves divided,
Is thy Commander, and surely He
For the vict'ry hath provided.
Trust in His power, and ever be
By His love and wisdom guided ;
Keep up the fight till the whole
world sings
Praise unto the King of kings.

892 LORD, bring some wand'rers
home to-night—
Some who have gone astray ;
Oh, give them grace to come to-night
Let them no more delay !

To-night, Lord ! to-night, Lord !
Bring wand'rers home to-night !
To-night, Lord ! to-night, Lord !
Bring wand'rers home to-night !

2 May none Thy mercy spurn to-night,
Thy Holy Spirit grieve ;
May prodigals return to-night ;
May sinners now believe.

3 Let none unblest depart to-night,
Unsaved and unforgiven ;
Over some yielding heart to-night
Let there be joy in heaven.

893 CONQUERORS and over-
comers now are we,
Thro' the precious blood of Christ
we've victory ;
If the Lord be for us, we can never
fail,
Nothing 'gainst His mighty power
can e'er prevail.

Con - - querors are we,..thro' the blood...
thro' the blood ;..
God will give...us victory,...thro' the blood,...
thro' the blood ;...
Thro' the Lamb for sinners slain,
Yet who lives and reigns again,
More than conquerors are we.

2 In the Name of Israel's God we'll
onward press,
Overcoming sin and all unrighteousness ;
Not to us, but unto Him the praise
shall be,
For salvation and for blood-bought
victory.

3 Unto him that overcometh shall be
giv'n
Here to eat of "hidden manna"
sent from heav'n ;
Over yonder he the victor's palm
shall bear,
And a robe of white and golden
crown shall wear.

894 WHEN out in sin and darkness
lost,
Love found me ;
My fainting soul was tempest tossed,
Love found me ;
I heard the Saviour's words so blest,
Love found me ;
Come, weary, heavy-laden rest,
Love found me.

Oh, 'twas love,..love,..
Love that moved the mighty God,
Love, love, 'twas love found me.

2 The Spirit roused me from my sleep,
Love found me ;
Conviction seized me strong and
deep,
Love found me ;
Although I long withstood His grace,
Love found me ;
He wooed me to His kind embrace,
Love found me.

3 I'll praise Him while He gives me
   breath,
    Love found me ;
For saving from an endless death,
    Love found me ;
Christ is my Advocate above,
    Love found me ;
I'm yoked to Him in perfect love,
    Love found me.

4 And when I reach the gold-paved
   street,
    Love found me ;
I'll sit adoring at His feet,
    Love found me ;
And sing hosanna round the throne,
    Love found me ;
Where I shall know as I am known,
    Love found me.

895 WHERE the flag is flying,
    where the fight is keen,
Where the trumpet call is ringing,
There you find the soldiers, steady
   and serene,   [singing.
  There you find the sound of
Servants of the Master, scorning fear
  or flight,
Fighting for the Truth, the Life, the
  Light !

  Soldiers of the Master, onward tread,
    Telling out the grand old story !
  Ready day by day Jesus to obey,
    Soldiers of the King of Glory.

2 Where the darkness reigneth, where
   the pow'r of sin,
  Binds the heart of man in sadness,
There you find the soldiers, waiting
   souls to win,
  Bringing them to light and glad-
   ness,
Servants of the Master, strong in
   love and might,
Fighting for the Truth, the Life, the
  Light !

3 Where the doubts are thickest,
   where the strength of youth
  Falls beneath the chains of error,
There you find the soldiers, with the
   lamp of truth,
  Freeing men from thoughts of
   terror.
Servants of the Master, strong in
   faith and sight,
Fighting for the Truth, the Life, the
  Light !

4 Where the pallid suff'rer, weary,
   worn, and weak,
  On his bed of pain is lying,
There you find the soldiers, words of
   hope to speak,
  Comforting the sick and dying.
Servants of the Master, watching in
   the night,   [Light !
Fighting for the Truth, the Life, the

5 Where from angel chorus thro' the
   heavenly dome,
  Rings a song of triumph splendid,
There you find the soldiers entering
   their home,
  By the heavenly hosts attended.
Servants of the Master, clad in spot-
   less white,   [Light !
One with Him in Truth, in Life, in

896 OUR heavenly home is bright
    and fair,
And we'll sing the new song ;
No pain or sorrow enter there,
We will sing the new song.

  Wait a little while,
  Then we'll sing the new song ;
  Wait a little while,
  Then we'll sing the new song.

2 Our Saviour and Lord to heav'n is
   gone,
  We will sing the new song ;
He whom we fix our hopes upon ;
And we'll sing the new song.

3 And when we behold His blessed face,
  We will sing the new song ;
We'll praise Him for His wondrous
   grace,
  And we'll sing the new song.

897 SADLY from the field of con-
    flict,
  Where the wounded and the slain...
Lay with pale and upturn'd faces,
  Some in peace and some in pain,
Slow we bore a dying soldier,
  Who had fallen in the fight,
And to us he faintly whisper'd,
  " Comrades, let me sleep to-night"

  Let him sleep,..calmly sleep,..
    While the days and the years go by,
  Let him sleep,..sweetly sleep,..
    Till the call of the roll on high,
  Let him sleep,..calmly sleep,..
    While the years go by.

2 On the ground we softly laid him,
    Thinking he no more will wake,.....
When, with eyelids widely open,
    Pointing upward, thus he spake :
" Comrades, listen ! don't you hear
        it,
    Hear the roll-call there on high ?
Hark ! my name the Saviour's
        calling,
    Jesus, Captain, here am I ! "

3 Oh ! from many a field of battle
    Earnest pray'r has gone to God,.....
From the lips of dying soldiers,
    As their life-blood drench'd the
        sod ;
And to many came the message :
    Son, thy sins are all forgiv'n ;
And their lips with joy responded,
    When the roll was called in heav'n.

Now they sleep,..calmly sleep,..
    While the days and the years go by,
Now they sleep,..sweetly sleep,..
    Till the call of the roll on high,
Now they sleep..calmly sleep,..
    While the years go by.

898   JESUS ! blessed Name,.....
        Jesus ! still the same,.....
    I will sing it more and more,
    Till we meet on heaven's shore.

899   HOMEWARD I go rejoicing !
        O lovely promised land,
    Far in the distance gleaming,
        I see thy shining strand.

Homeward,..to join the ransomed,..
    Beyond the borders of the crystal sea ;..
Homeward,..to joys eternal,..
    And oh, how sweet the rest will be !

2 Homeward to meet my Saviour
    On that eternal shore,
Wonderful land of Canaan,
    Where sorrows come no more.

3 Homeward I go believing
    That there shall be no night
In that eternal city,
    Where God Himself is light !

900   THERE is One who under-
        stands our hearts,
    Jesus, the best Friend of all ;
    And for ev'ry need His grace imparts,
    Jesus, the best Friend of all.

Jesus, the best Friend of all ;..
Jesus, the best Friend of all,..
    He knows our ev'ry care,
    And will ev'ry burden bear,
Jesus, the best Friend of all.

2 He will soothe and comfort in dis-
        tress,
    Jesus, the best Friend of all ;
He will sympathise, and help, and
        bless,
    Jesus, the best Friend of all.

3 In temptation He will help thee
        stand,
    Jesus, the best Friend of all ;
Will support thee with His strong,
        right hand,
    Jesus, the best Friend of all.

4 There is One who died for you and
        me,
    Jesus, the best Friend of all ;
He will give us pardon full and free,
    Jesus, the best Friend of all.

901   WE sing of a story the Master
        told
        Of God's great love ;
    A love that can never grow faint
        or cold,
        Where'er we rove ;
    A love that waits to welcome us
    When from our sins we turn,
    Whose depth and height are infinite
    Whose fulness none can learn.

Then arise and come to the Father !
    He will meet you on the way ;
All the lost to His arms He will gather,
    In His home of eternal day ;
For the bells of the city of God shall ring,
    And the choirs of heav'n shall sing,
" Let joy abound, let songs resound,
    For the loved and lost is found ! "

2 O all who have wander'd away and
        fed
        On husks of sin ;
    O ye who are faint for the Living
        Bread,
        And sad within ;
    Whose thoughts are turning long-
        ingly
    Towards the Father's home,
No longer stay, make no delay,
    For Jesus bids you come.

3 That house of the Father is full of
        light,
    Our home above ;

There waits you a robe of immortal
    white,
      A ring of love.
O Father, grant us all Thy grace
    To leave our sin behind,
To enter straight the narrow gate,
    And seek Thee till we find.

902 A BAND of faithful reapers we,
    Who gather for eternity,
The golden sheaves of ripened grain
From ev'ry valley, hill, and plain ;
Our song is one the reapers sing,
In honour of their Lord and King—
The Master of the harvest wide,
Who for a world of sinners died.

> To the harvest field away,
>   For the Master calleth ;
> There is work for all to-day,
>   Ere the darkness falleth.
> Swiftly do the moments fly,
> Harvest days are going by,
>   Going, going, going, going by.

2 We are a faithful gleaning band,
And labour at our Lord's command,
Unyielding, loyal, tried and true,
For lo ! the reapers are but few ;
Behold the waving harvest field
Abundant with a golden yield ;
And hear the Lord of the harvest say
To all : " Go reap for Me to-day."

3 The golden hours like moments fly,
And harvest days are passing by ;
Then take thy rusty sickle down,
And labour for a fadeless crown ;
Why will you idly stand and wait ?
Behold, the hour is growing late !
Can you to judgment bring but
    leaves,   [sheaves ?
While here are waiting golden

903 THE fight is on, the trumpet
    sound is ringing out,
The cry " To arms ! " is heard
    afar and near ;
The Lord of hosts is marching on to
    victory,   [appear.
The triumph of the Christ will soon

> The fight is on, O Christian soldier,
>   And face to face in stern array,
> With armour gleaming, and colours streaming,
>   The right and wrong engage to-day !
> The fight is on, but be not weary ;
>   Be strong, and in His might hold fast ;
> If God be for us, His banner o'er is,
>   We'll sing the victor's song at last !

2 The fight is on, arouse, ye soldiers
    brave and true !
Jehovah leads and vict'ry will
    assure ;
Go, buckle on the armour God has
    given you,
And in His strength unto the end
    endure.

3 The Lord is leading on to certain
    victory ;
The bow of promise spans the
    eastern sky ;
His glorious name in ev'ry land shall
    honoured be ;
The morn will break, the dawn of
    peace is nigh.

904 WHEN dark'ning clouds ob-
    scure our sky,   [nigh,
And friends are few, and troubles
On One alone we may rely,
    Jesus ! precious Saviour !

2 Friends, basking in the summer ray
Of brighter hours, have pass'd away ;
But One is left in sorrow's day,
    Jesus ! precious Saviour !

3 When hopes, like autumn leaves, are
    dead,
And ev'ry joy of earth is fled,
Sweet pillow—rest for heart and
    head,
    Jesus ! precious Saviour !

4 Jesus hath died thine heart to win,
His precious blood atones for sin,
His loving arms would take thee in ;
    Jesus ! precious Saviour !

5 Oh, let Him fold thee to His breast,
There find a true, a perfect rest,
And thou shalt be for ever blest,
    By Jesus ! precious Saviour !

905 CHRIST has need of soldiers,
    brave and staunch and true ;
In the front of battle there's a place
    for you ;
Ever marching onward through a
    world of sin,
For the heav'nly country is the prize
    we win.

> On - - ward !..soldiers of the Cross,
>   Doubting never..trusting ever ;..
> On - - ward !..soldiers of the Cross,
>   Trusting the Lord, heeding His Word,
>   Onward to victory !

2 Satan would oppose us, tempt our
   souls to stray,
But through Him who loves us we
   shall win the day ;
Other valiant soldiers in the ages
   past,
O'er this upward pathway reach'd
   their home at last.

3 Let us then with courage press our
   upward way,
With our gaze on Jesus, ever watch
   and pray ;
Blazon'd on our banner, " Christ, the
   Lord of all,"
While we shout, Hosanna, Satan's
   hosts must fall.

906   LET us never mind the scoffs
        or the jeers of the world,
For we all have a cross to bear ;
It will only make the crown the
   brighter to shine,
When we have the crown to wear.

907   AWAY to the harvest field,
        toilers, away ;
Go, gather the golden grain whilst it
   is day ;
Strength meet for thy labour thy
   Lord will bestow,
Away to the harvest field, labourers,
   go ;
For now is the time to be doing thy
   best,
Soon, soon will be coming the season
   for rest.
> Away,..away,..away,..away,..
> For soon..will be ended
> The bright, the bright harvest day.

2 Behold how the ripen'd grain bends
   to the earth !
The harvest is ready, oh, why such a
   dearth   [toil ?
Of labourers ready and willing to
Will they listlessly suffer the rich
   grain to spoil ?
No, it must not be so ; to the field
   hie away,
With heart and with hand to work
   whilst it is day.

3 O say not, " No work of that sort
   can I do ; "
For some kind of toil is there even
   for you ;

For if the keen sickle thy hand may
   not wield,
Bind together the sheaves, or else
   glean in the field.
If you follow the reapers over the
   ground,
Full many a rich golden ear shall be
   found.

4 And when the last sheaf to the garner
   has come,
And saints join with angels to shout
   " Harvest home,"
When labour is over, then rest and
   reward,
And the welcome " Well done ! "
   from the lips of the Lord.
Away to the harvest field, toil while
   you may,
Soon, soon will be ended the bright
   harvest day.

908   MAKE the Lord a full con-
        fession,
When on Him you call ;
Do not carry half the burden,
   Tell the Saviour all.
> Tell the Saviour all,....
> Tell the Saviour all,....
> Make to Him a full confession,
> Tell the Saviour all.

2 Not alone the great temptations
   That the heart appal,
But the little cares and burdens,
   Tell the Saviour all.

3 For the eye that guards creation,
   Sees a sparrow fall ;
All your troubles will not tire Him,
   Tell the Saviour all.

909   HARK to the sounds of voices !
        Hark to the tramp of feet !
Is it a mighty army
   Treading the busy street ?
Nearer it comes and nearer,
   Singing a glad refrain ;   [away,
List what they say as they haste
   To the sound of a martial strain—
> " Marching beneath the banner,
>   Fighting beneath the Cross,
> Trusting in Him who saves us,
>   Ne'er shall we suffer loss !
> Singing the songs of homeland,
>   Loudly the chorus rings,
> We march to the fight in our armour bright,
>   At the call of the King of kings."

2 Out of the mist of error,
   Out of the realms of night,
Out of the pride of learning,
   Seeking the home of light ;
Out of the strife for power,
   Out of the greed of gold,
Onward they roam to their heavenly
     home,
   And the treasure that grows not
     old.

3 Out of the bonds of evil,
   Out of the chains of sin,
Ever they're pressing onward,
   Fighting the fight within ;
Holding the passions under,
   Ruling the sense with soul ;
Wielding the sword in the Name of
     the Lord,
   As they march to their heavenly
     goal.

4 On then, ye gallant soldiers,
   On to your home above !
Yours is the truth and glory,
   Yours is the power and love.
Here are ye trained for heroes,
   Yonder to serve the King ;
Marching to the light, 'neath the
     banner white,
   With a song that ye love to sing.

910   BEAUTIFUL words of Jesus,
   Spoken so long ago,
Yet, as we sing them over,
   Dearer to us they grow ;
Calling the heavy laden,
   Calling to hearts oppressed,
" Come unto Me, ye weary,
   Come, I will give you rest."

   Hear the call of His voice so sweet ;
   Bring your load to the Saviour's feet ;
   Lean your heart on His loving breast,
   Come, O come and He will give you rest.

2 Beautiful words of Jesus,
   Cheering us day by day ;
Throwing a gleam of sunshine
   Over a cloudy way ;
Casting on Him the burden
   We are too weak to bear,
He will give grace sufficient,
   He will regard our pray'r.

3 Beautiful words of Jesus,
   Tokens of endless rest,
When, by and by, we enter
   Into His presence blest ;

There we shall see His beauty,
   Meet with Him face to face ;
There shall we sing His glory,
   Praising His matchless grace.

911   SAY, brother,* will you meet us,
   Say, brother, will you meet us,
Say, brother, will you meet us
   On Canaan's happy shore ?

   By the grace of God we'll meet you,
   By the grace of God we'll meet you,
   By the grace of God we'll meet you,
     On Canaan's happy shore !

May be sung " sister," " children."

912 WHAT are you building, brother?
   So busily day by day ?
Is it a mighty castle of stone ?
   Is it a house of clay ?
Whose is the plan you build on ?
   What are the stones and lime ?
Is it based on the Rock of eternity,
   Or the sands of the shores of time?

Then build on the Rock, the Rock that ever
   stands,
O build on the Rock, and not upon the sands ;
You need not fear the storm or the earthquake
   shock,
You're safe for evermore if you build on the
   Rock.

2 What are you building, brother ?
   You work at it every day ;
Something is added, something is
     changed,
   Something is cast away.
Is it a house of pleasure ?
   Is it a house of sin ?
Or a temple divine for the Light of
     lights
   To descend and abide within ?

3 Brother, a time is coming,
   When all shall be tried by fire ;
Storms of the world shall beat on
     your house,
   Winds of a fierce desire.
Then, if you based it wrongly,
   Great will the ruin be ;
But if built on the firm and un-
     changing Rock,
   It will stand for eternity.

4 Build on the Rock, then, brother,
   How grandly it towers above !
Piercing the clouds and the starry
     skies,
   Lost in the heights of love !

Heaven and earth shall perish,
  Grow like a garment old ;
But the Rock is the same, and it
  shall not fail,
  Through the ages of time untold.

913 AS of old, when the hosts of
    Israel,
Were compelled in the wilderness
  to dwell,
Trusted they in their God to lead
  the way
  To the light of perfect day.

So the sign of the fire by night,
  And the sign of the cloud by day,
Hov'ring o'er, just before,
  As they journey on their way,
Shall a guide and a leader be,
  Till the wilderness be past,
For the Lord our God in His own good time
  Shall lead to the light at last.

2 To and fro, as a ship without a sail,
  Not a compass to guide them through
    the vale ;
  But the sign of their God was ever
    near,
  Thus their fainting hearts to cheer.

3 All the days of their wand'rings
    they were fed,
  To the land of the promise they
    were led ;
  By the hand of the Lord, in guid-
    ance sure,
  They were brought to Caanan's shore

914 EV'RY morning the red sun
    Rises warm and bright ;
But the evening cometh on,
  And the dark cold night ;
There's a bright land far away,
Where 'tis never-ending day.

2 Ev'ry spring the sweet young flow'rs
    Open fresh and gay ;
  Till the chilly autumn hours
    Wither them away.
  There's a land we have not seen,
  Where the trees are always green.

3 Little birds sing songs of praise
    All the summer long ;
  But in colder, shorter days,
    They forget their song :
  There's a place where angels sing
  Ceaseless praises to their King.

4 Christ our Lord is ever near
    Those who follow Him ;
  But we cannot see Him here,
    For our eyes are dim :
  There's a happy, glorious place,
  Where His people see His face.

5 Who shall go to that fair land ?
    All who love the right ;
  Holy children there shall stand
    In their robes of white :
  For that heaven so bright and blest
  Is our everlasting rest.

915 WHAT will you do with the
    King called Jesus ?
  Many are waiting to hear you say ;
Some have despised Him, rejecting
    His mercy ;
What will you do with your King
    to-day ?
What can you witness concerning
    His goodness,
  Who died to save you from sin's
    bitter thrall ?
Who will declare Him the fairest of
    thousands ?
Who now will crown Him the Lord
    of all ?

What will you do with the King called Jesus ?
What, oh, what will you do with Jesus ?
He waits to bless all who humbly confess
Faith in His blood and righteousness.

2 What will you do for the King called
    Jesus ?
  He who for you left His throne
    above,
  Here 'mid the lowly and sinful to
    labour,
  Daily unfolding His Father's love.
  Look on the fields white already to
    harvest,
  Who now is willing to toil with
    the few ?
  What will you do for the dear
    Saviour, Jesus ?   [you !
  Lo, He is waiting—He calls for

3 What will you do with the King
    called Jesus ?
  Who will submit to His gentle
    sway ?
  Where are the hearts ready now to
    enthrone Him ?
  Who will His kind commands
    obey ?

Come with your ointments most
 costly and precious,
  Pour out your gifts at the dear
  Saviour's feet ;
Render to Him all your loyal devo-
 tion ;
Seek to exalt Him by praises meet.

916 BY AND BY we'll see the
   King,
  And crown Him Lord of all.

917 WHY are you marching along
   to war ?
   Soldiers true,
   Who are you ? [for ?
What is the cause you are fighting
 Why are you never sad ?
O we are only rank and file,
 Treading the path for many a mile ;
Still ev'ry face must bear a smile,
 For Jesus has made us glad.

We've enlisted in the cause victorious,
 Of the everlasting Lord,
We are marching in the ranks all glorious,
 Resplendent with the shield and sword.
Christ is our Captain, Christ our might,
  So we fight,
  Seeking right ;
Christ is leading us to light
 In the all victorious army.

2 Who are the foes that you fight
   withal,
   Ye who stand,
   Sword in hand ?
Do you not fear in the strife to fall,
 Struck by a deadly blow ?
Strong are the foes that bar our way,
Many the sins we have to slay,
Still we shall rise and win the day,
 Tho' oft in the dust laid low.

3 What is the secret of your great
   pow'r,
   Soldier bright,
   Full of might ?
Why are you fearless in danger's
 hour—
 Strong with the foe to cope ?
Jesus it is that makes us strong,
Trusting in Him we march along,
He ever fills our hearts with song,
 Our eyes with the light of hope.

4 Where is the home you are marching
  to,
   Hearts of youth,
   Hearts of truth ?
Is there a kingdom beyond the blue,
 Where you may rest from strife ?
Jesus has said that we shall stand,
Victors of faith at His right hand,
Crown'd in the light of God's own
 land
 With joy and eternal life.

918 THEY come and go, the seasons
   fair,
  And bring their spoil to vale and
  hills ;
But oh, there is waiting in the air,
 And a passionate hope the spirit
 fills.
Why doth He tarry, the absent
 Lord ?
When shall the kingdom be restor'd,
And earth and heav'n with one
 accord,
 Ring out the cry that the King
 comes ?

What will it be when the King comes ?
What will it be when the King comes ?
What will it be when He comes ?....
What will it be when the King comes ?

2 The floods have lifted up their voice ;
 The King hath come to His own,
 His own !
The little hills and vales rejoice,
 His right it is to take the crown.
Sleepers, awake, and meet Him first !
Now let the marriage hymn out-
 burst !
And powers of darkness flee, dis-
 perst :
 What will it be when the King
 comes ?

3 A ransomed earth breaks forth in
 song,
 Her sin-stain'd ages overpast ;
Her yearning, "Lord, how long,
 how long ? "
 Exchanged for joy at last, at last !
Angels carry the royal commands ;
Peace beams forth throughout all
 the lands ;
The trees of the field shall clap their
 hands ;
 What will it be when the King
 comes ?

4 Oh, brother, stand as men that
    wait,
    The dawn is purpling in the East,
And banners wave from heaven's
    high gate ;
    The conflict now, but soon the
    feast !
Mercy and truth shall meet again ;
    Worthy the Lamb that once was
    slain !
We can suffer now—He will know
    us then ;
    What will it be when the King
    comes ?

919   I KNOW that my Redeemer
        liveth,
    And on the earth....again shall
    stand !....
I know eternal life He giveth,
    That grace and power are in His
    hand.

I know, I know..that Jesus liveth,
  And on the earth..again shall stand ;
I know, I know..that life He giveth,
  That grace and power..are in His hand.

2 I know His promise never faileth,
    The word He speaks....it cannot
    die ;....
Tho' cruel death my flesh assaileth,
    Yet I shall see Him by and by.

3 I know my mansion He prepareth,
    That where He is....there I may
    be ;....
O wondrous thought, for me He
    careth,
    And He at last will come for me.

920   INTO the valleys of blessing
        My Shepherd leads ;
Peace is my spirit possessing,
    My soul He feeds.
Pastures so green are around me,
    Waters of life shall flow ;
Fairest of flowers surround me,
    Ever I onward go.

My Shepherd leads along the way,
  Kept by His care I cannot stray ;
    In tender love,
    To realms above,
My Shepherd leads me home !

2 Into the ways that are weary
    My Shepherd leads ;
Dark tho' the skies be, and dreary,
    He knows my needs,

Heavy the load I am bearing,
    Love hath my pathway planned ;
Trusting, I'm still forward faring,
    Led by my Shepherd's hand.

3 Into the land all immortal
        My Shepherd leads ;
Unto the glorious portal
        My way He heeds.
Mansions of heavenly splendour
    Wait me when I shall come.
Led by my Shepherd so tender,
    Unto my Father's home.

921   THERE is a place of rest,
        The sweetest and the best,
The saints have found it down the
    ages hoary ! !
    Life that is hid in Him
    Is full right to the brim
Of love, and peace, and ecstasy, and
    glory.

922   WHEN we have reached the
        heav'nly plains,
    And joined the hosts above,
One song shall swell the rapturous
    strains,
    The song of Jesus' love.
When we have reached the pearly
    gate,
    And passed its portals through,
The saints, with holy joy elate,
    Shall tune their harps anew.

..Rejoice,..rejoice, for Christ Himself is near..
His wondrous love I feel,..His tender voice I
  hear,..
And when..at last we meet with Him above..
One song shall swell the rapturous strains, the
  song of Jesus' love.

2 While years eternal roll along
    Their ever ceaseless round,
Like ocean's waves shall swell the
    song,
    The glad, triumphant sound.
There life's fair river, broad and
    deep,
    Reflects its golden ray ;
Where eyes have never learned to
    weep,
    Where joys shall ne'er decay.

3 Then we shall see as we are seen,
    And know as we are known,
And walk the fields of fadeless green,
    While gazing on the throne.

And when are tuned the harps of
    gold
  To ev'ry blissful sound,
And ages long have onward rolled,
  Jesus shall King be crowned.

923 I BELIEVE God answers
    prayer ;
I am sure God answers prayer ;
I have proved God answers prayer :
  Glory to His Name.

924 IN a world so full of weeping,
    While the years are rolling
    on,
Christian souls the watch are keeping
  While the years are rolling on !
While our journey we pursue,
With the haven still in view,
There is work for us to do,
  While the years are rolling on !

> Are rolling on !....
> Are rolling on !....
> Oh, the good we may be doing,
> While the years are rolling on !

2 There's no time to waste in sighing,
  While the years are rolling on !
Time is flying, souls are dying,
  While the years are rolling on !
Loving words a soul may win
From the wretched paths of sin ;
We may bring the wand'rers in,
  While the years are rolling on !

3 Let us strengthen one another,
  While the years are rolling on !
Seek to raise a fallen brother,
  While the years are rolling on !
This is work for ev'ry hand,
Till throughout creation's land,
Armies for the Lord shall stand,
  While the years are rolling on !

4 Friends we love are quickly flying,
  While the years are rolling on !
No more parting, no more dying,
  While the years are rolling on !
In the world beyond the tomb
Sorrow never more may come,
When we meet in that blest home,
  While the years are rolling on !

925 FROM Jesus' lips we hear the
    call,
In tones of tenderness to all,

" Ye burdened sinners, come to Me,
  Though heavy-laden you may be."

> He'll wash your sins away,
> He'll wash your sins away,
> The blood of Christ, the bleeding Lamb,
> Will wash your sins away.

2 He would not have one sinner lost,
For well He knows what pardon cost,
O seek His mercy while you may,
And Christ will wash your sins away.

3 Too long you have remained in sin,
Forsake it, hate it—now begin ;
Tho' Satan long has held the sway,
Yet Christ can wash your sins away.

4 And some have erred and turned
    aside,
And, Peter-like, their Lord denied,
To such He calls in love to-day,
And seeks to wash your sins away.

926 GO forth, go forth for Jesus
    now !
  Be working ! Be watching !
The Lord Himself will teach you how
  To watch and pray ;
'Tis not for thee thy field to choose,
No work He gives must thou refuse,
    Be working ! Be watching ! Be
    praying !

> Go forth to work, to watch and pray !
> 'Tis Jesus who calls thee ;
> The harvest waits for thee to-day,
> Go bring some sheaves for God !

2 Go forth, go forth to all the world !
  O stay not ! Delay not !
But let love's banner be unfurl'd,
  And grace be told ;
O let redeeming love be sung,
A song of joy on ev'ry tongue !
    Be working ! Be watching ! Be
    praying !

3 Go forth, let hearts and hands be
    strong !
  Be working ! Be watching !
O stay the mighty power of wrong
  Where'er ye may !
Equipped with love and strength
    divine,
The victory is surely thine ;
    Be working ! Be watching ! Be
    praying !

927 I HAVE a Friend, a precious Friend,
    A Helper in the time of need ;....
He will my soul keep to the end,
    A Helper in the time of need.....

O Jesus is a Friend, and He cares for me,
He cares for me, He cares for me ;
O Jesus is a Friend, and He cares for me,
    A Helper in the time of need....

2 He turns to light the darkest hour,
    A Helper in the time of need ;....
In pain He soothes with wondrous pow'r,
    A Helper in the time of need.....

3 Thro' dangers hid or dangers known,
    A Helper in the time of need ;....
His wings of love are o'er me thrown,
    A Helper in the time of need.....

4 Where'er I go, where'er I stray,
    A Helper in the time of need ;....
A Guardian all along my way,
    A Helper in the time of need.....

928 . WHEN my steps are slow and weary,
Shadows o'er me cast,
And the way seems long and dreary,
Jesus holds me fast.

He will hold me fast,
Till my journey's past :
Ransomed by His precious blood,
Jesus holds me fast.

2 Oft when storms and clouds surround me,
He has held me fast ;
With His strong right arm around me,
Jesus holds me fast.

3 When my faint heart dreads the morrow,
He will hold me fast ;
When my spirit bows in sorrow,
Jesus holds me fast.

4 When the summons, " Come up higher,"
Reaches me at last,
Face to face I'll see my Saviour :
He has held me fast.

929 IF you have heard that our God is love,
Go tell it, go tell it !

That He is reigning in heaven above,
Go tell of His love to-day.

Tell of a Saviour so kind and true,
Tell of His love and His mercy too,
Tell of the good He would have us do,
    Go tell of His love to-day.

2 If you can sing the dear Saviour's praise,
Go sing it, go sing it !
Unto Him gladly your voices now raise,
Go sing of His love to-day.

3 If you can turn other hearts to God,
Go do it, go do it !
Bid them to follow where Jesus has trod,
Go do what you can to-day.

930   *Choir Piece, for words see No. 460.*

931   *Choir Piece, for words see No. 21.*

932 THERE'S a city of such beauty
Mortal eye hath never seen,
Filled with radiance brighter than the noon-day sun,....
Streets of gold and streams of crystal,
Trees of ever living green,
Jesus reigns, exalted One, in glory land.

Then crowns of glory, palms of victory,
Harps of gold triumphant anthems blend,
Hosannahs ringing, praises singing,
  We shall come, our trophies bringing, in that glory land.

2 There the ransomed dwell eternal,
Out of tribulation come,
Undreamed music fills the soul thro' endless days,....
Hope so dear and aspirations
Down on earth there freely bloom,
Life's real treasures ne'er decay in glory land.

3 Would you see this heavenly city ?
Would you drink its rapture in ?
There's a place prepared for all who will believe,....
Jesus earnestly invites you,
He will guide you, cleanse your sin,
And a mansion freely give in glory land.

4 " Unto Him that overcometh,"
     Is the promise full of love ;
Fiery trials in the furnace proves the
     gold,....
After conquest in life's conflict,
     Faith sustained by grace above,
Comes the victor's joy untold in
     glory land.

933   OUR service for God has been
          barren and dry,
     And barren it shall remain,
Until we are blest with the fire from
     on high,
     And sound of abundance of rain.

There's sound of abundance of rain,
There's sound of abundance of rain ;
To God we draw near, and by faith we can hear,
The sound of abundance of rain.

2 The prophets of Pride and the priests
       of Desire
     Are " calling " and " cutting " in
       vain ;
The " halting " are waiting for wit-
       ness of fire,
     And sound of abundance of rain.

3 The altars of God that our sins have
       destroyed
     We must build with " the things
       that remain ; "
And prove to the world that no pro-
       mise is void
     By sound of abundance of rain.

4 To each may the faith of Elijah be
       given,
     To pray till the answer we gain,
And the sinners acknowledge the
       witness of heav'n
     And sound of abundance of rain.

934   GO tell to souls benighted, of
          the Lord who came,
Speak His Name—love proclaim ;
Go tell the Gospel story, that the lost
     may know,
     Bring salvation near.
O bid them come repenting, bid
     them come to-day,
Help them say, " I obey."
Bear the blessed message, hasten
     now to go,
     Go with love sincere.

Press on - - ward. . ere the night is falling,
On - - ward. . hear the Saviour calling,
     Hear Him gently, sweetly say,
     " I will be with thee alway,"
       Peace and joy to bring.
Press on - - ward. . never danger fearing,
On - - ward. . brightest hope is nearing,
     Darkness shall no more enthrall,
     Christ our light shall shine for all,
       He shall reign our King.

2 In lands beyond the rolling of the
       ocean foam,
Wand'rers roam—bring them home ;
O lead them to the Saviour and His
     pard'ning love—
     He will give them rest,
And they who long have wandered
     soon will learn to see
How to be truly free,
Living for the kingdom of the land
     above,
     Safe and glad and blest.

3 Go bear the joyful message ev'ry-
       where you may,
Work and pray—day by day ;
Lift burdens from the weary, cheer
     the grieving heart—
     Walk where Jesus trod.
O be a beam of sunshine that reflects
     His light,
Pure and bright, in the night,
Helping many sinners choose the
     " better part "
     In the love of God.

935   SING me the song that tells
          of Jesus,
     That is the song which has music's
       sweetest tone,
Coming from heaven like perfume
     on breezes,
     Fills all my soul with the joy that
       is His own.
Bears me in spirit to bright realms
     of glory,
     Holds me enraptured with visions
       of delight ;
Gives me to hear what the saint
     dar'd not utter,
     When He returned to the shadow
       and the night.

Sing me the song that tells of Jesus,
     Sing to this heart and bid its throbbing cease,
Sing me that song for it chastens my spirit,
     Calming my soul with its magic spell of peace.

2 This song has wings like eagle's
pinions,
    Oft has it borne me to God's own
paradise ;
There I have sung with angels in
chorus,
    Knows not my soul of a trance of
joy like this.
But when returning to life's din and
battle,
    Spells still are o'er me and sounds
are in mine ear,
Taking the glare from the earthly
and fleeting,
    Filling my life with what the
angels hear.

3 " Worthy the Lamb " who died to
save us ;
    " Worthy the Lamb "—let it
sound thro' earth and sky ;
" Worthy the Lamb " sing the
angels in chorus,
    " Worthy the Lamb " our redemp-
tion draweth nigh.
Worthy of honour from highest
archangels,
    Worthy of glory of the universe
around ;
Worthy of majesty, pow'r, adoration,
    " Worthy the Lamb," the lov'd
and lost are found.

936   *Choir Piece, for words see
No. 57.*

937   WHEN God sees the flowers
Need His tender care,
He sends little raindrops
With a blessing there.

     Busy little raindrops,
     Let us be to-day,
     As we strive to scatter blessings,
     All along the way,

     Helpful little raindrops
     Will we be to-day,
     Doing work for Jesus
     In a raindrop's way.

2   We are little raindrops,
    God has sent us here,
From His fount of blessing,
    Bringing hope and cheer.

3 Ev'ry drop reflecting
    God's most tender love,
Helps to light the pathway
    To the home above.

4 Tho' we are but raindrops,
    We are glad to know
That we have a mission
    In this world below.

938   I LOVE to think of Christ,
my King,
Who did salvation freely bring ;
So while I live I mean to sing,
    Hallelujah ! grace is free.

     O Hallelujah ! grace is free,
     This my song shall ever be ;
     Jesus died to set me free,
     Hallelujah ! grace is free.

2 O wondrous is the crimson flood !
O precious is the cleansing blood !
My Jesus as my surety stood,
    Hallelujah ! grace is free.

3 What greater love can ever be,
To die upon a cruel tree,
And ransom such a wretch as me ?
    Hallelujah ! grace is free.

4 And when I reach that silver strand,
And join that holy, happy band,
This song I'll sing in that bright
land,
    Hallelujah ! grace is free.

CLOSING

939   THRO' the love of God our
Saviour,
    All will be well.
Free and changeless is His favour,
    All, all is well.
Precious is the blood that heal'd us,
Perfect is the grace that seal'd us,
Strong the hand stretched forth to
shield us,
    All must be well.

2 Tho' we pass thro' tribulation,
    All will be well.
Ours is such a full salvation,
    All, all is well.
Happy still in God confiding,
Fruitful if in Christ abiding,
Holy thro' the Spirit's guiding.
    All must be well.

3 We expect a bright to-morrow ;
    All will be well.

Faith can sing thro' days of sorrow,
　All, all is well.
On our Father's love relying,
Jesus ev'ry need supplying,
Or in living or in dying,
　All must be well.

940 THE night draws near, our
　　　day of praise is o'er,
Our songs, our hearts uplifted rise
　once more,
As at Thy feet, O Lord, our off'rings
　pour,
　And then, "Good night, good
　night!"

2 The day of life has oft-times dark-
　ened been,
Fierce storms have raged, with
　fitful lights between;
But still at even, o'er the changing
　scene,
　Has come—sweet word—"Good
　night!"

3 The task will soon be o'er, however
　hard,
The lonely struggle, watched still
　by the Lord,
With Him is thine exceeding great
　reward,
　Till then, "Good night, good
　night!"

4 Go forth in earnest, steadfast lives
　to prove
Thy teaching true; deep rooted in
　His love,
Fruits budding here, to ripen soon
　above,
　Where none shall say, "Good
　night!"

5 "Good night!" The longest day
　must have an end,
The happiest hours will to their
　closing tend,
Beyond, afar, th' eternal day we'll
　spend,
　"Good night, good night, good
　night!"

941 OUR friends on earth we meet
　　　with pleasure,
While swift the moments fly,
Yet ever comes the thought of sad-
　ness
That we must say good-bye.

We'll never say good-bye in heav'n,
　We'll never say, good-bye,..
For in that land of joy and song
　We'll never say, good-bye.

2 How joyful is the thought that
　lingers,
　When lov'd ones cross death's sea,
That when our labours here are
　ended,
　With them we'll ever be.

3 No parting words shall e'er be spoken
　In that bright land of flow'rs;
But songs of joy and peace and glad-
　ness
　Shall evermore be ours.

942 GOD be with you till we meet
　　　again,
　By His counsels guide, uphold you,
　With His sheep securely fold you;
God be with you till we meet again.

Till we meet,..till we meet,..
Till we meet at Jesus' feet;..
Till we meet,..till we meet,..
　God be with you till we meet again..

2 God be with you till we meet again,
　'Neath His wings protecting hide
　you,
　Daily manna still provide you;
God be with you till we meet again.

3 God be with you till we meet again,
　When life's perils thick confound
　you,
　Put His arms unfailing round you;
God be with you till we meet again.

4 God be with you till we meet again,
　Keep love's banner floating o'er
　you,
　Smite death's threat'ning wave
　before you;
God be with you till we meet again.

943 GLORY be to the Father, and
　　　to the Son, and to the Holy
　　　Ghost.
As it was in the beginning, is now,
　and ever shall be, world without
　end.　　　　　　　AMEN.

944 FATHER, in high heaven
　　　dwelling,
May our ev'ning song be telling
Of Thy mercy large and free;

Through the day Thy love hath fed
us, [us,
Through the day Thy care hath led
With divinest charity.

2 This day's sins O pardon, Saviour,
Evil thoughts, perverse behaviour,
Envy, pride, and vanity;
From the world, the flesh, deliver,
Save us how, and save us ever,
O Thou Lamb of Calvary.

3 From enticements of the devil,
From the might of spirits evil,
Be our shield and panoply;
Let Thy power this night defend us,
And a heav'nly peace attend us,
And angelic company.

4 Whilst the night dews are distilling,
Holy Ghost, each heart be filling
With Thine own serenity;
Softly let our eyes be closing,
Loving souls on Thee reposing,
Ever blessed Trinity.

945 LORD, dismiss us with Thy
blessing,
Fill our hearts with joy and peace;
Let us each, Thy love possessing,
Triumph in redeeming grace;
Oh, refresh us, oh, refresh us,
Travelling through this wilder-
ness!

2 Thanks we give, and adoration,
For Thy Gospel's joyful sound;
May the fruits of Thy salvation
In our hearts and lives abound;
May Thy presence, may Thy presence
With us evermore be found.

3 So whene'er the signal's given,
Us from earth to call away,
Borne on angels' wings to heaven,
Glad the summons to obey,
We shall surely, we shall surely
Reign with Christ in endless day.

946 BLEST be the tie that binds
Our hearts in Christian love;
The fellowship of kindred minds
Is like to that above.

2 Before our Father's throne
We pour our ardent pray'rs;
Our fears, our hopes, our aims are
one,
Our comforts and our cares.

3 We share our mutual woes;
Our mutual burdens bear;
And often for each other flows
The sympathising tear.

4 When we asunder part,
It gives us inward pain;
But we shall still be joined in heart,
And hope to meet again.

947 SUN of my soul, Thou Saviour
dear,
It is not night if Thou be near;
Oh, may no earth-born cloud arise,
To hide Thee from Thy servant's
eyes!

2 When the soft dews of kindly sleep
My wearied eyelids gently steep,
Be my last thought, how sweet to
rest
For ever on my Saviour's breast.

3 Abide with me from morn till eve,
For without Thee I cannot live;
Abide with me when night is nigh,
For without Thee I dare not die.

4 If some poor wand'ring child of
Thine
Have spurn'd to-day the voice divine
Now, Lord, the gracious work begin,
Let him no more lie down in sin.

5 Watch by the sick, enrich the poor
With blessings from Thy boundless
store;
Be ev'ry mourner's sleep to-night,
Like infant's slumbers, pure and
light.

6 Come near and bless us when we
wake,
Ere thro' the world our way we take;
Till, in the ocean of Thy love,
We lose ourselves in heav'n above.

948 ABIDE with me; fast falls the
eventide;
The darkness deepens; Lord, with
me abide;
When other helpers fail, and comforts flee,
Help of the helpless, oh, abide with
me!

2 I need Thy presence ev'ry passing
hour;
What but Thy grace can foil the
tempter's pow'r?

Who like Thyself my guide and stay
  can be ?
Thro' cloud and sunshine, oh, abide
  with me !

3 Swift to its close ebbs out life's little
  day ;
Earth's joys grow dim, its glories
  pass away ;
Change and decay in all around I see ;
O Thou, who changest not, abide
  with me !

4 I fear no foe with Thee at hand to
  bless,   [bitterness ;
Ills have no weight, and tears no
Where is death's sting ? where,
  grave, thy victory ?   [me.
I triumph still if Thou abide with

949 THE day Thou gavest, Lord,
  is ended ;
The darkness falls at Thy behest ;
To Thee our morning hymns as-
  cended,
Thy praise shall sanctify our rest.

2 We thank Thee that Thy Church
  unsleeping,   [light,
While earth rolls onward into
Thro' all the world her watch is
  keeping,
And rest not now by day or night.

3 As o'er each continent and island
The dawn leads on another day,
The voice of pray'r is never silent,
Nor dies the strain of praise away.

4 The sun that bids us rest is waking
Our brethren 'neath the western
  sky ;
And hour by hour fresh lips are
  making   [high.
Thy wondrous doings heard on

5 So be it, Lord ! Thy throne shall
  never,   [away ;
Like earth's proud empires, pass
Thy kingdom stands and grows for
  ever,   [sway.
Till all Thy creatures own Thy

950 SAVIOUR, again to Thy dear
  Name we raise
With one accord our parting hymn
  of praise ;
We stand to bless Thee ere our wor-
  ship cease,   [of peace.
Then, lowly kneeling, wait Thy word

2 Grant us Thy peace upon our home-
  ward way ;
With Thee began, with Thee shall
  end the day ;
Guard Thou the lips from sin, the
  hearts from shame,
That in this house have called upon
  Thy Name.

3 Grant us Thy peace, Lord, thro' the
  coming night,   [light ;
Turn Thou for us its darkness into
From harm and danger keep Thy
  children free,   [Thee.
For dark and light are both alike to

4 Grant us Thy peace throughout our
  earthly life ;
Our balm in sorrow and our stay in
  strife ;
Then, when Thy voice shall bid our
  conflict cease,   [peace.
Call us, O Lord, to Thine eternal

951 PRAISE God, from whom all
  blessings flow ;
Praise Him, all creatures here below ;
Praise Him above, ye heav'nly host,
Praise Father, Son, and Holy Ghost.

952 I HOPE to meet you all in
  glory,
When the storms of life are o'er ;
I hope to tell the dear old story,
On the blessed shining shore.

  On the shining shore,
    On the golden strand,
  In our Father's home,
    In the happy land :
  I hope to meet you there,
  I hope to meet you there—
  A crown of vict'ry wear—
    In glory.

2 I hope to meet you all in glory,
By the tree of life so fair ;
I hope to praise our dear Redeemer,
For the grace that brought me
  there.

3 I hope to meet you all in glory,
Round the Saviour's throne above ;
I hope to join the ransomed army,
Singing now redeeming love.

4 I hope to meet you all in glory,
When my work on earth is o'er ;
I hope to clasp your hands rejoicing
On the bright eternal shore.

CHORUSES

None of the following Choruses are to be found in any other part of the book.

GOSPEL

1 I AM the Door, I am the Door,
By Me if any man enter in
He shall be saved, he shall be saved,
He shall be saved.

For Gospel Temperance Meetings.

2 A CERTAIN man of whom we read,
Who lived in days of old,
Though he was rich he felt his need
Of something more than gold.
Oh, yes, my friend, there's something more,
  something more than gold :
To know your sins are all forgiv'n is something
  more than gold.

2 It happened on a certain day
This little man was told
That Jesus soon would pass that way
With something more than gold.

3 He climbed a tree above the crowd,
So that he might behold
The Blessed One with power to give
Something more than gold.

4 The Saviour came along the way,
And saw him on the tree,
Then calling to him Jesus said,
" I must abide with thee."

5 So he obeyed, and soon he found,
The half had not been told,
The blessing Jesus brought to him
Was better far than gold.

3 LOOK to Him now, look to Him
    now,
Jesus is waiting to save ;
Look to Him now, look to Him now,
Jesus is waiting to save.

4 WHO'LL be the next ?
Who'll be the next ?
Who'll be the next to follow Jesus ?
Who'll be the next to follow Jesus
  now,
    Follow Jesus now ?

5 TELL the Saviour all,....
Tell the Saviour all ;....
Make to Him a full confession,
    Tell the Saviour all.

6 COME away, come away,
    Come away to Jesus ;
Come away, come away home !
For Jesus waits to save you.

7 STEAL away, steal away,
    Steal away to Jesus,
Steal away, steal away home,
For Jesus waits to save you.

8 ETERNITY, eternity,
Where will you spend eternity ?
Eternity, eternity,
Where will....you spend eternity?

TESTIMONY

9 O GLORY ! O glory, what rap-
    ture is mine !
The King in His beauty I see ;
I'm singing His praises since Jesus
  divine
Extended His mercy to me.

10 I KNOW,....I know,....
I have another building ;
I know,....I know,....
'Tis not made with hands.

11 I WANT ev'rybody to know
Of Jesus who loveth me so !
My time I will give as long as I
  live
To help ev'rybody to know.

12 O....WHAT He's done for me !
O....what He's done for me !
If I tried to eternity, I never could
  tell
All He's done for me !

13 OH, wondrous bliss! oh, joy
     sublime!
I've Jesus with me all the time!
Oh, wondrous bliss! oh, joy sub-
     lime!
I've Jesus with me all the time!

14 'TIS Jesus in the morning hour,
     'Tis Jesus thro' the day;
'Tis Jesus in the eventide,
     'Tis Jesus all the way.

2 I'll praise Him in the morning hour,
     I'll praise Him thro' the day;
I'll praise Him in the eventide,
     I'll praise Him all the way.

15 GET right with God,....
     Get right with God,....
Oh, do not let the Spirit now de-
     part;....
     Get right with God,....
     Get right with God,....
And grant Him glad admission to
     thy heart.

16 SAVED, saved, oh glory to God!
     I have the assurance divine;
Saved, saved, oh glory to God!
     His Spirit bears witness with
     mine.

17 SINCE I....have learned the
     sto - - ry,
This song I love to sing,....
Oh, Jesus has the world redeemed
From darkness unto glory.

18 I'M satisfied with Jesus here,
     He's ev'rything to me;
His dying love has won my heart,
And now He sets me free.

19 HALLELUJAH to His Name!
     Hallelujah to His Name!
He is guiding, cheering, loving all
     the way!
     O glory to His Name!

20 THE Lamb, the Lamb, the bleed-
     ing Lamb,
I love the sound of Jesus' Name,
It sets my spirit in a flame—
     Glory to the bleeding Lamb!

21 AND when I reach the pearly
     gates,
     Then I'll put in this plea;
I was a guilty sinner,
     But Jesus died for me.

22 OH! the blood, the precious
     blood,
     Jesus shed on Calvary;
Oh! the blood, the precious blood;
     Praise the Lord, it cleanseth me....

CONSECRATION AND HOLINESS

23 EV'RY step of the way, my Lord,
     Yes, ev'ry step of the way;
Thy all is mine, and I am Thine,
For ev'ry step of the way.

24 I'M going thro', Jesus, I'm going
     thro';
I'll pay the price whatever others do;
I'll take the way with the world-
     despised few;
I've started out, Jesus, I'm going
     thro'.

25 I'LL be true, Lord, to Thee,
     I'll be true, Lord, to Thee;
     And whate'er befall,
     I shall conquer all,
If I'm only true to Thee.

26 JESUS, Master, search me, prove
     me,
With Thy fire try my heart;
All I am and have I yield Thee;
     All I want Thou art.

27 MORE, more like Jesus
     I would ever grow;
More of His love constantly prove—
More of His likeness show.

28 HE will break ev'ry fetter,
He will break ev'ry fetter,
He will break ev'ry fetter,
     And will set you free.

2 He has broken ev'ry fetter,
He has broken ev'ry fetter,
He has broken ev'ry fetter,
     And has set me free.

29 JESUS, keep me in Thy ful-
     ness;
     Keep me yielded, keep me
     pure;
Keep me telling of Thy glory;
     Keep me steady, keep me sure.

30 STEP by step, step by step,
    I will follow Jesus,
    Ev'ry day, all the way,
    Keeping step with Jesus.

31 POW'R to cleanse the leper,
    pow'r to raise the dead, [oil,
Pow'r filled the empty cruse with
Ready waiting for the workers, who
    in Jesu's step will tread, [toil.
And leave a life of ease for one of

32 NEARER, yes, nearer, my Saviour,
    Oh draw me yet nearer to Thee !
Nearer, yes, nearer, my Saviour,
    And perfect Thy likeness in me !

33 THY love,..Thy boundless love,..
    Thy love,..all-conq'ring love,..
    Shed in..my heart abroad ;
    Give me this perfect love.

34 THERE'S nothing **too** hard for
    Thee,....
There's nothing too hard for Thee ;
    Nothing, nothing,
There's nothing too hard for Thee.

2 I'm trusting alone in Thee,....
I'm trusting alone in Thee ;
    Trusting, trusting,
I'm trusting alone in Thee.

GENERAL

35 MARCH on ! we shall win the
    day ;
March on ! hear the Saviour say :
" March on till the vict'ry's won,"
And you shall hear the glad " Well
    done."

36 MY burden's great, my faith is
    small ;
Ah, that's the trouble with us all !
A little more faith ! a little more
    faith !
A little more faith in Jesus.

37 COMING by and by, 'tis coming
    by and by ;
A better day is dawning in yonder
    sky ;
So never give up trusting, nor ques-
    tion Him or why,
For victory is coming by and by.

38 SATISFIED,....satisfied,....
I know I'll be fully satisfied ;....
When mine eyes shall behold
All the wonders untold,
I know I'll be satisfied...

39 I SHALL be like Him, I shall be
    like Him,
And in His beauty shall shine ;
I shall be like Him, wondrously like
    Him,
Jesus, my Saviour divine.

40 I FEEL like going on, brother,
    I feel like going on ;
I'm on my way to Zion,
    And I feel like going on.

41 'TIS well, 'tis well,
    'Tis well with the righteous, well ;
    In sorrow's night,
    In pleasures bright,
    'Tis well with the righteous, well.

42 CONFIDE it to Jesus, He'll
    comfort and cheer you,
    Each burden and sorrow He'll
    share ;
Confide it to Jesus, He's waiting to
    hear you,
Go, tell Him the story in prayer.

43 SOME thro' the waters,
    Some thro' the flood,
Some thro' the fire,
    But all thro' the blood ;
Some thro' deep sorrow, trial and
    pains,
God leads His dear children along.

44 SOMETHING whispers, can it
    be,....
There is hope for one like me ?...
I will seek His mercy full and free,
Jesus bled and died for me.

45 IN tune with Thee,....in tune with
    Thee,...
Lord, keep my heart in tune....with
    Thee.

46 SINCE I have been forgiven,
    His dear face I see ;....
While we walk together,
    This world's a heaven to me.....

47 A LITTLE talk with Jesus makes
things right, all right,
A little talk with Jesus makes things
right, all right ;
Thank God, I always find,
In trouble of ev'ry kind,
That a little talk with Jesus makes
things right, all right.

48 I AM determined to hold out to
the end,
Jesus is with me, on Him I can
depend ;
And I know I have salvation, for I
feel it in my soul,
I am determined to hold out to the
end.

INDEX TO FIRST LINES

INDEX OF CHORUSES

The following appear throughout the Hymn Book

The following Refrains are suitable as Choruses